PROBABILITY MEASURES ON METRIC SPACES

Probability and Mathematical Statistics

A Series of Monographs and Textbooks

---

1. Thomas Ferguson. Mathematical Statistics: A Decision Theoretic Approach. 1967
2. Howard Tucker. A Graduate Course in Probability. 1967
3. K. R. Parthasarathy. Probability Measures on Metric Spaces. 1967

In preparation

B. V. Gnedenko, Yu. K. Belyayev, and A. D. Solovyev. Mathematical Methods of Reliability Theory

PROBABILITY MEASURES ON METRIC SPACES

K. R. Parthasarathy

DEPARTMENT OF PROBABILITY AND STATISTICS
THE UNIVERSITY OF SHEFFIELD
SHEFFIELD, ENGLAND

1967

ACADEMIC PRESS New York and London

ACADEMIC PRESS INC.
111 Fifth Avenue, New York, New York 10003

United Kingdom Edition published by
ACADEMIC PRESS INC. (LONDON) LTD.
Berkeley Square House, London W.1

Library of Congress Catalog Card Number: 66-30096

PRINTED IN THE UNITED STATES OF AMERICA

PREFACE

Ever since Yu. V. Prohorov wrote his fundamental paper "Convergence of random processes and limit theorems in the theory of probability" in the year **1956** [**33**], the general theory of stochastic processes has come to be regarded as the theory of probability measures in complete separable metric spaces. The subsequent work of A. V. Skorohod of which a detailed account is given in the book by I. I. Gikhman and A. V. Skorohod [**9**] gave a great impetus to the subject of limit theorems in probability theory. The present monograph deals with the general theory of probability measures in abstract metric spaces, complete separable metric groups, locally compact abelian groups, Hilbert spaces, and the spaces of continuous functions and functions with discontinuities of the first kind only. Emphasis is given to the work done by the Indian School of probabilists consisting of, among others, V. S. Varadarajan, R. Ranga Rao, S. R. S. Varadhan, and the author.

In Chapter I a detailed description of the Borel σ-field of a metric space is given. The isomorphism theorem which states that two Borel subsets of complete separable metric spaces are isomorphic if and only if they have the same cardinality is proved. The by now classical theorem of Kuratowski on the measurability of the inverse of a measurable map from a Borel set of a complete separable metric space into a separable metric space is established.

Chapter II deals with properties such as regularity, tightness, and perfectness of measures defined on metric spaces. The weak topology in the space of probability measures is investigated and Prohorov's theorems on metrizability and compactness are proved. Convergence of sample distributions and existence of nonatomic measures in separable metric spaces are investigated.

Chapters III and IV deal with the arithmetic of probability distributions in topological groups. The nature of idempotent measures, existence of indecomposable and nonatomic indecomposable measures, and representation of infinitely divisible distributions and its relevance in the theory of limit theorems for "sums" of infinitesimal summands are discussed in great detail.

Chapter V contains the proofs of the classical extension theorems and existence of conditional and regular conditional probabilities in standard Borel spaces. This is included for the sake of completeness.

Chapter VI gives a detailed account of the subject of limit theorems in a Hilbert space. Prohorov's theorems on the description of weakly compact subsets of the space of measures on a Hilbert space [**33**], Sazonov's criterion for a characteristic function [**37**], and Varadhan's results on the Lévy-Khinchine representation of infinitely divisible laws and limit theorems for sums of infinitesimal summands [**45**] are established.

Chapter VII is devoted to a study of probability measures on the spaces $C[0, 1]$ and $D[0, 1]$. Properties of the Skorohod topology [**9, 20**] in the space $D[0, 1]$ are proved. The compactness criteria for sets of probability measures and their applications to testing statistical hypotheses are given.

The account of the subject given herein is by no means complete. The topic of measures on Lie groups and homogeneous spaces, for example, is not touched on at all. Some of the references on this subject have been included, however, and for further comments the reader may refer to the bibliographical notes at the end of the book.

Theorem numbers refer to theorems in the same chapter if they are not accompanied by a chapter number.

The author wishes to express his thanks to R. Ranga Rao, V. S. Varadarajan, and S. R. S. Varadhan with whom he had the opportunity of collaboration over several years. It is a pleasure to offer thanks to F. Topsøe and O. Bjornsson who read the first two chapters of the manuscript carefully and made valuable suggestions. He is grateful to V. Rohatgi and K. Vijayan who also helped with proofreading.

He is deeply indebted to the Research and Training School of the Indian Statistical Institute, Calcutta, for providing facilities to carry out research work during 1960–1965, a substantial portion of which has been included in the present monograph. He is grateful to the Department of Probability and Statistics of the University of Sheffield for the invaluable assistance rendered in the preparation of the book.

Thanks are finally due to Miss J. Bowden for her efficient typing of the manuscript.

Sheffield, England
March 1967

K. R. Parthasarathy

CONTENTS

I

THE BOREL SUBSETS OF A METRIC SPACE

1. GENERAL PROPERTIES OF BOREL SETS

Here we shall concern ourselves with the study of the properties of Borel subsets of metric spaces. The precise metric which gives rise to the topology will be usually unimportant. Generally speaking all we shall use is the fact that the topology arises through a metric.

Let X be any metric space. We define by $\mathscr{B}_X$, or $\mathscr{B}$ when no confusion can arise, the smallest σ-algebra of subsets of X which contains all the open subsets of X. $\mathscr{B}_X$ is called the Borel σ-field of X and elements of $\mathscr{B}_X$ are called Borel sets. $\mathscr{B}_X$ satisfies the following conditions:

(1) $X \in \mathscr{B}_X$, $\phi \in \mathscr{B}_X$;

(2) $A \in \mathscr{B}_X$ implies that $A' \in \mathscr{B}_X$ where A' stands for the complement of A;

(3) $A_1, A_2, \ldots, \in \mathscr{B}_X$ implies that $\bigcup_1^\infty A_i \in \mathscr{B}_X$, $\bigcap_1^\infty A_i \in \mathscr{B}_X$.

Since every closed set is the complement of an open set and vice versa, $\mathscr{B}_X$ is also the smallest σ-algebra of subsets of X which contains all the closed subsets of X.

We shall now examine how far the metric nature of the space X allows us to reduce the number of axioms in the definition of $\mathscr{B}_X$.

Definition 1.1

A set $A \subseteq X$ is called a G_δ if it can be expressed as the intersection of a denumerable sequence of open sets. A set $A \subseteq X$ is called an F_σ if it can be expressed as the union of a denumerable sequence of closed sets.

Let d be the metric in X. For any set $A \subseteq X$ and $x \in X$ we shall write $d(x, A) = \inf_{y \in A} d(x, y)$. $d(x, A)$ is called the distance of the set A from the point x.

Theorem 1.1

The function $d(x, A)$ satisfies the inequality

$$|d(x, A) - d(y, A)| \leqslant d(x, y).$$

In particular, $d(x, A)$ is uniformly continuous.

PROOF. By the triangular inequality we have for any $z \in A$ and any $x, y \in X$,

$$\begin{aligned} d(x, A) &\leqslant d(x, z) \\ &\leqslant d(x, y) + d(y, z). \end{aligned}$$

Taking infimum over $z \in A$ we obtain

$$d(x, A) \leqslant d(x, y) + d(y, A).$$

By the symmetry of $d(x, y)$ we have

$$d(y, A) \leqslant d(x, y) + d(x, A).$$

The two preceding inequalities yield

$$|d(x, A) - d(y, A)| \leqslant d(x, y).$$

Theorem 1.2

Every closed subset of X is a G_δ and every open set is an F_σ.

PROOF. Let $A \subseteq X$ be closed. It is clear that $d(x, A) = 0$ if and only if $x \in A$. Thus

$$A = \bigcap_{n=1}^{\infty} \{x : d(x, A) < 1/n\}.$$

The continuity of $d(x, A)$ (Theorem 1.1) implies that the sets $\{x: d(x, A) < 1/n\}$ are open, and hence A is a G_δ. Since the complement of a G_δ is an F_σ, the second part of the theorem follows from the first. This completes the proof.

Theorem 1.3

Let X be any metric space. Then $\mathscr{B}_X$ is the smallest class of subsets of X which contains all the open (closed) subsets of X, and which is closed under countable unions and countable intersections.

PROOF. Let $\mathscr{D}$ be the smallest class of subsets of X containing all the open sets and closed under countable unions and intersections. Since $\mathscr{B}_X$ has both the properties, we have $\mathscr{D} \subseteq \mathscr{B}_X$. It is enough to show that $\mathscr{D}$ is closed under complementation. Let $\mathscr{D}'$ be the class of all sets A such that $A' \in \mathscr{D}$. By Theorem 1.2 every closed set is a G_δ, and hence belongs to $\mathscr{D}$. Thus every open set belongs to $\mathscr{D}'$, which is closed under countable intersections and unions. Hence $\mathscr{D} \subseteq \mathscr{D}'$. This implies that $\mathscr{D}$ is closed under complementation.

Theorem 1.4

Let X be any metric space. Then $\mathscr{B}_X$ is the smallest class of subsets of X which contains all the open subsets of X, and which is closed under countable intersections and countable disjoint unions.

PROOF. Let $\mathscr{H}_0$ be the smallest class containing the open sets and closed under countable intersections and countable disjoint unions. In order to prove the theorem it is enough to show that $\mathscr{H}_0$ is closed under complementation.

By Theorem 1.2 it is clear that $\mathscr{H}_0$ contains all closed sets. Let $\mathscr{V} = \{E: E \text{ is either closed or open}\}$. Let $\mathscr{H}_1 = \{E: E \in \mathscr{H}_0, E' \in \mathscr{H}_0\}$. Then $\mathscr{V} \subseteq \mathscr{H}_1 \subseteq \mathscr{H}_0$. We shall now prove that $\mathscr{H}_1$ is closed under countable unions and countable intersections. Indeed, let $E_i \in \mathscr{H}_1$, $i = 1, 2, \ldots$. Since $E_i \in \mathscr{H}_0$, $i = 1, 2, \ldots$, $\bigcap_{i=1}^\infty E_i \in \mathscr{H}_0$. $(\bigcap_{i=1}^\infty E_i)' = \bigcup_{i=1}^\infty E_i' = \bigcup_{i=1}^\infty (E_i' \cap E_1 \cap E_2 \cap \ldots \cap E_{i-1})$ is a countable disjoint union of sets in $\mathscr{H}_0$ and hence belongs to $\mathscr{H}_0$. Thus $\bigcap_{i=1}^\infty E_i \in \mathscr{H}_1$. $\bigcup_{i=1}^\infty E_i = \bigcup_{i=1}^\infty (E_i \cap E_1' \cap E_2' \cap \ldots \cap E_{i-1}')$ is a countable disjoint union of sets in $\mathscr{H}_0$ and hence belongs to $\mathscr{H}_0$. $(\bigcup_{i=1}^\infty E_i)' = \bigcap_{i=1}^\infty E_i'$

is a countable intersection of sets in $\mathscr{H}_0$ and hence belongs to $\mathscr{H}_0$. Thus $\bigcup_{i=1}^{\infty} E_i \in \mathscr{H}_1$. Thus $\mathscr{H}_0 = \mathscr{H}_1$. This completes the proof.

The next two theorems relate the σ-algebra $\mathscr{B}_X$ and the continuous functions on X.

Theorem 1.5

Let X and Y be metric spaces and f a map of X into Y. If f is continuous, then f is measurable.

PROOF. For every open set $U \subseteq Y$, $f^{-1}(U)$ is open in X, and hence belongs to $\mathscr{B}_X$. This implies that for every Borel set $B \subseteq Y$, $f^{-1}(B) \in \mathscr{B}_X$. Hence f is measurable.

Theorem 1.6

If X is a metric space and A and B are two disjoint closed subsets of X, then there exists a continuous function $f(x)$ on X with the properties: (1) $0 \leqslant f(x) \leqslant 1$; (2) $f(x) = 0$ for $x \in A$, $= 1$ for $x \in B$. If $\inf_{x \in A, y \in B} d(x, y) = \delta > 0$, then the function f can be chosen to be uniformly continuous.

PROOF. Let $f(x) = d(x, A)/[d(x, A) + d(x, B)]$. It is easy to verify that f satisfies (1) and (2). The second part of the theorem follows immediately from Theorem 1.1 and the fact that $d(x, A) + d(x, B) \geqslant \delta$.

Theorem 1.7

If X is a metric space, the σ-algebra $\mathscr{B}_X$ is the smallest σ-algebra of subsets of X with respect to which all real-valued bounded continuous functions on X are measurable.

PROOF. Let $\mathscr{H}$ be the smallest σ-algebra with respect to which all real valued bounded continuous functions are measurable. By Theorem 1.5, $\mathscr{H} \subseteq \mathscr{B}_X$. We shall now prove that every closed set C belongs to $\mathscr{H}$. By Theorem 1.2, $C = \bigcap_1^{\infty} U_n$ where $U_1, U_2, \ldots,$ are open sets and $U_1 \supseteq U_2 \supseteq, \ldots$. Since C and $X - U_n$ are disjoint closed sets, by Theorem 1.6, there exists a continuous function $f_n(x)$ such that $0 \leqslant f_n(x) \leqslant 1$ and $f_n(x) = 1$ for all $x \in C$ and $= 0$ for all $x \in X - U_n$. Let $f = \sum_1^{\infty} 2^{-n} f_n$. Since the series is uniformly convergent, f is also continuous and bounded. It is clear that $f(x) = 1$ if and only if $f_n(x) = 1$ for all n, and hence $C = \{x: f(x) = 1\}$. Thus $C \in \mathscr{H}$. This proves that $\mathscr{H} = \mathscr{B}_X$.

We shall now examine the situation when X is a separable metric space.

Theorem 1.8

Let X be a separable metric space. Then $\mathscr{B}_X$ has a denumerable subfamily $\mathscr{D}$ such that $\mathscr{B}_X$ is the smallest σ-algebra of subsets of X containing $\mathscr{D}$.

PROOF. Since X is a separable metric space, it satisfies the second axiom of countability. Hence there exists a denumerable family $\mathscr{D}$ of open sets $U_1, U_2, \ldots,$ such that every open set can be expressed as the union of sets from $\mathscr{D}$. Now it is obvious that $\mathscr{B}_X$ is generated by $\mathscr{D}$.

We shall now discuss various methods of constructing new metric spaces out of given ones and see how the corresponding Borel σ-fields are made up. Given any metric space X and a set $Y \subseteq X$, Y is a metric space when we restrict the metric on X to Y. A set $A \subseteq Y$ is open in Y if and only if there exists an open set $U \subseteq X$ such that $A = U \cap Y$.

Theorem 1.9

Let X be a metric space and $Y \subseteq X$. Then $\mathscr{B}_Y = \{E \cap Y: E \in \mathscr{B}_X\}$. In particular, if Y is itself a Borel set in X (i.e., $Y \in \mathscr{B}_X$), *$\mathscr{B}_Y$ is precisely the class of all subsets of Y which are Borel sets in X.*

PROOF. $\mathscr{B}_Y$ is the class of Borel sets of the metric space Y, and hence is the σ-algebra generated by the open sets of Y. If $\mathscr{U}_Y$ is the class of all open sets of Y and $\mathscr{U}_X$ the class of all open sets of X, it is clear that $\mathscr{U}_Y = \{U \cap Y, U \in \mathscr{U}_X\}$. Hence $\mathscr{B}_Y = \{E \cap Y: E \in \mathscr{B}_X\}$ (Halmos [12], p. 25). For the second part, notice that if $Y \in \mathscr{B}_X$ and $E \in \mathscr{B}_X$, then $E \cap Y \in \mathscr{B}_X$.

Another method of generating new metric spaces is by taking cartesian product. If X_1 and X_2 are metric spaces we can form their cartesian product $X = X_1 \times X_2$. X, under the product topology, is a metric space. The question naturally arises whether $\mathscr{B}_X$ is the smallest σ-algebra containing all sets of the form $A_1 \times A_2$ where $A_1 \in \mathscr{B}_{X_1}$ and

$A_2 \in \mathscr{B}_{X_2}$. It can be shown that in general this is not true. The class of Borel sets in X is in general much wider than the σ-algebra generated by "rectangles" of the form $A_1 \times A_2$. However, when the spaces X_1 and X_2 are separable these complications do not arise. Let $X_1, X_2, \ldots$ be a sequence of separable metric spaces, and let X be their cartesian product. Let $\mathscr{D}_n = \{U_{n1}, U_{n2}, \ldots\}$ be a denumerable base for the topology of X_n and for $(x_1, x_2, \ldots) \in X$ let $\pi_n: (x_1, \ldots, x_k, \ldots) \to x_n$ be the "projection" on X_n. The sets $\pi_n^{-1}(U_{nj}) = V_{nj}$ $(n = 1, 2, \ldots, j = 1, 2, \ldots)$ are open and the class of all finite intersections of the V_{nj} is a denumerable base for the topology of X. X is a separable metric space.

Definition 1.2

A *Borel space* $(X, \mathscr{B})$ is a pair where X is an abstract set and $\mathscr{B}$ is a σ-algebra of subsets of X. If $(X_\alpha, \mathscr{B}_\alpha)$ $(\alpha \in \Delta)$ are Borel spaces, $X = \prod_{\alpha \in \Delta} X_\alpha$ is the cartesian product of the X_α (= the set of all functions x from Δ to $\bigcup_{\alpha \in \Delta} X_\alpha$ such that $x(\alpha) \in X_\alpha$ for all $\alpha \in \Delta$) and if π_α is the map $x \to x(\alpha)$ of X onto X_α, then the *cartesian product* of the Borel spaces $(X_\alpha, \mathscr{B}_\alpha)$ is defined as the Borel space $(X, \mathscr{B})$ where X is as defined above and $\mathscr{B}$ is the smallest σ-algebra of subsets of X with respect to which the π_α are measurable. $\mathscr{B}$ is the σ-algebra generated by sets of the form $\pi_\alpha^{-1}(A)$, where α runs over Δ and A runs over any subclass $\mathscr{D}_\alpha \subseteq \mathscr{B}_\alpha$ which generates $\mathscr{B}_\alpha$. In symbols $(X, \mathscr{B}) = \prod_{\alpha \in \Delta} (X_\alpha, \mathscr{B}_\alpha)$.

Theorem 1.10

Let $X_1, X_2, \ldots$ be separable metric spaces, and X their cartesian product. Then the Borel space $(X, \mathscr{B}_X)$ is the cartesian product of the Borel spaces $(X_n, \mathscr{B}_{X_n})$, $n = 1, 2, \ldots$.

PROOF. Let $(X, \mathscr{B}')$ be the cartesian product of the Borel spaces $(X_n, \mathscr{B}_{X_n})$. We have to show that $\mathscr{B}' = \mathscr{B}_X$. Since $\mathscr{D}_n = \{U_{n1}, U_{n2}, \ldots\}$ is a basis for the topology of X_n, $\mathscr{D}_n$ generates $\mathscr{B}_{X_n}$, and consequently $\mathscr{B}'$ is the σ-algebra generated by V_{nj} $(n = 1, 2, \ldots; j = 1, 2, \ldots)$. Since $V_{nj} \in \mathscr{B}_X$ for all n and j, it follows that $\mathscr{B}' \subseteq \mathscr{B}_X$. On the other hand, the class $\mathscr{V}$ of all sets which are finite intersections of V_{nj}'s is a basis for the topology of X. Now clearly $\mathscr{V} \subseteq \mathscr{B}'$. Since $\mathscr{V}$ is countable and any open set in X is a union of sets in $\mathscr{V}$ it follows that every open set of X is in $\mathscr{B}'$. Since $\mathscr{B}'$ is a σ-algebra, $\mathscr{B}_X \subseteq \mathscr{B}'$. Hence $\mathscr{B}_X = \mathscr{B}'$.

2. THE ISOMORPHISM THEOREM

In this section we shall make a detailed analysis of Borel subsets of a complete separable metric space. The main result of this section asserts that Borel subsets of complete separable metric spaces are isomorphic if and only if they have the same cardinality.

Given metric spaces X_1 and X_2 and Borel sets $B_1 \subseteq X_1$ and $B_2 \subseteq X_2$ we shall say that B_1 and B_2 are isomorphic, $B_1 \sim B_2$ in symbols, if there exists a map φ, called an isomorphism such that (1) φ maps B_1 onto B_2, (2) φ is one-to-one, and (3) φ and φ^{-1} are both measurable. Clearly, $\sim$ is an equivalence relation. The obvious question is to decide when are two Borel sets isomorphic. We shall study this problem when X_1 and X_2 are complete separable metric spaces.

We write I for the unit interval $[0, 1]$ in the real line. For any separable metric space X, we write X^0 for the space of all functions x from the positive integers to X. A point $x \in X^0$ can be expressed as a sequence $(x_1, x_2, \ldots)$, where each $x_n \in X$. We shall use the same symbol to denote the space X, as well as the Borel space of which it is the underlying set. We shall denote by M the countable product of the space consisting of two points 0 and 1. M is the space of sequences of 0's and 1's. M is a compact metric space in its natural (product) topology.

Theorem 2.1

There exists a Borel set $E \subseteq M$ such that $E \sim I$.

Proof. Let E be the set of all functions x from the positive integers into $\{0, 1\}$ (the space consisting of two points 0 and 1 only) such that $x(n) = 1$ for all n or $x(n) = 0$ for infinitely many n. $E \subseteq M$ and $M - E$ is a countable set. Hence E is a Borel set. For any $x \in M$ we write

$$\tau(x) = \sum_{n=1}^{\infty} \frac{x(n)}{2^n}.$$

We shall prove that τ, when restricted to E, is an isomorphism onto I.

Since the series for $\tau(x)$ is uniformly convergent it follows that τ is a continuous map. τ is onto since every number in $[0, 1]$ has a binary expansion. τ is one-one since the binary expansion is unique if we impose the condition that in the expansion all the elements are 1 or 0 occurs infinitely often. Since τ is measurable and E is a Borel set, τ restricted to E is a measurable map of E onto I. We shall now prove that τ^{-1} is measurable.

To prove this we must show that if $A \subseteq E$ is a Borel set then $\tau(A)$ is a Borel set in I. It is enough to prove this for all A of a class which generates the class of Borel sets of E. If we write

$$B_j = \{x : x \in M, x(j) = 1\}$$

and

$$A_j = B_j \cap E$$

for $j = 1, 2, \ldots$, it is enough to prove that $\tau(A_j)$ is a Borel set for $j = 1, 2, \ldots$. It is easy to see that $\tau(A_j)$ is a finite union of intervals whose end points are of the form $m/2^n$. This completes the proof.

Theorem 2.2

There exists a Borel set $E_1 \subseteq M$ such that $E_1 \sim I^0$.

PROOF. Let τ, E have the same meaning as in Theorem 2.1. Form M^0 and define $E^0 = \{y : y(n) \in E \text{ for all } n\}$. Then the map τ' from M^0 onto I^0 defined by

$$\tau'(y)(n) = \tau(y(n))$$

is a measurable map. τ' restricted to E^0 is clearly an isomorphism of E^0 onto I^0. Thus $E^0 \sim I^0$. It is clear that M and M^0 are homeomorphic. Hence E^0 is isomorphic to a Borel set $E_1 \subseteq M$. Hence $E_1 \sim I^0$.

Theorem 2.3

Let X be a complete separable metric space and $E \subseteq X$ a Borel set. Then there exists a Borel set $E_1 \subseteq M$ such that $E \sim E_1$.

PROOF. Because of Theorem 2.2 it is enough to prove that $E \sim E_2$ where E_2 is a Borel set in I^0. However, by the well-known theorems of Urysohn and Alexandroff ([21], pp. 215–216) there exists a G_δ in I^0, say E_3, such that X is homeomorphic to E_3 so that $X \sim E_3$. This completes the proof.

Thus from Theorems 2.1–2.3 it follows that the problem of deciding when two Borel subsets of complete separable metric spaces are isomorphic reduces to the same problem for Borel subsets of M. We shall now examine this problem.

We write $\mathcal{N}$ for the space of all sequences $(n_1, n_2, \ldots)$ where $n_1, n_2, \ldots$ are all integers $\geqslant 1$. $\mathcal{N}$ is the product of countably many copies of the set of positive integers, and a complete separable metric space in the product topology, the integers being given the discrete topology.

Theorem 2.4

Let X be any complete separable metric space. Then there exists a continuous map φ on $\mathcal{N}$ such that φ maps $\mathcal{N}$ onto X.

PROOF. For any set $A \subseteq X$ we write $\delta(A)$ for its diameter. Since X is separable we can write $X = \bigcup_1^\infty A_j$ where each A_j is closed, nonempty and $\delta(A_j) \leqslant 1$. If $n_1, \ldots, n_k$ are integers $\geqslant 1$ and $A_{n_1 n_2, \ldots, n_k}$ is defined we write $A_{n_1, \ldots, n_k} = \bigcup_{j=1}^\infty A_{n_1, \ldots, n_k j}$ where the $A_{n_1 n_2, \ldots, n_k j}$ $(j = 1, 2, \ldots)$ are nonempty, closed, and $\delta(A_{n_1, \ldots, n_k j}) \leqslant 1/(k+1)$ for all j. By induction we can thus ensure that $A_{n_1, \ldots, n_k}$ is defined for all $k = 1, 2, \ldots$, and all positive integers $n_1, n_2, \ldots, n_k$ such that

(1) $A_{n_1 n_2, \ldots, n_k} = \bigcup_{j=1}^\infty A_{n_1 n_2, \ldots, n_k j}$;

(2) $A_{n_1 n_2, \ldots, n_k}$ is closed and nonempty for all $n_1, \ldots, n_k$;

(3) $\delta(A_{n_1 n_2, \ldots, n_k}) \leqslant 1/k$.

For any point $\mathbf{n} = (n_1, \ldots, n_k, \ldots)$ of $\mathcal{N}$ consider $A_{n_1}, A_{n_1 n_2}, \ldots$. Clearly, $A_{n_1} \supseteq A_{n_1 n_2} \supseteq \ldots$ and $\delta(A_{n_1, \ldots, n_k}) \to 0$ as $k \to \infty$. Since X is complete and the A's are nonempty and closed, there exists exactly one point, say x_0, common to all of these. We define $\varphi(\mathbf{n}) = x_0$. In symbols,

$$\{\varphi(\mathbf{n})\} = \bigcap_k A_{n_1 n_2, \ldots, n_k};$$

φ is well-defined on $\mathcal{N}$. If $x_0 \in X$ is an arbitrary point then there is an n_1^0 such that $x_0 \in A_{n_1^0}$, and hence an n_2^0 such that $x_0 \in A_{n_1^0 n_2^0}$, and so on. If $\mathbf{n}^0 = (n_1^0, n_2^0, \ldots)$ then $\varphi(\mathbf{n}^0) = x_0$. This shows that φ maps $\mathcal{N}$ onto X. We shall now show that φ is continuous.

Suppose $\mathbf{n}^0 \in \mathcal{N}$, say $\mathbf{n}^0 = (n_1^0, n_2^0, \ldots)$ and $x_0 = \varphi(\mathbf{n}^0)$. Let $\varepsilon > 0$ be arbitrary but fixed and S the open sphere with x_0 as center and radius ε. Since $\delta(A_{n_1^0,\ldots,n_k^0}) \to 0$ and $x_0 \in A_{n_1^0,\ldots,n_k^0}$ it follows that there exists an integer N such that, for $k \geqslant N$, $A_{n_1^0,\ldots,n_k^0} \subseteq S$. Let now $U = \{\mathbf{n}\colon \mathbf{n} = (n_1, n_2, \ldots)$ and $n_1 = n_1^0,\ n_2 = n_2^0, \ldots,\ n_N = n_N^0\}$. Then U is an open neighborhood of the point $\mathbf{n}^0$ in $\mathcal{N}$. If $\mathbf{n} \in U$, it is clear that for $k \geqslant N$, $A_{n_1,\ldots,n_k} \subseteq A_{n_1^0,\ldots,n_N^0} \subseteq S$. Hence, for $\mathbf{n} \in U$,

$$\{\varphi(\mathbf{n})\} = \bigcap_{k=1}^{\infty} A_{n_1,\ldots,n_k} \subseteq S,$$

i.e., $\varphi(U) \subseteq S$. Thus for every sphere S of arbitrarily small radius $\varepsilon > 0$ with center x_0 we can find an open neighborhood U of $\mathbf{n}^0$ such that $\varphi(U) \subseteq S$. In other words, φ is continuous.

Theorem 2.5

Let X be a complete separable metric space and let $E \subseteq X$ be a Borel set. Then there exists a continuous map φ of $\mathcal{N}$ into X such that φ maps $\mathcal{N}$ onto E.

PROOF. Let $\mathscr{D}$ be the class of subsets A of X which are the ranges of continuous mappings of $\mathcal{N}$ into X. We shall prove that $\mathscr{D}$ contains every Borel set.

Since closed subsets of X with relative topology are complete separable metric spaces in their own right, we conclude from Theorem 2.4 that $\mathscr{D}$ includes all closed sets.

If $A_1, A_2, \ldots, \in \mathscr{D}$, then $\bigcap_{n=1}^{\infty} A_n \in \mathscr{D}$. To prove this let $\varphi_n\colon \mathcal{N} \to X$ be a continuous map such that $\varphi_n(\mathcal{N}) = A_n$. Let $\mathcal{N}^0$ be the cartesian product of countably many copies of $\mathcal{N}$. Let $\tilde{\mathcal{N}} \subseteq \mathcal{N}^0$ be defined by

$$\tilde{\mathcal{N}} = \{(\eta_1, \eta_2, \ldots)\colon \eta_k \in \mathcal{N} \quad \text{for all} \quad k,\ \varphi_1(\eta_1) = \varphi_2(\eta_2) = \ldots\}.$$

Since all the φ_n are continuous $\tilde{\mathcal{N}}$ is a closed subset of $\mathcal{N}^0$. If we define φ on $\tilde{\mathcal{N}}$ by

$$\varphi\colon (\eta_1, \eta_2, \ldots) \to \varphi_1(\eta_1) \qquad (= \varphi_j(\eta_j) \quad \text{for all } j),$$

then it is obvious that φ is continuous and $\varphi(\tilde{\mathcal{N}}) = \bigcap_{n=1}^{\infty} A_n$. $\tilde{\mathcal{N}}$ being closed in $\mathcal{N}^0$ which is itself homeomorphic to $\mathcal{N}$, is a complete separable metric space. Hence by Theorem 2.4 there exists a continuous map ψ from $\mathcal{N}$ onto $\tilde{\mathcal{N}}$. The map $\varphi \cdot \psi$ is continuous, and maps $\mathcal{N}$ onto $\bigcap_{n=1}^{\infty} A_n$. Thus $\mathscr{D}$ is closed under countable intersections.

If $A_1, A_2, \ldots, \in \mathscr{D}$, then $\bigcup_{n=1}^{\infty} A_n \in \mathscr{D}$. To prove this let $\mathscr{N}_k = \{(n_1, n_2, \ldots); n_1 = k\}$. Then $\mathscr{N}_k$ is open and closed in $\mathscr{N}$ for every k. $\mathscr{N}_j$'s are all disjoint and $\mathscr{N} = \bigcup_{j=1}^{\infty} \mathscr{N}_j$. $\mathscr{N}_j$ and $\mathscr{N}$ are homeomorphic. Since $A_j \in \mathscr{D}$, there exists a continuous map

$$\varphi_j : \mathscr{N}_j \to A_j.$$

Define φ on $\mathscr{N}$ by defining it as φ_j in $\mathscr{N}_j$. Then φ is continuous and $\varphi(\mathscr{N}) = \bigcup_{j=1}^{\infty} A_j$.

Now an application of Theorem 1.3 completes the proof.

We shall now examine Borel sets which are uncountable.

Theorem 2.6

Let X be a separable metric space which is uncountable. Then there exists a countable set N such that if $x \in X - N$, every neighborhood of x contains uncountably many points of $X - N$. In particular, $X - N$ is dense in itself.

Proof. Let N be the set of all points $x \in X$ having the property that some open set containing x has only countably many points. For $x \in N$, let N_x be such an open set. Clearly $N = \bigcup_{x \in N} N_x$, and since X is separable, we can find $x_1, x_2, \ldots, \in N$ such that $N = \bigcup_k N_{x_k}$. Thus N is countable. It is obvious that N has the required properties.

Theorem 2.7

Let X be a complete separable metric space, Y a separable metric space with uncountably many points, and let there exist a continuous map φ of X onto Y. Then there exists a subset $C \subseteq X$ such that (1) φ restricted to C is a homeomorphism, and (2) C is homeomorphic to M. In particular, $\varphi(C)$ is a compact subset of Y homeomorphic to M.

Proof. For each $y \in Y$ let $x_y \in X$ be a point such that $\varphi(x_y) = y$. Let $A = \{x_y : y \in Y\}$. A is an uncountable set, and hence by Theorem 2.6, there exists an uncountable subset $D \subseteq A$ such that D is dense in itself. φ is one-one on D.

We can find x_0 and $x_1 \in D$ such that $\varphi(x_0) \neq \varphi(x_1)$. Since φ is continuous we can find closed spheres A_0 and A_1 around x_0 and x_1, respectively, such that (1) $\delta(A_0) \leqslant 1$, $\delta(A_1) \leqslant 1$; and (2) $\varphi(A_0) \cap \varphi(A_1) = \phi$. If this were not possible we can find sequences r_n and s_n in X such that $r_n \to x_0$, $s_n \to x_1$, $\varphi(r_n) = \varphi(s_n)$, which is impossible, since $\varphi(x_0) \neq \varphi(x_1)$.

Since D is dense in itself, the interiors of A_0 and A_1 have infinite intersections with D. Hence, by the same argument as above, we can find points $x_{00}, x_{01} \in D$ such that $x_{00} \neq x_{01}$, and two closed spheres A_{00} and A_{01} such that (1) $x_{00} \in A_{00} \subseteq A_0$, $x_{01} \in A_{01} \subseteq A_0$; (2) $\delta(A_{00}) \leqslant \frac{1}{2}$, $\delta(A_{01}) \leqslant \frac{1}{2}$; and (3) $\varphi(A_{00}) \cap \varphi(A_{01}) = \phi$. Similarly, we can construct A_{10} and A_{11}.

Proceeding successively we have, for each k-tuple $(c_1, c_2, \ldots, c_k)$ of 0's and 1's a closed sphere $A_{c_1c_2,\ldots,c_k}$ such that the family $\{A_{c_1,\ldots,c_k}\}$ has the following properties:

(i) $A_{c_1,\ldots,c_{k+1}} \subseteq A_{c_1,\ldots,c_k}$ for any $c_1, \ldots, c_{k+1}$ and all k;

(ii) $\varphi(A_{c_1,\ldots,c_k}) \cap \varphi(A_{d_1,\ldots,d_k}) = \phi$ if $(c_1, \ldots, c_k) \neq (d_1, \ldots, d_k)$;

(iii) $\delta(A_{c_1,\ldots,c_k}) \leqslant 1/k$ for all k and $c_1, \ldots, c_k$;

(iv) $A_{c_1,\ldots,c_k} \cap D$ is nonempty for all k and $c_1, \ldots, c_k$.

For any $\mathbf{c} = (c_1, c_2, \ldots) \in M$ we let $\tau(\mathbf{c}) = x$ where x is the unique point common to $A_{c_1}, A_{c_1c_2}, \ldots$. An argument similar to the one in Theorem 2.4 shows that τ is a continuous map of M onto a subset $C \subseteq X$. Moreover, condition (ii) implies that $A_{c_1,\ldots,c_k} \cap A_{d_1,\ldots,d_k} = \phi$ if $(c_1, \ldots, c_k) \neq (d_1, \ldots, d_k)$ so that τ is even one-one. Since M is compact it follows that C is homeomorphic to M. We shall now complete the proof by showing that φ is a homeomorphism on C. Since C is compact it is enough to show that φ is one-one on C. If $x, x' \in C$ and $x \neq x'$, then $x = \tau(\mathbf{c})$ and $x' = \tau(\mathbf{c}')$ for $\mathbf{c}, \mathbf{c}' \in M$ with $\mathbf{c} \neq \mathbf{c}'$. Consequently, there are two k-tuples $(c_1, \ldots, c_k)$ and $(d_1, \ldots, d_k)$ of 0's and 1's with $(c_1, \ldots, c_k) \neq (d_1, \ldots, d_k)$ such that $x \in A_{c_1,\ldots,c_k}$ and $x' \in A_{d_1,\ldots,d_k}$. By condition (ii) it is clear that $\varphi(x) \neq \varphi(x')$. This completes the proof.

Theorem 2.8

Let X be a complete separable metric space and $E \subseteq X$ an uncountable Borel set. Then there exists a compact set $C \subseteq E$ homeomorphic to M. In particular, E has the power of the continuum.

PROOF. By Theorem 2.5 there exists a continuous map of $\mathcal{N}$ onto E. Theorem 2.8 follows from Theorem 2.7.

Theorem 2.9

Let $E_1, E_2, \ldots,$ *and* $F_1, F_2, \ldots$ *be Borel subsets of* M *such that* (i) $E_i \cap E_j = F_i \cap F_j = \phi$, $i \neq j$ *and* (ii) $E_i \sim F_i$. *Then* $\bigcup_i E_i \sim \bigcup_i F_i$.

PROOF. Obvious.

Theorem 2.10

If E *and* F *are Borel subsets of* M, $E \sim F$ *and if* $E = E_1 \cup E_2$ *where* E_1, E_2 *are disjoint Borel sets, then there are disjoint Borel sets* F_1 *and* F_2 *such that* $E_1 \sim F_1$, $E_2 \sim F_2$ *and* $F = F_1 \cup F_2$.

PROOF. Let φ be any isomorphism from E onto F. Let $F_1 = \varphi(E_1)$, $F_2 = \varphi(E_2)$. F_1 and F_2 satisfy the required conditions.

Theorem 2.11

If E, E_1, *and* F *are Borel subsets of* M *such that* (i) $E \sim E_1$, *and* (ii) $E_1 \subseteq F \subseteq E$, *then* $E \sim F$.

PROOF. Let $D_1 = E - E_1$. Since $E \sim E_1$ and $E = E_1 \cup D_1$ we can find disjoint Borel sets E_2 and D_2 such that $E_1 = E_2 \cup D_2$, $E_1 \sim E_2$, $D_1 \sim D_2$. Proceeding successively we can write $E_{n-1} = E_n \cup D_n$ where E_n and D_n are disjoint Borel sets with $E_{n-1} \sim E_n$, $D_{n-1} \sim D_n$. Clearly, $D_1, D_2, \ldots$ are disjoint Borel sets. Let $E_\infty = \bigcap_n E_n$. Then $E = E_\infty \cup D_1 \cup D_2 \cup, \ldots$.

Let now $A_1 = E - F$ and $B_1 = F - E_1$. Then $D_1 = A_1 \cup B_1$. Since $D_1 \sim D_2 \sim, \ldots$, we can find disjoint Borel sets A_n and B_n such that $A_1 \sim A_n$, $B_1 \sim B_n$ and $D_n = A_n \cup B_n$. We then obtain

$$\begin{aligned}
E &= E_\infty \cup \left\{\bigcup_1^\infty D_i\right\} \\
&= E_\infty \cup \left\{\bigcup_1^\infty A_i\right\} \cup \left\{\bigcup_1^\infty B_i\right\} \\
&\sim E_\infty \cup \left(\bigcup_2^\infty A_i\right) \cup \left(\bigcup_1^\infty B_i\right) \\
&= B_1 \cup E_\infty \cup \left(\bigcup_2^\infty D_i\right) \\
&= B_1 \cup E_1 \\
&= F.
\end{aligned}$$

This proves Theorem 2.11.

Theorem 2.12

Let X_1 and X_2 be two complete separable metric spaces and let $E_1 \subseteq X_1$ and $E_2 \subseteq X_2$ be two Borel sets. Then E_1 and E_2 are isomorphic if and only if they have the same cardinality.

PROOF. The "only if" part is trivial. By virtue of Theorem 2.3 we may take $X_1 = X_2 = M$. If one of the E_i's is finite or countably infinite we are through. Suppose E_1 and E_2 are uncountable. We shall prove that $E_1 \sim M$, $E_2 \sim M$. By Theorem 2.8, there exists a Borel set $M_1 \subseteq E_1$ such that $M_1 \sim M$. Since $M_1 \subseteq E_1 \subseteq M$ and $M_1 \sim M$, it follows from Theorem 2.11 that $E_1 \sim M$. Similarly, $E_2 \sim M$. This completes the proof.

We finish this section with another important proposition on Borel sets.

Theorem 2.13

Let X be a complete separable metric space. Then there exists a complete separable totally disconnected metric space Y and a continuous one-one map φ such that φ maps Y onto X.

PROOF. We recall that a totally disconnected separable metric space has the property that every open set can be expressed as a disjoint union of countably many open and closed sets. The class of totally disconnected separable metric spaces is closed under taking countable cartesian products and passing to subspaces.

The space M consisting of all sequences of 0's and 1's is totally disconnected. By Theorem 2.1, the unit interval I is a one-one continuous image of E where $M - E$ is countable. E is a G_δ in M and hence, by Alexandroff's theorem, E is a complete separable metric space which is totally disconnected. Thus the theorem holds when $X = I$.

The class of spaces for which the present theorem holds is obviously closed under taking countable cartesian products. Thus the theorem holds when $X = I^0$. Suppose now X is an arbitrary complete separable metric space. By the well-known theorems of Urysohn and Alexandroff we may regard X as a G_δ subset of I^0. Let Y_1 be a complete separable, totally disconnected metric space and φ a continuous one-one map of

Y_1 onto I^0. If $Y = \varphi^{-1}(X)$, then Y is a G_δ in Y_1, and hence a complete separable totally disconnected metric space. φ restricted to Y is a continuous one-one map onto X.

Theorem 2.14

Let X be a complete separable metric space and $E \subseteq X$ a Borel set. Then there exists a complete separable totally disconnected metric space Y and a continuous map φ of Y such that φ is one-one and φ maps Y onto E.

PROOF. Let $\mathscr{D}$ be the class of all Borel sets E having the required property. Since any open subset of X is, under a suitable equivalent metric, a complete separable metric space, Theorem 2.13 implies that $\mathscr{D}$ contains all open sets. It is proved exactly as in Theorem 2.5 that $\mathscr{D}$ is closed under countable intersections. We claim further that $\mathscr{D}$ is closed under countable disjoint unions. In fact if $A_1, A_2, \ldots, \in \mathscr{D}$ and are mutually disjoint, we write $A_n = \varphi_n(X_n)$ where the X_n are disjoint complete separable metric spaces which are totally disconnected and φ_n is a one-one continuous map for each n. Let $X = \bigcup X_n$. We topologize X so that $U \subseteq X$ is open if and only if $U \cap X_n$ is open for each n. Then X_n is open and closed in X, and X is a complete, separable, totally disconnected metric space. If we write $\varphi(x) = \varphi_n(x)$ whenever $x \in X_n$, then φ is one-one, continuous on X and $\varphi(X) = \bigcup A_n$.

Now an application of Theorem 1.4 completes the proof.

3. THE KURATOWSKI THEOREM

The main purpose of this section is to establish an important theorem due to Kuratowski which asserts that if φ is a one-one measurable map from a Borel subset E_1 of a complete separable metric space onto a Borel subset E_2 of another complete separable metric space then φ^{-1} is also measurable, i.e., φ is an isomorphism.

In order to prove this result we need the notion of analytic sets. Let X be a complete separable metric space.

Definition 3.1

A subset E of X is called analytic if there exists a continuous map φ of $\mathscr{N}$ onto E.

We denote by $\mathscr{A}_X$, or $\mathscr{A}$ when no confusion can arise, the class of analytic subsets of X.

Theorem 3.1

If X is a complete separable metric space, the class $\mathscr{A}$ of analytic subsets of X is closed under countable unions and countable intersections. Every Borel set is analytic.

PROOF. The proof of Theorem 2.5 contains the proof of both these assertions.

Theorem 3.2

Let $X_1, X_2, \ldots$ be complete separable metric spaces, and let $A_n \subseteq X_n$ be an analytic set for each n. Let X be the cartesian product of the X_n and $A = \prod_n A_n$. Then A is analytic in X.

PROOF. Let φ_n be a continuous map of $\mathscr{N}$ onto A_n. Let $\mathscr{N}^0$ be the cartesian product of countably many copies of $\mathscr{N}$ and let, for any $(\mathbf{n}^1, \mathbf{n}^2, \ldots) \in \mathscr{N}^0$ ($\mathbf{n}^j \in \mathscr{N}$ for all $j = 1, 2, \ldots$), $\varphi(\mathbf{n}^1, \mathbf{n}^2, \ldots) = (\varphi_1(\mathbf{n}^1), \varphi_2(\mathbf{n}^2), \ldots)$. Then φ is continuous on $\mathscr{N}^0$ and onto A. Since $\mathscr{N}^0$ and $\mathscr{N}$ are homeomorphic it follows that A is analytic.

Theorem 3.3

Let X_1, X_2 be two separable metric spaces and let φ be a measurable map of X_1 onto X_2. If $E = \{(x_1, \varphi(x_1)) : x_1 \in X_1\}$, then E is a Borel set in $X_1 \times X_2$.

PROOF. The maps $\tau_1: (x_1, x_2) \to x_2$ and $\tau_2: (x_1, x_2) \to \varphi(x_1)$ are both measurable maps of $X = X_1 \times X_2$ into X_2. Hence, the map $\tau: (x_1, x_2) \to [\tau_1(x_1, x_2), \tau_2(x_1, x_2)] = [x_2, \varphi(x_1)]$ is a measurable map of X into $X_2 \times X_2$. If $D = \{(x_2, x_2) : x_2 \in X_2\}$, then D is a Borel subset of $X_2 \times X_2$. Clearly, $E = \tau^{-1}(D)$, and so E is a Borel set in $X_1 \times X_2$.

Theorem 3.4

Let X_1, X_2 be complete separable metric spaces, $E_1 \subseteq X_1$ be analytic, and φ a measurable map of E_1 into X_2. If $E_2 = \varphi(E_1)$, then E_2 is analytic in X_2.

PROOF. We shall first suppose that E_1 is a Borel set. Let $X = X_1 \times X_2$ and $E = \{(x_1, \varphi(x_1)) : x_1 \in E_1\}$. By Theorem 3.3, E is a Borel set in X. Let σ be the map $(x_1, x_2) \to x_2$ of X onto X_2. σ is a continuous map and $\sigma(E) = E_2$. Since E is the range of a continuous map ψ of $\mathcal{N}$ into X, it follows that E_2 is the range of the continuous map $\sigma \cdot \psi$ from $\mathcal{N}$ into X_2. Thus E_2 is analytic.

In the general case when E_1 need not be a Borel set we choose a continuous map φ_1 of $\mathcal{N}$ into X_1 such that $\varphi_1(\mathcal{N}) = E_1$ and write $\psi_1 = \varphi \cdot \varphi_1$. From the special case proved above it is seen that $\psi_1(\mathcal{N})$ is analytic in X_2. But $\psi_1(\mathcal{N}) = E_2$. This completes the proof.

Theorem 3.5

Let X_1, X_2 be complete separable metric spaces and let $E_1 \subseteq X_1$, $E_2 \subseteq X_2$ be two analytic sets thereof. If φ is a measurable map of E_1 into X_2, then $\varphi^{-1}(E_2) \cap E_1 = \varphi^{-1}(E_2)$ is an analytic subset of X_1.

PROOF. Let $E = \{(x_1, \varphi(x_1)) : x_1 \in E_1\}$. E is a Borel subset of $E_1 \times X_2$. Since $E_1 \times X_2$ is an analytic subset of $X_1 \times X_2$, it follows that E is analytic in $X_1 \times X_2$. Let τ be the map $(x_1, x_2) \to x_1$ of $X_1 \times X_2$ onto X_1. Then

$$\varphi^{-1}(E_2) \cap E_1 = \tau[(X_1 \times E_2) \cap E]$$

and hence is an analytic set.

Theorem 3.6

Let X be a complete separable metric space and $E \subseteq X$ an analytic set. If E is uncountable there exists a compact set $C \subseteq E$ such that C is homeomorphic to M. In particular, E has the power of the continuum.

PROOF. This is an immediate consequence of Theorem 2.7.

We shall now make a deeper analysis of analytic sets by a more careful analysis of continuous maps of the space $\mathcal{N}$.

Definition 3.2

Suppose that $A_{n_1,\ldots,n_k}$ is a set in some space and that $A_{n_1,\ldots,n_k}$ is defined for each k and each k-tuple $(n_1,\ldots, n_k)$ of positive integers. Then the set

$$E = \bigcup_{(n_1, n_2, \ldots)} \left[\bigcap_{k=1}^{\infty} A_{n_1 n_2,\ldots,n_k}\right]$$

is said to be the result of performing *operation* (A) on the system $\{A_{n_1,\ldots,n_k}\}$. The system $\{A_{n_1,\ldots,n_k}\}$ is said to be *regular* if $A_{n_1,\ldots,n_{k+1}} \subseteq A_{n_1,\ldots,n_k}$ for all k and $n_1,\ldots, n_{k+1}$.

Theorem 3.7

Let X be a complete separable metric space and let $\{A_{n_1,\ldots,n_k}\}$ be a regular system of closed subsets of X such that for each fixed $(n_1, n_2,\ldots)$, $\delta(A_{n_1n_2,\ldots,n_k}) \to 0$ as $k \to \infty$. Then the result of performing operation (A) on this system is an analytic set. Conversely, every analytic subset of X can be so obtained.

PROOF. Let E be the set obtained from $\{A_{n_1,\ldots,n_k}\}$ by performing operation (A). We write $\tilde{\mathcal{N}} = \{(n_1, n_2,\ldots) : A_{n_1n_2,\ldots,n_k} \neq \phi \text{ for all } k\}$. Since X is complete, $\bigcap_{k=1}^{\infty} A_{n_1n_2,\ldots,n_k} \neq \phi$ if and only if $(n_1, n_2,\ldots) \in \tilde{\mathcal{N}}$ so that

$$E = \bigcup_{(n_1, n_2,\ldots) \in \tilde{\mathcal{N}}} \left[\bigcap_{k=1}^{\infty} A_{n_1 n_2,\ldots,n_k}\right]$$

For $(n_1, n_2,\ldots) \in \tilde{\mathcal{N}}$ we define $\varphi(\mathbf{n})$ to be the unique point common to all $A_{n_1n_2,\ldots,n_k}$. φ is well defined on $\tilde{\mathcal{N}}$ and $E = \varphi(\tilde{\mathcal{N}})$.

$\tilde{\mathcal{N}}$ is a closed subset of $\mathcal{N}$. In fact, if $(n_1, n_2,\ldots) \in \mathcal{N} - \tilde{\mathcal{N}}$, then for some integer N, $A_{n_1n_2,\ldots,n_N} = \phi$ so that $\mathcal{N}_{n_1n_2,\ldots,n_N} = \{(m_1, m_2,\ldots) : m_1 = n_1,\ldots, m_N = n_N\} \subseteq \mathcal{N} - \tilde{\mathcal{N}}$. $\mathcal{N}_{n_1n_2,\ldots,n_N}$ is open in $\mathcal{N}$. Hence $\mathcal{N} - \tilde{\mathcal{N}}$ is open and $\tilde{\mathcal{N}}$ is closed.

By exactly the same argument as in Theorem 2.4 we conclude that φ is continuous. Since $E = \varphi(\tilde{\mathcal{N}})$ it follows that E is analytic.

To prove the converse, let $E \subseteq X$ be analytic and φ a continuous map of $\mathcal{N}$ onto E. Let $A_{n_1n_2,\ldots,n_k} = \overline{\{\varphi(\mathcal{N}_{n_1n_2,\ldots,n_k})\}}$ where the bar denotes closure and

$$\mathcal{N}_{n_1 n_2,\ldots,n_k} = \{(m_1, m_2,\ldots) : m_1 = n_1, m_2 = n_2,\ldots, m_k = n_k\}.$$

Using the continuity of φ it is easy to verify that

$$E = \bigcup_{(n_1, n_2,\ldots)} \left[\bigcap_{k=1}^{\infty} A_{n_1 n_2,\ldots,n_k}\right].$$

Definition 3.3

Given two disjoint subsets A and B of a metric space we shall say that A and B can be *separated by Borel sets* if there are Borel sets E and F such that $A \subseteq E$, $B \subseteq F$, and $E \cap F = \phi$.

Lemma 3.1

Let $\{A_m\}$ and $\{B_n\}$ be two sequences of subsets of X and let $A_m \cap B_n = \phi$ for all m and n. If A_m and B_n can be separated by Borel sets for all m and n, then $\bigcup_m A_m$ and $\bigcup_n B_n$ can be separated by Borel sets.

PROOF. Let E_{mn} and F_{mn} be disjoint Borel sets such that $A_m \subseteq E_{mn}$, $B_n \subseteq F_{mn}$. Let $\tilde{E}_m = \bigcap_{n=1}^{\infty} E_{mn}$ and $\tilde{E} = \bigcup_m \tilde{E}_m$, $F = \bigcap_m \bigcup_n F_{mn}$. Then $\bigcup_m A_m \subseteq \tilde{E}$, $\bigcup_n B_n \subseteq \tilde{F}$. The sets $\tilde{E}$ and $\tilde{F}$ are disjoint Borel sets.

Theorem 3.8

Let X be a complete separable metric space and let A and B be two disjoint analytic subsets of X. Then there are two disjoint Borel subsets E and F of X such that $A \subseteq E$, $B \subseteq F$.

PROOF. Let φ and ψ be two continuous maps of $\mathcal{N}$ such that $\varphi(\mathcal{N}) = A$, $\psi(\mathcal{N}) = B$. Since $\mathcal{N} = \bigcup_k \mathcal{N}_k$, $A = \bigcup_k \varphi(\mathcal{N}_k)$, $B = \bigcup_k \psi(\mathcal{N}_k)$. If A and B cannot be separated by Borel sets then by Lemma 3.1 we can conclude that there exist n_1 and m_1 such that $\varphi(\mathcal{N}_{n_1})$ and $\psi(\mathcal{N}_{m_1})$ cannot be separated by Borel sets. Since $\mathcal{N}_k = \bigcup_l \mathcal{N}_{kl}$ it follows that for some integers n_2 and m_2, $\varphi(\mathcal{N}_{n_1 n_2})$ and $\psi(\mathcal{N}_{m_1 m_2})$ cannot be separated by Borel sets. Repeating the argument we obtain two points $\mathbf{n} = (n_1, n_2, \ldots)$, $\mathbf{m} = (m_1, m_2, \ldots)$ of $\mathcal{N}$ such that for all k, $\varphi(\mathcal{N}_{n_1 n_2, \ldots, n_k})$ and $\psi(\mathcal{N}_{m_1 m_2, \ldots, m_k})$ cannot be separated by Borel sets.

Since $\varphi(\mathbf{n}) \in A$ and $\psi(\mathbf{m}) \in B$, $\varphi(\mathbf{n}) \neq \psi(\mathbf{m})$, and hence there exists an $\varepsilon_0 > 0$ such that spheres of radius ε_0 with centers $\varphi(\mathbf{n})$ and $\psi(\mathbf{m})$ are disjoint. Since φ and ψ are continuous, we can choose N so large that

$$\delta(\varphi[\mathcal{N}_{n_1 n_2, \ldots, n_N}]) < \varepsilon_0, \qquad \delta(\psi[\mathcal{N}_{m_1 m_2, \ldots, m_N}]) < \varepsilon_0$$

This means that $\varphi[\mathcal{N}_{n_1 n_2, \ldots, n_N}]$ and $\psi[\mathcal{N}_{m_1 m_2, \ldots, m_N}]$ can be separated by open spheres. This is a contradiction. This completes the proof.

Corollary 3.1

Let $A \subseteq X$ be analytic. Then $X - A$ is analytic if and only if A is Borel.

Corollary 3.2

Let $A_1, A_2, \ldots$ be a sequence of mutually disjoint analytic sets. Then there is a sequence of mutually disjoint Borel sets $E_1, E_2, \ldots$ such that $A_n \subseteq E_n$ for all n.

PROOF. Since A_m and A_n are disjoint for $m \neq n$, A_1 and $\bigcup_{n \geqslant 2} A_n$ are disjoint analytic sets. Thus by theorem 3.8 we can find disjoint Borel sets E_1 and F_1 such that $A_1 \subseteq E_1$, $\bigcup_{n \geqslant 2} A_n \subseteq F_1$. We can then separate similarly A_2 and $\bigcup_{n \geqslant 3} A_n$ by Borel sets E_2 and F_2 such that $E_2 \subseteq F_1$, $F_2 \subseteq F_1$. Repeating the argument we complete the proof.

Lemma 3.2

Let X be a complete separable metric space, Y a complete separable totally disconnected metric space. Let $E \subseteq X$ be such that $\varphi(Y) = E$ where φ is a continuous one-one map of Y into X. Then E is a Borel set.

PROOF. Since Y is totally disconnected we can find a system $\{A_{n_1 n_2, \ldots, n_k}\}$ of open-closed subsets of Y such that

(i) $A_{n_1 n_2, \ldots, n_k} \cap A_{m_1 m_2, \ldots, m_k} = \phi$

if $(n_1, n_2, \ldots, n_k) \neq (m_1, m_2, \ldots, m_k)$;

(ii) $A_{n_1 n_2, \ldots, n_k} = \bigcup_l A_{n_1 n_2, \ldots, n_k l}$, $Y = \bigcup A_n$;

(iii) $\delta(A_{n_1 n_2, \ldots, n_k}) \leqslant 1/k$.

Let $E_{n_1 n_2, \ldots, n_k} = \varphi(A_{n_1 n_2, \ldots, n_k})$. Then by Theorem 3.4, $E_{n_1 n_2, \ldots, n_k}$ are disjoint analytic sets, and hence by Corollary 3.2 of Theorem 3.8 we can find disjoint Borel sets $B_1, B_2, \ldots$ such that $E_n \subseteq B_n$ for all n. For given n_1, $E_{n_1 1}, E_{n_1 2}, \ldots$ are disjoint analytic sets $\subseteq E_{n_1}$ and thus, using the same corollary once again, we can find disjoint Borel sets $B_{n_1 1}$, $B_{n_1 2}, \ldots$ such that $E_{n_1 l} \subseteq B_{n_1 l}$ for all l. By replacing $B_{n_1 l}$ by $B_{n_1 l} \cap B_{n_1}$ we may and do assume that $B_{n_1 l} \subseteq B_{n_1}$ for all n_1. Proceeding successively we obtain a regular system $\{B_{n_1n_2,\ldots,n_k}\}$ of Borel sets such that $E_{n_1n_2,\ldots,n_k} \subseteq B_{n_1n_2,\ldots,n_k}$ and $B_{n_1n_2,\ldots,n_k} \cap B_{m_1,\ldots,m_k} = \phi$ if $(n_1,\ldots,n_k) \neq (m_1,m_2,\ldots,m_k)$. Let $B^*_{n_1n_2,\ldots,n_k} = B_{n_1n_2,\ldots,n_k} \cap \bar{E}_{n_1n_2,\ldots,n_k}$. Clearly, $E_{n_1n_2,\ldots,n_k} \subseteq B^*_{n_1n_2,\ldots,n_k}$ and $B^*_{n_1n_2,\ldots,n_k} \cap B^*_{m_1,\ldots,m_k} = \phi$ if $(n_1n_2,\ldots,n_k) \neq (m_1m_2,\ldots,m_k)$.

Let $E^* = \bigcup_{\mathbf{n}} \bigcap_{k=1}^{\infty} B^*_{n_1n_2,\ldots,n_k}$. Since $B^*_{n_1,\ldots,n_k} \cap B^*_{m_1m_2,\ldots,m_k} = \phi$ if $(n_1,\ldots,n_k) \neq (m_1m_2,\ldots,m_k)$, it is easily verified that $E^* = \bigcap_{k=1}^{\infty} \bigcup_{(n_1n_2,\ldots,n_k)} B^*_{n_1n_2,\ldots,n_k}$, and hence E^* is a Borel set. We shall prove that $E = E^*$.

Notice that if $x \in E$, $x = \varphi(y)$ for some $y \in Y$, and hence there is an $\mathbf{n} = (n_1, n_2, \ldots)$ such that $y \in A_{n_1}, A_{n_1n_2}, \ldots$. This shows that $x \in E_{n_1}, E_{n_1n_2}, \ldots$, and hence that $x \in E^*$. Thus $E \subseteq E^*$.

Suppose now $x \in E^*$. Since $B^*_{n_1n_2,\ldots,n_k} \subseteq \bar{E}_{n_1,\ldots,n_k}$, it follows that $x \in \bigcup_{\mathbf{n}} \bigcap_{k=1}^{\infty} \bar{E}_{n_1,\ldots,n_k}$ and hence there exists an $\mathbf{n}$ such that $x \in \bar{E}_{n_1}, \bar{E}_{n_1n_2}, \ldots, \bar{E}_{n_1}, \bar{E}_{n_1n_2}, \ldots$ are nonempty, and hence so are $E_{n_1}, E_{n_1n_2}, \ldots$. Consequently, $A_{n_1}, A_{n_1n_2}, \ldots$ are nonempty, and hence $\bigcap_k A_{n_1n_2,\ldots,n_k}$ consists of exactly one point, say y. Since φ is continuous at y, and since $\delta(A_{n_1n_2,\ldots,n_k}) \to 0$ as $k \to \infty$, $\delta(E_{n_1n_2,\ldots,n_k}) \to 0$. But $\delta(E_{n_1n_2,\ldots,n_k}) = \delta(\bar{E}_{n_1n_2,\ldots,n_k})$ so that $\delta(\bar{E}_{n_1n_2,\ldots,n_k}) \to 0$. This means that exactly one point is common to all the $\bar{E}_{n_1n_2,\ldots,n_k}$. Since x and $\varphi(y)$ are both in all the $\bar{E}_{n_1n_2,\ldots,n_k}$, we have $x = \varphi(y)$. Thus $x \in E$. As x was an arbitrary point of E^*, we have $E^* \subseteq E$.

The two inclusions show that $E^* = E$, and hence E is a Borel set.

Theorem 3.9

Let X_1, X_2 be complete separable metric spaces and $E_1 \subseteq X_1$, $E_2 \subseteq X_2$ two sets, E_1 being a Borel set. Let φ be a measurable one-one map of E_1 into X_2 such that $\varphi(E_1) = E_2$. Then E_2 is a Borel set.

Proof. Let $E \subseteq X = X_1 \times X_2$ be the set $\{(x_1, \varphi(x_1)) : x_1 \in E_1\}$. Then by Theorem 3.3, E is a Borel set in X. Let τ be the continuous map $(x_1, x_2) \to x_2$ of X onto X_2. Since φ is one-one, τ is a one-one continuous map of E onto E_2. By Theorem 2.14, E is the range of a one-one continuous map ψ of some totally disconnected complete separable metric space Y. Hence, if $\psi' = \tau \cdot \psi$, then ψ' is one-one and continuous and maps Y onto E_2. By Lemma 3.2, E_2 is a Borel set.

Corollary 3.3

If E_1 is a Borel subset of a complete separable metric space X_1 and φ is a one-one measurable map of E_1 into a separable metric space X_2, then $\varphi(E_1)$ is a Borel subset of X_2, E_1, and $\varphi(E_1)$ are isomorphic and φ is an isomorphism.

PROOF. This follows immediately from Theorem 3.9 by considering φ as a map from X_1 into the completion of X_2.

4. BOREL CROSS SECTIONS IN COMPACT METRIC SPACES

In this section we shall prove an important property of continuous mappings of compact metric spaces.

Theorem 4.1

Let X be a compact metric space. Then there exists a nowhere dense closed subset A of the unit interval and a continuous map h of A onto X.

PROOF. Since X is compact, it is a finite union of sets of arbitrarily small diameter. Hence we may write $X = \bigcup_{i=1}^{s_1} M_i$, where M_i is nonempty and $\delta(M_i) \leqslant 1$ for $i = 1, 2, \ldots, s_1$. Let $N_i = \bar{M}_i$. Then $X = \bigcup_{i=1}^{s_1} N_i$, where N_i are closed and hence compact, nonempty and $\delta(N_i) \leqslant 1$ for $i = 1, 2, \ldots, s_1$. Similarly, each of the sets N_i can be expressed as the union of a finite number of closed sets N_{ij}, $j = 1, 2, \ldots, s_2$ and $\delta(N_{ij}) \leqslant \frac{1}{2}$. Repeating this construction, we obtain an infinite sequence $s_1, s_2, \ldots$ of natural numbers (where $s_k > 1$ for $k > 1$) such that for every finite set $n_1, n_2, \ldots, n_k$ of indices, where $n_i \leqslant s_i$ for $i = 1, 2, \ldots, k$, the compact set $N_{n_1 n_2, \ldots, n_k}$ is nonempty, $\delta(N_{n_1 n_2, \ldots, n_k}) \leqslant 1/k$, and $N_{n_1 n_2, \ldots, n_k} = \bigcup_{l=1}^{s_{k+1}} N_{n_1 n_2, \ldots, n_k l}$.

For each finite sequence $n_1, n_2, \ldots, n_k$ of indices such that $n_i \leqslant s_i$ for $i = 1, 2, \ldots, k$, we now define a closed interval $I_{n_1 n_2, \ldots, n_k}$ in the following manner. Divide the closed interval $[0, 1]$ into $2s_1$ equal intervals. Denote by $I_1, I_2, \ldots, I_{s_1}$ every second one of these intervals, endpoints included. Suppose we have chosen $I_{n_1 n_2, \ldots, n_k}$ for some $n_i \leqslant s_i$, $i = 1, 2, \ldots, k$. Then divide the interval $I_{n_1 n_2, \ldots, n_k}$ into $2s_{k+1}$ equal intervals and denote every second one of these intervals by $I_{n_1 n_2,\ldots,n_k l}$, $l = 1, 2,\ldots, s_{k+1}$. Let

$$S_k = \bigcup_{\substack{n_i \leqslant s_i \\ i=1,2\ldots k}} I_{n_1 n_2,\ldots,n_k}.$$

Then S_k are nonempty, closed and $S_{k+1} \subseteq S_k$ for all k. Hence, $A = \bigcap_{k=1}^{\infty} S_k$ is a nonempty closed set. It is clear that A is nowhere dense in $[0, 1]$.

Let now $x \in A$. Since $x \in S_1$ and $I_1, I_2,\ldots, I_{s_1}$ are disjoint there exists a unique $n_1 \leqslant s_1$ such that $x \in I_{n_1}$. Since $x \in S_2$, by the same argument there exists a unique $n_2 \leqslant s_2$ such that $x \in I_{n_1 n_2}$.

Continuing in this manner we obtain an infinite sequence $n_1, n_2,\ldots,$ determined uniquely by the number $x \in A$ and such that

(i) $n_k \leqslant s_k$;

(ii) $x \in I_{n_1 n_2,\ldots,n_k}$, for $k = 1, 2,\ldots.$

Let

$$h(x) = \bigcap_{k=1}^{\infty} N_{n_1 n_2,\ldots,n_k}.$$

Since $N_{n_1 n_2,\ldots,n_k}$ is a decreasing sequence of closed subsets of a compact metric space such that $\delta(N_{n_1 n_2,\ldots,n_k}) \to 0$ as $k \to \infty$, $h(x)$ is a single point set in X. Exactly as in the proof of Theorem 2.4 it follows that h is continuous on A and maps A onto X.

Theorem 4.2

Let X and Y be compact metric spaces and g a continuous map of X onto Y. Then there is a Borel set $B \subseteq X$ such that $g(B) = Y$ and g is one-one on B.

Proof. By Theorem 4.1, we can select a closed set A of the unit interval and a continuous map h from A onto X.

Let now

$$A_n = \{t : t \in A, \quad g(h(s)) \neq g(h(t)) \quad \text{for all} \quad s \in A, \quad s \leqslant t - 1/n\}.$$

Then it is easy to verify that $A - A_n$ is closed in A, and hence A_n is open in A. Let

$$B_n = h(A_n).$$

Since A_n is open, it is an F_σ set and since images of compact sets are compact, it follows that B_n is an F_σ in X. Let

$$B = \bigcap_{n=1}^{\infty} B_n.$$

Then B is a Borel set. Let now $y_0 \in Y$ and

$$t_0 = \inf \{t : t \in A \cap h^{-1}(g^{-1}(\{y_0\}))\},$$
$$x_0 = h(t_0).$$

Then it is clear that

$$t_0 \in \cap A_n, \qquad x_0 \in B, \qquad g(x_0) = y_0.$$

If $x_0 \neq x_1$, $x_1 \in B$ and $g(x_1) = y_0$, then we infer that the set $A \cap h^{-1}[\{x_1\}]$ is a closed set lying entirely to the right of t_0 with distance $d > 0$ from t_0; hence $n > d^{-1}$ implies that $A \cap h^{-1}[\{x_1\}] \subseteq A - A_n$ which in turn implies $x_1 \in X - B_n \subseteq X - B$. This contradicts the fact that $x_1 \in B$, and completes the proof of the theorem.

REMARK. The set B occurring in Theorem 4.2 is called a Borel cross section for the map g.

5. BOREL CROSS SECTIONS IN LOCALLY COMPACT GROUPS

We shall now establish a lemma due to Mackey [25] (cf. p. 102), which will be used in Chapter IV.

Let X be a locally compact second countable group and H a closed subgroup of X. Let Y be the homogeneous space of right H cosets and let $\tau(x \to \tau(x))$ denote the canonical mapping of X onto Y. τ maps x to the unique right H coset to which x belongs.

Lemma 5.1

There exists a Borel set B in X such that (a) *B intersects each right H coset in exactly one point and* (b) *for each compact set $K \subseteq X$, $\tau^{-1}[\tau(K)] \cap B$ has compact closure.*

PROOF. First of all we note that X and Y are topologically complete separable spaces, i.e., their topologies admit metrics under which they are complete and separable. Choose a compact neighborhood V of the identity such that $V = V^{-1}$ where $V^{-1} = \{x: x^{-1} \in V\}$. If X is connected then $X = \bigcup_{n=1}^{\infty} V^n$ and every compact subset of X is in some V^n. If X is not connected then $\bigcup_1^{\infty} V^n$ is an open and closed subgroup with only countably many cosets. In any case it is clear that there exists in X a countable family $K_1 \subseteq K_2 \subseteq \ldots$ of compact subsets of X such that any compact set is contained in some K_n. By Theorem 4.2 there exists for each j, a Borel subset $B_j \subseteq K_j$ such that $\tau(B_j) = \tau(K_j)$ and such that τ is one-one on B_j. We now claim that B_j may be so chosen that $B_{j+1} \supseteq B_j$ for $j = 1, 2, \ldots$. In fact, suppose $B_1, B_2, \ldots, B_j$ have been chosen such that $B_1 \subseteq B_2 \subseteq \ldots \subseteq B_j$. By Theorem 3.9, $\tau(B_j)$ is a Borel set. Let $\tilde{B}_{j+1} \subseteq K_{j+1}$ be any Borel set such that $\tau(\tilde{B}_{j+1}) = \tau(K_{j+1})$ and τ is one-one on $\tilde{B}_{j+1}$. Choose $B_{j+1} = [\tilde{B}_{j+1} - \tau^{-1}(\tau(B_j))] \cup B_j$. Then B_{j+1} has the required properties. Since B_j's are Borel sets in a complete separable metric space, it follows from Theorem 3.9 that $\tau(B_j)$ is a Borel set for every j and the set $B = \bigcup_{j=1}^{\infty} B_j$ has all the required properties.

II

PROBABILITY MEASURES IN A METRIC SPACE

1. REGULAR MEASURES

By a *measure* μ on a metric space we shall understand a countably additive nonnegative set function μ on the class of Borel sets $\mathscr{B}_X$ with the property that $\mu(X) = 1$.[1] The main aim of this section is to show that in a metric space a measure μ is uniquely determined by its values for the topologically important sets such as closed sets or open sets.

Definition 1.1

Let μ be a measure on the metric space X. A Borel subset A of X is said to be *μ-regular* if

$$\begin{aligned}\mu(A) &= \sup\{\mu(C): C \subseteq A, \quad C \text{ closed}\}\\ &= \inf\{\mu(U): A \subseteq U, \quad U \text{ open}\}.\end{aligned}$$

If every Borel set is μ-regular we shall say that μ is *regular*.

Theorem 1.1

Let X be a metric space and μ a measure in X. Then an $A \in \mathscr{B}_X$ is μ-regular if and only if for each $\varepsilon > 0$ there is an open set U_ε and a closed set C_ε such that

---

[1] For the sake of simplicity the term "measure" will be used for probability measures until further notice.

(i) $C_\varepsilon \subseteq A \subseteq U_\varepsilon$;

(ii) $\mu(U_\varepsilon - C_\varepsilon) < \varepsilon$.

PROOF. Obvious.

Theorem 1.2

Let X be a metric space and μ any measure on X. Then μ is regular.

PROOF. Let $\mathscr{R}$ denote the class of all Borel sets of X which are μ-regular. Then $\mathscr{R} \subseteq \mathscr{B}_X$. Since ϕ and X are open and closed it follows that $\phi \in \mathscr{R}$, $X \in \mathscr{R}$. $\mathscr{R}$ is closed under complementation. In fact, let $A \in \mathscr{R}$ and $\varepsilon > 0$. There exists an open set $U_\varepsilon \supseteq A$ and a closed set $C_\varepsilon \subseteq A$ such that $\mu(U_\varepsilon - C_\varepsilon) < \varepsilon$. We have $U_\varepsilon' \subseteq A' \subseteq C_\varepsilon'$, $C_\varepsilon' - U_\varepsilon' = U_\varepsilon - C_\varepsilon$, U_ε' is closed and C_ε' is open. This shows that $A' \in \mathscr{R}$.

$\mathscr{R}$ is closed under countable unions. Indeed let $A_1, A_2, \ldots, \in \mathscr{R}$ and $A = \bigcup_1^\infty A_i$. Let $\varepsilon > 0$ be fixed but arbitrary. Since $A_n \in \mathscr{R}$, there exists an open set $U_{n,\varepsilon}$ and a closed set $C_{n,\varepsilon}$ such that $C_{n,\varepsilon} \subseteq A_n \subseteq U_{n,\varepsilon}$ and $\mu(U_{n,\varepsilon} - C_{n,\varepsilon}) < \varepsilon/3^n$. Let $U_\varepsilon = \bigcup_{n=1}^\infty U_{n,\varepsilon}$. Let $C = \bigcup_n C_{n,\varepsilon}$. Since μ is a measure we can choose a k so large that $\mu(C - \bigcup_{n=1}^k C_{n,\varepsilon}) < \varepsilon/2$. Let $C_\varepsilon = \bigcup_{n=1}^k C_{n,\varepsilon}$. Then U_ε is open, C_ε is closed, $C_\varepsilon \subseteq A \subseteq U_\varepsilon$, and $\mu(U_\varepsilon - C_\varepsilon) \leqslant \mu(U_\varepsilon - C) + \mu(C - C_\varepsilon) \leqslant \sum_{n=1}^\infty \mu(U_{n,\varepsilon} - C_{n,\varepsilon}) + \varepsilon/2 < \sum_{n=1}^\infty \varepsilon/3^n + \varepsilon/2 = \varepsilon$.

The two preceding arguments show that $\mathscr{R}$ is a σ-algebra. To complete the proof it is enough to show that $\mathscr{R}$ contains all closed sets. Let $C \subseteq X$ be a closed set and $\varepsilon > 0$. By Theorem 1.2, Chapter I, C is a G_δ, and hence there exist open sets $U_1, U_2, \ldots, U_1 \supseteq U_2 \supseteq \ldots$ such that $C = \bigcap_{n=1}^\infty U_n$. Since $\mu(U_n) \to \mu(C)$ we can find an n_0 such that $\mu(U_{n_0} - C) < \varepsilon$. If we define $C_\varepsilon = C$, $U_\varepsilon = U_{n_0}$ we see that $\mu(U_\varepsilon - C_\varepsilon) < \varepsilon$. This completes the proof.

2. SPECTRUM OF A MEASURE

We shall now discuss the notion of spectrum or support of a measure.

Theorem 2.1

Let X be a separable metric space and μ a measure in X. Then there exists a unique closed set C_μ satisfying (i) $\mu(C_\mu) = 1$, (ii) *if D is any* *closed set such that* $\mu(D) = 1$, *then* $C_\mu \subseteq D$. *Moreover,* C_μ *is the set of all points* $x \in X$ *having the property that* $\mu(U) > 0$ *for each open set* U *containing* x.

PROOF. Let $\mathscr{U} = \{U: U \text{ open}, \mu(U) = 0\}$. Since X is separable, there are countably many open sets $U_1, U_2, \ldots$ such that $\bigcup_n U_n = \bigcup\{U: U \in \mathscr{U}\}$. Let us denote this union by U_μ and set $C_\mu = X - U_\mu$. Since $\mu(U_\mu) = \mu(\bigcup_n U_n) \leqslant \sum_n \mu(U_n) = 0$, $\mu(C_\mu) = 1$. Further, if D is any closed set with $\mu(D) = 1$, $X - D \in \mathscr{U}$ and hence $X - D \subseteq U_\mu$, i.e., $C_\mu \subseteq D$. The uniqueness of C_μ is obvious. To prove the last assertion notice that for any $x \in X - C_\mu$, U_μ is an open set containing x and $\mu(U_\mu) = 0$, whereas if $x \in C_\mu$ and U is an open set containing x, $\mu(U)$ must be positive, as otherwise $U \subseteq U_\mu$ by the definition of U_μ.

Definition 2.1

The closed set C_μ in Theorem 2.1 is called the *spectrum* or *support* of μ.

Corollary 2.1

Let X be any metric space and μ a measure on X such that for some separable Borel set $E \subseteq X$, $\mu(X - E) = 0$. Then μ has a spectrum C_μ which is separable and $C_\mu \subseteq \bar{E}$.

3. TIGHT MEASURES

We shall now investigate a smaller class of measures on metric spaces, the so-called tight measures. Tight measures have the property that they are determined by their values for compact sets.

Definition 3.1

A measure μ on a metric space X is said to be *tight* if for each $\varepsilon > 0$ there exists a compact set $K_\varepsilon \subseteq X$ such that $\mu(X - K_\varepsilon) < \varepsilon$.

It will be shown that a very extensive class of metric spaces has the property that every measure is tight.

Theorem 3.1

Let X be a metric space and μ a tight measure on X. Then μ has a separable support and for any Borel set E and any $\varepsilon > 0$, there is a compact set $K_\varepsilon \subseteq E$ with $\mu(E - K_\varepsilon) < \varepsilon$.

PROOF. Let K_n be a compact set such that $\mu(X - K_n) < 1/n$. A compact set in a metric space is separable, and hence $\bigcup_n K_n$ is separable. If $E_0 = \bigcup_n K_n$, then $\mu(E_0) = 1$. Hence, the first part follows from Corollary 2.1. Let now $E \in \mathscr{B}_X$. By Theorem 1.2 there exists a closed set $C_\varepsilon \subseteq E$ such that $\mu(E - C_\varepsilon) < \varepsilon/2$. For sufficiently large N, $\mu(X - K_N) < \varepsilon/2$. Let $K_\varepsilon = C_\varepsilon \cap K_N$. Since C_ε is closed, K_ε is compact. Further, $K_\varepsilon \subseteq C_\varepsilon \subseteq E$. Finally, $\mu(E - K_\varepsilon) \leqslant \mu(E - C_\varepsilon) + \mu(X - K_N) < \varepsilon$.

Lemma 3.1

Let X be a complete metric space and $K \subseteq X$ a closed subset of X. Let, for each n, there exist an integer k_n such that $K \subseteq \bigcup_{j=1}^{k_n} \bar{S}_{nj}$, where each $\bar{S}_{nj}$ is a closed sphere of radius $1/n$ in X. Then K is compact.

PROOF. Let $x_1, x_2, \ldots$ be an infinite sequence of distinct points of K. We shall prove that this has a limit point. We can find an integer $n_1 (\leqslant k_1)$ such that $K \cap \bar{S}_{1n_1} = K_1$ contains infinitely many x_j's. Since $K_1 \subseteq \bigcup_1^{k_2} \bar{S}_{2j}$ we can find $n_2 (\leqslant k_2)$ such that $K_1 \cap \bar{S}_{2n_2} = K_2$ contains infinitely many x_j's. Moreover, $K_1 \supseteq K_2 \supseteq \ldots$, and the diameter of K_n is $\leqslant 2/n$ since K_n is contained in a closed sphere of radius $1/n$. The completeness of X implies that $\bigcap_n K_n$ consists of a single point x_0. Since $K_n \subseteq K$ it follows that $x_0 \in K$. Further, every neighborhood of x_0 contains infinitely many x_j's. This shows that K is compact.

Theorem 3.2

Let X be a separable metric space with the property that there exists a complete separable metric space $\tilde{X}$ such that X is contained in $\tilde{X}$ as a topological subset and X is a Borel subset of $\tilde{X}$. Then every measure μ on X is tight. In particular, if X itself is a complete separable metric space, every measure on X is tight.

PROOF. Let $X \subseteq \tilde{X}$ where $\tilde{X}$ is a complete separable metric space and X is a Borel set in $\tilde{X}$. Given a measure μ on $\mathscr{B}_X$ we define $\tilde{\mu}$ on the class $\mathscr{B}_{\tilde{X}}$ by setting $\tilde{\mu}(\tilde{A}) = \mu(\tilde{A} \cap X)$, $\tilde{A} \in \mathscr{B}_{\tilde{X}}$. Since $X \in \mathscr{B}_{\tilde{X}}$, $\tilde{\mu}(\tilde{X} - X) = 0$.

We claim that it is enough to prove that $\tilde{\mu}$ is a tight measure on $\tilde{X}$. Indeed, suppose this has been established. Since X is a Borel set in $\tilde{X}$, there will exist, for each $\varepsilon > 0$, a set $K_\varepsilon \subseteq X$, compact in $\tilde{X}$, such that $\tilde{\mu}(X - K_\varepsilon) < \varepsilon$ (Theorem 3.1). K_ε is also compact in X since X is a topological subset of $\tilde{X}$. Further, $\mu(X - K_\varepsilon) = \tilde{\mu}(X - K_\varepsilon) < \varepsilon$. This implies that μ is tight. Thus we may and do assume that X is itself a complete separable metric space.

Choose and fix $\varepsilon > 0$. Let d be the distance in X. For any integer n, the spheres of radius $1/n$ around each point constitute a covering of X, and since X is separable, we can find countably many such, say $S_{n1}, S_{n2}, \ldots$, such that $X = \bigcup_j S_{nj}$. Clearly, $X = \bigcup_j \bar{S}_{nj}$ and hence there exists an integer k_n such that $\mu(\bigcup_{j=1}^{k_n} \bar{S}_{nj}) \geqslant 1 - \varepsilon/2^n$. Let $X_n = \bigcup_{j=1}^{k_n} \bar{S}_{nj}$. X_n is closed. Let $K_\varepsilon = \bigcap_{n=1}^{\infty} X_n$. Since $K_\varepsilon \subseteq \bigcup_{j=1}^{k_n} \bar{S}_{nj}$ for each n, K_ε is compact (Lemma 3.1). Further, $\mu(X - K_\varepsilon) \leqslant \sum_n \mu(X - X_n) \leqslant \sum_n \varepsilon/2^n = \varepsilon$. This completes the proof.

REMARK. It follows as a consequence of Theorem 3.9, Chapter I, that if the separable metric space X is a Borel set in some complete separable metric space $\tilde{X}$, then it has the same property with respect to every complete separable metric space in which it is imbedded as a topological subset. In particular, it is enough to verify that X is a Borel set in its completion.

4. PERFECT MEASURES

Another notion which is of some interest is that of perfectness.

Definition 4.1

A measure space $(X, \mathscr{B}, \mu)$ is said to be *perfect* if for any $\mathscr{B}$-measurable real valued function f and any set A on the real line such that $f^{-1}(A) \in \mathscr{B}$, there are Borel sets A_1 and A_2 on the real line such that $A_1 \subseteq A \subseteq A_2$ and $\mu f^{-1}(A_2 - A_1) = 0$.

Lemma 4.1

Let X be a metric space and μ a measure on X. If f is any Borel measurable function on X and $\varepsilon > 0$ arbitrary, there exists a closed set C_ε such that (i) $\mu(X - C_\varepsilon) \leqslant \varepsilon$; (ii) *$f$ restricted to C_ε ($f|C_\varepsilon$ in symbols) is continuous.*

PROOF. Let $\{f_n\}$ be a sequence of simple functions converging pointwise to f. Given $\varepsilon > 0$, by Egoroff's theorem there exists a Borel set $E \subseteq X$ such that $\mu(X - E) < \varepsilon/2$ and f_n converges uniformly to f on E. Since f_n is simple on E we can write $f_n = \sum_{i=1}^{k_n} a_{ni}\, \chi_{E_{ni}}$, where $E_{n1}, E_{n2}, \ldots, E_{nk_n}$ are disjoint Borel sets whose union is E and χ_A is the characteristic function of A. Since μ is regular we can take a closed set $C_{ni} \subseteq E_{ni}$ such that $\mu(E_{ni} - C_{ni}) \leqslant \varepsilon/(4^n \cdot k_n)$. Let $C_n = \bigcup_{i=1}^{k_n} C_{ni}$. Since the C_{ni} are disjoint closed sets whose union is C_n, and since f_n is constant on C_{ni}, it follows that $f_n|C_n$ is continuous. Let $C_\varepsilon = \bigcap_{n=1}^{\infty} C_n$. Since each C_n is closed so is C_ε. Further, $\mu(X - C_\varepsilon) = \mu(X - E) + \mu(E - C_\varepsilon) \leqslant \mu(X - E) + \sum_n \mu(E - C_n) < \varepsilon/2 + \sum_n k_n \cdot \varepsilon/(4^n \cdot k_n) < \varepsilon$. Finally, $C_\varepsilon \subseteq C_n$ for each n, $f_n|C_\varepsilon$ is continuous for each n and $f|C_\varepsilon$ is also continuous since f is a uniform limit of f_n on C_ε. This proves the lemma.

REMARK. It should be noted that it is only the continuity of f on C_ε that is asserted. In fact, no point of C_ε need be a continuity point of f.

Lemma 4.2

Let X be any metric space and μ a tight measure on X. If f is a measurable function and $\varepsilon > 0$, there exists a compact set K_ε such that (i) $\mu(X - K_\varepsilon) \leqslant \varepsilon$; (ii) *$f|K_\varepsilon$ is continuous.*

PROOF. This follows immediately from Lemma 4.1 and Theorem 3.1.

Theorem 4.1

Let X be any metric space and μ a tight measure on X. Then $(X, \mathscr{B}_X, \mu)$ is a perfect measure space.

PROOF. Let f be any real valued measurable function. It is sufficient to prove that for any $A \subseteq R^1$ (the real line) such that $f^{-1}(A) \in \mathscr{B}_X$, there exists a Borel set $A_1 \subseteq A$ with $\mu(f^{-1}(A - A_1)) = 0$; A_2 can then be defined as a Borel set such that $A_2' \subseteq A'$ and $\mu(f^{-1}(A' - A_2')) = 0$. Suppose then $A \subseteq R^1$ is a set such that $E = f^{-1}(A) \in \mathscr{B}_X$. Let $\{C_n\}$, $n = 1, 2, \ldots$, and $\{K_n\}$, $n = 1, 2, \ldots$ be two sequences of sets such that (i) $K_1 \subseteq K_2 \subseteq, \ldots$, each K_n is compact, $f|K_n$ is continuous, and $\mu(X - K_n) \to 0$, (ii) $C_1 \subseteq C_2 \subseteq \ldots \subseteq E$, each C_n is closed and $\mu(E - C_n) \to 0$. If we write $\tilde{K}_n = K_n \cap C_n$, then $\tilde{K}_1 \subseteq \tilde{K}_2 \subseteq \ldots \subseteq E$, each $\tilde{K}_n$ is compact, $f|\tilde{K}_n$ is continuous and $\mu(E - \tilde{K}_n) \to 0$ as $n \to \infty$.

If $B_n = f(\tilde{K}_n)$ then B_n is a compact subset of the real line since $f|\tilde{K}_n$ is continuous, and hence $A_1 = \bigcup_n B_n$ is a Borel set. Since $f[\bigcup_n \tilde{K}_n] = A_1$ it follows that $f^{-1}(A_1) \supseteq \bigcup_n \tilde{K}_n$. Clearly, $A_1 \subseteq A$ and $f^{-1}(A_1) \subseteq f^{-1}(A) = E$. Since $\mu(E - \bigcup_n \tilde{K}_n) = 0$, $\mu(E - f^{-1}(A_1)) = 0$. This completes the proof.

5. LINEAR FUNCTIONALS AND MEASURES

Here we shall examine the relationship between linear functionals and measures. Let X be a metric space and $C(X)$ the space of all bounded real valued continuous functions on X. For any $f \in C(X)$ we write $||f|| = \sup_{x \in X} |f(x)|$. Under the norm $||\cdot||$, $C(X)$ becomes a Banach space.

Definition 5.1

A *linear functional* Λ on $C(X)$ is a map $f \to \Lambda(f)$ of $C(X)$ into the real line such that for any two constants α and β and any two elements f and g of $C(X)$ the equation $\Lambda(\alpha f + \beta g) = \alpha\Lambda(f) + \beta\Lambda(g)$ holds. A linear functional Λ is called positive if $\Lambda(f) \geqslant 0$ whenever $f \geqslant 0$.

Notice that if Λ is a positive linear functional, then $\Lambda(f) \leqslant \Lambda(g)$ whenever $f \leqslant g$. Let 1 denote the function which takes the value 1 everywhere.

Given any measure μ on X the functional Λ_μ: $g \to \int g \, d\mu$ is easily seen to be a positive linear functional on $C(X)$ with $\Lambda_\mu(1) = 1$. We shall prove in this section that at least when X is compact, every positive linear functional can be obtained in this manner. Hereafter we shall consider a fixed positive linear functional Λ on $C(X)$ with $\Lambda(1) = 1$. X is a metric space. $\mathscr{F}_0$ will denote the class of all closed subsets and $\mathscr{G}_0$ the class of all open subsets of X.

For any $C \in \mathscr{F}_0$, let

$$\lambda(C) = \inf \{\Lambda(f) : f \geqslant \chi_C\}$$

where χ_C denotes the characteristic function of C. Throughout this section the symbol C, with or without suffixes, will denote a closed set and G an open set.

Theorem 5.1

λ is a well-defined function on $\mathscr{F}_0$ and possesses the following properties: (i) $0 \leqslant \lambda(C) \leqslant 1$ *for all* $C \in \mathscr{F}_0$; (ii) *if* $C_1 \subseteq C_2$, $\lambda(C_1) \leqslant \lambda(C_2)$; (iii) *if*

$C_1 \cap C_2 = \phi$, $\lambda(C_1 \cup C_2) = \lambda(C_1) + \lambda(C_2)$; (iv) $\lambda(C_1 \cup C_2) \leqslant \lambda(C_1) + \lambda(C_2)$ *for all* C_1, C_2; *and* (v) $\lambda(\phi) = 0$, $\lambda(X) = 1$.

PROOF. Since $1 \geqslant \chi_C$ for any C it is clear that $\lambda(C) \leqslant \Lambda(1) = 1$. Further, if $f \geqslant \chi_C$ then $f \geqslant 0$, and hence $\Lambda(f) \geqslant 0$ so that $\lambda(C) \geqslant 0$. This proves (i); (ii) is trivial. We now prove (iv). If $f_1 \geqslant \chi_{C_1}$, $f_2 \geqslant \chi_{C_2}$ are such that $\Lambda(f_1) \leqslant \lambda(C_1) + \varepsilon$ and $\Lambda(f_2) \leqslant \lambda(C_2) + \varepsilon$ then $\Lambda(f_1 + f_2) \leqslant \lambda(C_1) + \lambda(C_2) + 2\varepsilon$. Since $f_1 + f_2 \geqslant \chi_{C_1 \cup C_2}$, we have $\lambda(C_1 \cup C_2) \leqslant \Lambda(f_1 + f_2) \leqslant \lambda(C_1) + \lambda(C_2) + 2\varepsilon$. Letting $\varepsilon \to 0$ we obtain (iv). To prove (iii) it is now sufficient to prove that $\lambda(C_1 \cup C_2) \geqslant \lambda(C_1) + \lambda(C_2)$ if $C_1 \cap C_2 = \phi$. By Theorem 1.6, Chapter I, there exists a function $h \in C(X)$ such that $0 \leqslant h \leqslant 1$ and $h(x) = 1$ for $x \in C_1$ and $= 0$ for $x \in C_2$. If $f \in C(X)$ and $f \geqslant \chi_{C_1 \cup C_2}$ then clearly $fh \geqslant \chi_{C_1}$ and $f(1-h) \geqslant \chi_{C_2}$. We now have $\Lambda(f) = \Lambda(fh) + \Lambda(f(1-h)) \geqslant \lambda(C_1) + \lambda(C_2)$ so that $\lambda(C_1 \cup C_2) \geqslant \lambda(C_1) + \lambda(C_2)$; (v) is trivial. This completes the proof.

Define now for any open set G,

$$\tau(G) = \sup \{\lambda(C) : G \supseteq C \in \mathscr{F}_0\}.$$

Theorem 5.2

τ is a well-defined function on $\mathscr{G}_0$ and has the following properties: (i) $0 \leqslant \tau(G) \leqslant 1$ *for all* $G \in \mathscr{G}_0$; (ii) $\tau(G_1) \leqslant \tau(G_2)$ *if* $G_1 \subseteq G_2$; (iii) $\tau(\bigcup_1^N G_i) \leqslant \sum_1^N \tau(G_i)$; and (iv) $\tau(\phi) = 0$, $\tau(X) = 1$.

PROOF. Since $0 \leqslant \lambda(C) \leqslant 1$ for all $C \in \mathscr{F}_0$, it is clear that τ is well-defined and $0 \leqslant \tau(G) \leqslant 1$ for all G. (ii) and (iv) are trivial. It only remains to prove (iii), and it is enough to do it when $N = 2$. The general case of N can be settled by induction. Let G_1, G_2 be two open sets and $C \subseteq G_1 \cup G_2$. Then $C - G_1$ and $C - G_2$ are disjoint closed sets, and hence there are disjoint open sets $\tilde{G}_1$ and $\tilde{G}_2$ such that $C - G_1 \subseteq \tilde{G}_1$, $C - G_2 \subseteq \tilde{G}_2$. Let $C_1 = C - \tilde{G}_1$, $C_2 = C - \tilde{G}_2$. Then $C_1, C_2 \in \mathscr{F}_0$. $C = C_1 \cup C_2$, $C_1 \subseteq G_1$, $C_2 \subseteq G_2$. Consequently, $\lambda(C) \leqslant \lambda(C_1) + \lambda(C_2) \leqslant \tau(G_1) + \tau(G_2)$. Since $C \subseteq G_1 \cup G_2$ is an arbitrary closed set it follows that $\tau(G_1 \cup G_2) \leqslant \tau(G_1) + \tau(G_2)$.

Define now, for *any* set $A \subseteq X$,

$$\mu^*(A) = \inf \{\tau(G) : A \subseteq G\}.$$

Theorem 5.3

μ^* is a well-defined function on the class of all subsets of X and has the following properties: (i) $\mu^*(\phi) = 0$, $\mu^*(X) = 1$; (ii) $\mu^*(G) = \tau(G)$ *if* $G \in \mathscr{G}_0$; (iii) $\mu^*(A) \leqslant \mu^*(B)$ *if* $A \subseteq B$; (iv) $\mu^*(\bigcup_1^N A_j) \leqslant \sum_{j=1}^N \mu^*(A_j)$; *and* (v) *if* $G \subseteq C$ *then* $\mu^*(G) \leqslant \lambda(C)$.

PROOF. (i), (ii), and (iii) are trivial. For proving (iv) choose $G_j \supseteq A_j$ such that $\tau(G_j) \leqslant \mu^*(A_j) + \varepsilon/N$. Then we have, since $\bigcup_1^N A_j \subseteq \bigcup_1^N G_j$, $\mu^*(\bigcup_1^N A_j) \leqslant \tau(\bigcup_1^N G_j) \leqslant \sum_j \tau(G_j) \leqslant \sum_j \mu^*(A_j) + \varepsilon$. Letting $\varepsilon \to 0$ we get (iv). For (v) note that if $C_1 \subseteq G$ then $C_1 \subseteq C$ and $\lambda(C_1) \leqslant \lambda(C)$, so that $\mu^*(G) = \sup \lambda(C_1) \leqslant \lambda(C)$.

Theorem 5.4

For any closed set C,

$$\lambda(C) = \mu^*(C).$$

PROOF. By the definition of τ, $\lambda(C) \leqslant \tau(G)$ if $C \subseteq G$. Hence $\lambda(C) \leqslant \mu^*(C)$ if $C \in \mathscr{F}_0$. We shall now prove the reverse inequality. Given $\varepsilon > 0$ we can find an $f \in C(X)$ such that $f \geqslant \chi_C$ and $\Lambda(f) \leqslant \lambda(C) + \varepsilon/2$. For any number γ with $0 < \gamma < 1$ write $G_\gamma = \{x : f(x) > \gamma\}$ and $C_\gamma = \{x : f(x) \geqslant \gamma\}$. Since $G_\gamma \subseteq C_\gamma$, $\mu^*(G_\gamma) \leqslant \lambda(C_\gamma)$. But $f/\gamma \geqslant \chi_{C_\gamma}$, and so $\Lambda(f/\gamma) \geqslant \lambda(C_\gamma)$ so that we have $\mu^*(G_\gamma) \leqslant \lambda(C_\gamma) \leqslant \Lambda(f)/\gamma \leqslant (\lambda(C) + \varepsilon/2)/\gamma$. By choosing γ near enough to 1 we can assume that $(\lambda(C) + \varepsilon/2)/\gamma \leqslant \lambda(C) + \varepsilon$ so that $\mu^*(G_\gamma) \leqslant \lambda(C) + \varepsilon$ and since $C \subseteq G_\gamma$, $\mu^*(C) \leqslant \lambda(C) + \varepsilon$. Letting $\varepsilon \to 0$ we get $\mu^*(C) \leqslant \lambda(C)$.

Theorem 5.5

If G is any open set, then for any set $A \subseteq X$,

$$\mu^*(A) \geqslant \mu^*(G \cap A) + \mu^*(G' \cap A).$$

PROOF. Let G_1 be any open set such that $A \subseteq G_1$. Let C_1 be a closed set $\subseteq G \cap G_1$ such that $\lambda(C_1) \geqslant \tau(G \cap G_1) - \varepsilon$ and let C_2 be a closed subset of $G_1 - C_1$ such that $\lambda(C_2) \geqslant \tau(G_1 - C_1) - \varepsilon$. Since C_1 and C_2 are disjoint, $\lambda(C_1 \cup C_2) = \lambda(C_1) + \lambda(C_2) \geqslant \tau(G \cap G_1) + \tau(G_1 - C_1) - 2\varepsilon \geqslant \mu^*(G \cap G_1) + \mu^*(G' \cap G_1) - 2\varepsilon$. Since $C_1 \cup C_2 \subseteq G_1$ we thus have $\tau(G_1) \geqslant \mu^*(G \cap G_1) + \mu^*(G' \cap G_1) - 2\varepsilon$. Since $\mu^*(A) = \inf \tau(G_1)$ and

$\mu^*(G \cap G_1) \geqslant \mu^*(G \cap A)$, $\mu^*(G' \cap G_1) \geqslant \mu^*(G' \cap A)$ we see that $\mu^*(A) \geqslant \mu^*(G \cap A) + \mu^*(G' \cap A) - 2\varepsilon$. Letting $\varepsilon \to 0$ we complete the proof of the theorem.

Theorem 5.6

Let $\mathscr{A}_X$ be the algebra (not the σ-algebra) generated by the class $\mathscr{G}_0$ of all open subsets of X. μ^* is a finitely additive regular measure over $\mathscr{A}_X$.

PROOF. This follows from Theorems 5.1–5.5 and by the well-known argument that μ^*-measurable sets form an algebra (cf. Halmos [12], p. 44).

For any finitely additive measure μ (with $\mu(X) = 1$) on $\mathscr{A}_X$ we define integrability and integral of a function exactly as in the case of an ordinary measure. We consider partitions of the whole space into sets belonging to $\mathscr{A}_X$ and form the upper and lower Darboux sums. If the infimum of all the upper Darboux sums is equal to the supremum of all lower Darboux sums the function is said to be integrable. Every bounded real valued function with the property that $f^{-1}((a, b]) \in \mathscr{A}_X$ for all intervals $(a, b]$ can be shown to be integrable. In particular, bounded continuous functions are integrable. The integral of f with respect to μ is denoted by $\int f\, d\mu$. It is easy to verify the following properties of the integral: (i) if α and β are constants and f and g are integrable functions $\alpha f + \beta g$ is integrable and $\int (\alpha f + \beta g)\, d\mu = \alpha \int f\, d\mu + \beta \int g\, d\mu$; (ii) $\int f\, d\mu \geqslant 0$ if $f \geqslant 0$; (iii) $\int 1\, d\mu = 1$; and (iv) $|\int f\, d\mu| \leqslant ||f||$.

Theorem 5.7

Let X be a metric space and $C(X)$ be the space of all bounded real valued continuous functions. Let Λ be a nonnegative linear functional on $C(X)$ such that $\Lambda(1) = 1$. Then there exists a unique finitely additive regular measure μ on $\mathscr{A}_X$ (the algebra generated by all the open subsets of X) such that

$$\Lambda(f) = \int f\, d\mu, \qquad f \in C(X)$$

Conversely, if μ is a finitely additive measure on $\mathscr{A}_X$ then the map Λ: $f \to \int f\, d\mu$ is nonnegative, linear, and $\Lambda(1) = 1$.

PROOF. Let μ be the finitely additive measure obtained by restricting μ^* to $\mathscr{A}_X$, where μ^* is defined as in Theorem 5.3. Let f be any function in $C(X)$ such that $0 \leqslant f \leqslant 1$. We shall first establish that $\Lambda(f (\geqslant \int_X f\, d\mu$. To this end let n be any integer and let $G_i = \{x: f(x) > i/n\}$. Then $G_0 \supseteq G_1 \supseteq \ldots \supseteq G_n = \phi$. Let φ_i be the continuous function on the unit interval $[0, 1]$ which is 0 for $0 \leqslant t \leqslant (i-1)/n$ and 1 for $i/n \leqslant t \leqslant 1$ and is linear in between. Let $f_i(x) = \varphi_i(f(x))$, $i = 1, 2, \ldots, n$. Since $(1/n)(\varphi_1(t) + \ldots + \varphi_n(t)) \equiv t$, we have $(1/n)(f_1 + \ldots + f_n) = f$. Thus $\Lambda(f) = 1/n(\sum_i \Lambda(f_i))$. Now $f_i \geqslant \chi_{G_i}$, and hence $\Lambda(f_i) \geqslant \mu(G_i)$. Thus

$$
\begin{aligned}
\Lambda(f) &= \frac{1}{n}\left(\sum_i \Lambda(f_i)\right) \\
&\geqslant \frac{1}{n}\left(\sum_i \mu(G_i)\right) \\
&= \sum_{i=1}^{n}\left(\frac{i}{n} - \frac{i-1}{n}\right)\mu(G_i) \\
&= \sum_{i=1}^{n-1} \frac{i}{n}\mu(G_i - G_{i+1}) \\
&= \sum_{i=1}^{n-1} \frac{i+1}{n}\mu(G_i - G_{i+1}) - \frac{1}{n}\mu(G_1) \\
&\geqslant \sum_{i=1}^{n-1} \int_{G_i - G_{i+1}} f\, d\mu - \frac{1}{n}\mu(G_1) \\
&= \int_{G_1} f\, d\mu - \frac{1}{n}\mu(G_1) \\
&\geqslant \int_X f\, d\mu - \frac{1}{n}\mu(G_0).
\end{aligned}
$$

Letting $n \to \infty$ we have

$$
\Lambda(f) \geqslant \int_X f\, d\mu.
$$

If f is any nonnegative function in $C(X)$ we can find a positive constant c such that $0 \leqslant cf \leqslant 1$. Then

$$\Lambda(f) = \frac{1}{c}\Lambda(cf) \geqslant \frac{1}{c}\int_X cf\,d\mu = \int f\,d\mu.$$

If f is any function in $C(X)$ we can find a constant c' such that $f + c' \geqslant 0$, and hence

$$\Lambda(f) = \Lambda(f + c') - c' \geqslant \int (f + c')\,d\mu - c' = \int f\,d\mu.$$

Thus for any $f \in C(X)$, $\Lambda(f) \geqslant \int f\,d\mu$. Changing f to $-f$ we have $\Lambda(-f) \geqslant -\int f\,d\mu$ or $\Lambda(f) \leqslant \int f\,d\mu$. Hence $\Lambda(f) = \int f\,d\mu$.

Let us now suppose that ν is another regular finitely additive measure in $\mathscr{A}_X$ such that $\Lambda(f) = \int f\,d\nu$. Then we have

$$\int f\,d\mu = \int f\,d\nu, \qquad \text{for every} \quad f \in C(X).$$

Let C be any closed set. Since μ and ν are regular we can find two sequences $\{G_n\}$ and $\{H_n\}$ of open sets such that $G_1 \supseteq G_2 \supseteq \ldots$ and $H_1 \supseteq H_2 \supseteq \ldots$, C is contained in all the G_i and H_i and

$$\lim_{n\to\infty} \mu(G_n) = \mu(C),$$

$$\lim_{n\to\infty} \nu(H_n) = \nu(C).$$

If we write $U_n = G_n \cap H_n$, then it is clear that

$$\lim_{n\to\infty} \mu(U_n) = \mu(C),$$

$$\lim_{n\to\infty} \nu(U_n) = \nu(C).$$

By Theorem 1.6, Chapter I, we can construct a continuous function f_n such that $0 \leqslant f_n \leqslant 1$, $f_n(x) = 1$ for $x \in C$, $f_n(x) = 0$ for $x \in X - U_n$. Then we have

$$\int f_n\,d\mu = \int f_n\,d\nu$$

for all n. Since $f_n = 0$ on $X - U_n$, we have

$$\mu(C) + \int_{U_n - C} f_n \, d\mu = \nu(C) + \int_{U_n - C} f_n \, d\nu.$$

But

$$\int_{U_n - C} f_n \, d\mu \leqslant \mu(U_n - C) = \mu(U_n) - \mu(C),$$

$$\int_{U_n - C} f_n \, d\nu \leqslant \nu(U_n - C) = \nu(U_n) - \nu(C).$$

Letting $n \to \infty$, we obtain

$$\mu(C) = \nu(C).$$

Since C is an arbitrary closed set and μ and ν are regular, it follows that $\mu = \nu$.

The last part of the theorem is an easy consequence of the properties of the integral mentioned earlier.

Theorem 5.8

Let X be a compact metric space and Λ be a nonnegative linear functional on $C(X)$ with $\Lambda(1) = 1$. Then there exists a unique measure on $\mathscr{B}_X$ such that $\Lambda(f) = \int f \, d\mu$, $f \in C(X)$.

PROOF. It is enough to prove that the set function μ^* of Theorem 5.3 is actually an outer measure. Then the theorem will follow from theorem 5.5. Thus we have to only show that $\mu^*(\bigcup_1^\infty A_i) \leqslant \sum_1^\infty \mu^*(A_i)$. By a routine argument this reduces to showing that $\mu^*(\bigcup_1^\infty G_j) \leqslant \sum_1^\infty \mu^*(G_j)$ for arbitrary open sets $G_1, G_2, \ldots$, i.e., $\tau(\bigcup_1^\infty G_j) \leqslant \sum_1^\infty \tau(G_j)$ (see the definition before Theorem 5.3). If $C \subseteq \bigcup_1^\infty G_j$, the compactness of C implies that $C \subseteq \bigcup_1^N G_j$ for some N. Then we have $\lambda(C) \leqslant \tau(\bigcup_1^N G_j) \leqslant \sum_{j=1}^N \tau(G_j) \leqslant \sum_j \tau(G_j)$. Thus $\tau(\bigcup_1^\infty G_j) = \sup_{C \subseteq \bigcup_1^\infty G_j} \lambda(C) \leqslant \sum_j \tau(G_j)$. This completes the proof since the class of μ^*-measurable sets is a σ-algebra, and by Theorem 5.5 open sets are μ^*-measurable.

From the proof of Theorem 5.7 it is clear that if μ and ν are two measures and $\int f \, d\mu = \int f \, d\nu$ for every $f \in C(X)$, then $\mu = \nu$. We shall now prove a useful result which asserts that a measure in a metric space is completely determined by the values of the integral of uniformly continuous functions.

Theorem 5.9

Let X be a metric space, $U(X)$ be the space of all bounded real valued uniformly continuous functions and μ and ν be two measures such that

$$\int f\,d\mu = \int f\,d\nu, \qquad \text{for all } f \in U(X).$$

Then $\mu = \nu$.

PROOF. Let C be any closed set and let $G_n = \{x: d(x, C) < 1/n\}$. G_n is open (Theorem 1.1, Chapter I) and $\bigcap_1^\infty G_n = C$. C and G_n' are disjoint closed sets such that $\inf_{x \in C,\, y \in G_n'} d(x, y) \geqslant 1/n$. Hence, by Theorem 1.6, Chapter I, there exists a function $f_n \in U(X)$ such that $f_n(x) = 0$ for $x \in G_n'$, $f_n(x) = 1$ for $x \in C$ and $0 \leqslant f_n(x) \leqslant 1$. Integrating f_n with respect to μ and ν, we get

$$\mu(C) \leqslant \int f_n\,d\mu = \int f_n\,d\nu$$

$$= \int_{G_n} f_n\,d\nu \leqslant \nu(G_n).$$

Letting $n \to \infty$, we have $\mu(C) \leqslant \nu(C)$. Interchanging μ and ν in the above argument we get $\nu(C) \leqslant \mu(C)$. Thus $\mu(C) = \nu(C)$ for all closed sets. The regularity of measures implies that $\mu = \nu$. This completes the proof.

6. THE WEAK TOPOLOGY IN THE SPACE OF MEASURES

Till now we studied properties of individual measures. In this section we shall endow the space of all measures with a certain topology and investigate its properties.

Let X be a metric space and $\mathcal{M}(X)$ the space of all measures defined on $\mathcal{B}_X$. An element $\mu \in \mathcal{M}(X)$ is a nonnegative, countably additive set function defined on $\mathscr{B}_X$ with the property $\mu(X) = 1$. $C(X)$ stands for the space of all bounded real valued continuous functions on X. We shall now topologize the space $\mathscr{M}(X)$ by defining a base of open neighborhoods for any point μ. Consider the family of sets of the form

$$V_\mu(f_1, f_2, \ldots, f_k; \varepsilon_1, \ldots, \varepsilon_k) = \Big\{\nu : \nu \in \mathscr{M}(X),$$

$$\left| \int f_i \, d\nu - \int f_i \, d\mu \right| < \varepsilon_i, \quad i = 1, 2, \ldots, k\Big\},$$

where $f_1, f_2, \ldots, f_k$ are elements from $C(X)$ and $\varepsilon_1, \varepsilon_2, \ldots, \varepsilon_k$, are positive numbers. It is easy to verify that the family of sets obtained by varying $k, f_1, f_2, \ldots, f_k, \varepsilon_1, \ldots, \varepsilon_k$ satisfies the axioms of a basis for a topology. We shall refer to this as *the weak topology*[2] in $\mathscr{M}(X)$. It is then clear that a net $\{\mu_\alpha\}$ of measures converges in the weak topology to a measure μ if and only if $\int f \, d\mu_\alpha \to \int f \, d\mu$ for every $f \in C(X)$. In such a case we shall say that μ_α converges "weakly" to μ or $\mu_\alpha \Rightarrow \mu$ in symbols. Unless otherwise stated, $\mathscr{M}(X)$ will always be considered as a topological space with the weak topology.

We shall first prove a theorem which yields several useful equivalent definitions of the weak topology.

Theorem 6.1

Let μ_α be a net in $\mathscr{M}(X)$. Then the following statements are equivalent:

(a) $\mu_\alpha \Rightarrow \mu$;

(b) $\lim_\alpha \int g \, d\mu_\alpha = \int g \, d\mu$ *for all* $g \in U(X)$ *where* $U(X)$ *is the space of all bounded real valued uniformly continuous functions;*

(c) $\overline{\lim}_\alpha \, \mu_\alpha(C) \leqslant \mu(C)$ *for every closed set* C;

(d) $\underline{\lim}_\alpha \, \mu_\alpha(G) \geqslant \mu(G)$ *for every open set* G;

(e) $\lim_\alpha \mu_\alpha(A) = \mu(A)$ *for every Borel set* A *whose boundary has* μ*-measure* 0.

---

[2] Note that the same definition of weak topology holds good in the space of all totally finite (not necessarily probability) measures.

PROOF. Since $U(X) \subseteq C(X)$, it follows that (a) → (b). We shall now prove that (b) → (c). Let C be any closed set and $G_n = \{x: d(x, C) < 1/n\}$ where $d(x, C)$ is defined as in Theorem 1.1, Chapter I. Then C and G_n' are disjoint closed sets such that $\inf_{x \in C, y \in G_n'} d(x, y) \geqslant 1/n$. Hence, by Theorem 1.6, Chapter I, there exists a function $f_n \in U(X)$ such that $0 \leqslant f_n \leqslant 1$, $f_n(x) = 1$ for $x \in C$, $f_n(x) = 0$ for $x \in G_n'$. Further, $G_1 \supseteq G_2 \supseteq \ldots$ and $\bigcap G_n = C$. Thus

$$\overline{\lim_{\alpha}}\, \mu_\alpha(C) \leqslant \overline{\lim_{\alpha}} \int f_n \, d\mu_\alpha$$

$$= \int f_n \, d\mu \leqslant \mu(G_n)$$

Now letting $n \to \infty$ we obtain

$$\overline{\lim_{\alpha}}\, \mu_\alpha(C) \leqslant \mu(C).$$

That (c) ↔ (d) is obvious since open sets are complements of closed sets and vice versa, and the whole space has mass unity for all measures. We shall now show that (c) and (d) → (e). Let $\bar{A}$ denote the closure of A and A^0 the interior of A. Then $\bar{A} \supseteq A \supseteq A^0$. $\bar{A}$ is closed and A^0 is open. Let A be such that $\mu(\bar{A} - A^0) = 0$. Hence

$$\overline{\lim_{\alpha}}\, \mu_\alpha(A) \leqslant \overline{\lim_{\alpha}}\, \mu_\alpha(\bar{A}) \leqslant \mu(\bar{A}) = \mu(A),$$

$$\underline{\lim_{\alpha}}\, \mu_\alpha(A) \geqslant \underline{\lim_{\alpha}}\, \mu_\alpha(A^0) \geqslant \mu(A^0) = \mu(A).$$

Thus $\lim_\alpha \mu_\alpha(A)$ exists and equals $\mu(A)$.

We shall now complete the proof of the theorem by showing that (e) → (a). Let g be any element of $C(X)$ and $\lim_\alpha \mu_\alpha(A) = \mu(A)$ for every Borel set A such that $\mu(\bar{A} - A^0) = 0$. Let μ^g denote the measure on the real line defined by $\mu^g(E) = \mu\{x: g(x) \in E\}$ for any Borel set E in the real line. Since g is a bounded function μ^g is concentrated in a bounded interval (a, b). The measure μ^g can have at most a countable number of mass points. Hence we can find, given any $\varepsilon > 0$, numbers $t_1, t_2, \ldots, t_m$ such that (i) $a = t_0 < t_1 < \cdots < t_m = b$; (ii) $a < g(x) < b$ for all $x \in X$; (iii) $t_j - t_{j-1} < \varepsilon$ for all $j = 1, 2, \ldots, m$; and (iv) $\mu(\{x: g(x) = t_j\}) = 0$ for all $j = 1, 2, \ldots, m$.

Let $A_j = \{x: t_{j-1} \leqslant g(x) < t_j\}$. $A_1, A_2, \ldots, A_m$ are disjoint Borel sets with $X = \bigcup_j A_j$. Moreover, $\bar{A}_j - A_j^0 \subseteq \{x: g(x) = t_{j-1}\} \cup \{x: g(x) = t_j\}$ so that $\mu(\bar{A}_j - A_j^0) = 0$. We have therefore $\lim_\alpha \mu_\alpha(A_j) = \mu(A_j)$, $j = 1, 2, \ldots, m$. Consequently, writing g^* for the simple function $\sum_j t_{j-1}\chi_{A_j}$, and noting that $|g^*(x) - g(x)| < \varepsilon$ for all $x \in X$, we have

$$\left|\int g\,d\mu_\alpha - \int g\,d\mu\right| \leqslant \left\{\int |g - g^*|\,d\mu_\alpha + \int |g - g^*|\,d\mu + \left|\int g^*\,d\mu_\alpha - \int g^*\,d\mu\right|\right\}$$

$$\leqslant 2\varepsilon + \sum_{j=1}^{m} |\mu_\alpha(A_j) - \mu(A_j)|\,|t_{j-1}|.$$

Letting $\alpha \to \infty$,

$$\overline{\lim_\alpha} \left|\int g\,d\mu_\alpha - \int g\,d\mu\right| \leqslant 2\varepsilon.$$

Letting $\varepsilon \to 0$, we obtain the required result.

We shall now proceed to analyze the problem of metrization of the topological space $\mathscr{M}(X)$.

For each point $x \in X$ we shall denote by p_x the measure degenerate at the point x.

Lemma 6.1

X is homeomorphic to the (topological) subset $D = \{p_x: x \in X\}$.

PROOF. For any point x and $g \in C(X)$, we have $\int g\,dp_x = g(x)$. If $x_\alpha \to x_0$ then $g(x_\alpha) \to g(x_0)$. Hence $p_{x_\alpha} \Rightarrow p_{x_0}$. Conversely, let $p_{x_\alpha} \Rightarrow p_{x_0}$. If x_α does not converge to x_0, there is an open set G and a subnet $\{x_\beta\}$ such that $x_0 \in G$ and $x_\beta \in X - G$ for all β. Let g be a continuous function such that $0 \leqslant g \leqslant 1$, $g(x_0) = 0$ and $g(x) = 1$ for $x \in X - G$. Then $\int g\,dp_{x_\beta} = 1$, while $\int g\,dp_{x_0} = 0$. This is a contradiction. This completes the proof.

Lemma 6.2

D is a sequentially closed subset of $\mathscr{M}(X)$.

PROOF. Let $\{x_n\}$ be a sequence of points in X such that $p_{x_n} \Rightarrow q$. Suppose $\{x_n\}$ does not have any convergent subsequence. Then the set $S = \{x_1, x_2, \ldots\}$ is closed and thus is any subset C of S. Since $p_{x_n} \Rightarrow q$, we have by Theorem 6.1, $q(C) \geqslant \overline{\lim}\, p_{x_n}(C)$ for $C \subseteq S$. It follows that for every infinite subset $S_1 \subseteq S$, $q(S_1) = 1$. This is a contradiction since q is a measure.

Thus there is a subsequence $\{x_{n_k}\}$, $x_{n_k} \to x$. By Lemma 6.1, $q = p_x$. Hence D is sequentially closed.

Lemma 6.3

If X is a totally bounded metric space, then $U(X)$ is a separable Banach space under the supremum norm.

PROOF. We recall that a totally bounded metric space has the property that for every $r > 0$ the whole space has a finite covering consisting of spheres of radius r. The completion of such a metric space is compact. Let X_1 be the completion of X. Then X is dense in X_1. Any $g \in U(X)$ can be extended uniquely to a $\hat{g} \in C(X_1)$. Further, $\sup_{x \in X} |g(x)| = \sup_{x \in X_1} |\hat{g}(x)|$. In other words, the Banach spaces $U(X)$ and $C(X_1)$ are isomorphic. Since X_1 is a compact space, $C(X_1)$ is separable. This shows that $U(X)$ is separable.

Theorem 6.2

$\mathcal{M}(X)$ can be metrized as a separable metric space if and only if X is a separable metric space.

PROOF. Suppose X is a separable metric space. Then by the celebrated theorem of Urysohn (cf. Kelley [16], p. 125), X can be topologically imbedded in a countable product of unit intervals. Consequently, there exists an equivalent totally bounded metrization of X. We will impose this metric on X. It follows from Lemma 6.3 that $U(X)$ is separable. Let $\{g_1, g_2, \ldots\}$ be a countable dense subset of $U(X)$.

Let R^∞ be the countable product of the real lines. Define the map T of $\mathcal{M}(X)$ into R^∞ as follows. For each $\mu \in \mathcal{M}(X)$, $T(\mu) = (\int g_1\, d\mu, \int g_2\, d\mu, \ldots)$. We will now show that T is a homeomorphism on $\mathcal{M}(X)$.

First, T is one-one. For, if $T(\mu) = T(\nu)$, then $\int g_r\, d\mu = \int g_r\, d\nu$ for all r. Since $\{g_1, g_2, \ldots\}$ is dense in $U(X)$, it follows that $\int g\, d\mu = \int g\, d\nu$ for all $g \in U(X)$. Hence by Theorem 5.9, $\mu = \nu$.

Second, T is continuous. Suppose $\mu_\alpha \Rightarrow \mu$. Then $\int g_r\, d\mu_\alpha \to \int g_r\, d\mu$ for $r = 1, 2, \ldots$. This implies that $T(\mu_\alpha) \to T(\mu)$.

Last, T^{-1} is continuous. For, let $\{\mu_\alpha\}$ be a net in $\mathscr{M}(X)$ and let $T(\mu_\alpha) \to T(\mu)$, i.e., $\int g_r\, d\mu_\alpha \to \int g_r\, d\mu$ for $r = 1, 2, \ldots$. We have for any $g \in U(X)$,

$$\left|\int g\, d\mu_\alpha - \int g\, d\mu\right| \leqslant 2\|g - g_r\| + \left|\int g_r\, d\mu_\alpha - \int g_r\, d\mu\right|.$$

Hence

$$\overline{\lim_\alpha}\left|\int g\, d\mu_\alpha - \int g\, d\mu\right| \leqslant 2\|g - g_r\|.$$

Since there exists a sequence $\{g_{n_k}\}$ such that $\|g - g_{n_k}\| \to 0$, it follows that

$$\overline{\lim_\alpha}\left|\int g\, d\mu_\alpha - \int g\, d\mu\right| = 0,$$

for all $g \in U(X)$. An application of Theorem 6.1 yields $\mu_\alpha \Rightarrow \mu$. This shows that T is a homeomorphism.

Since R^∞ is a separable metric space and $\mathscr{M}(X)$ is homeomorphic to a subset of R^∞ it follows that $\mathscr{M}(X)$ is a separable metric space.

Conversely, let $\mathscr{M}(X)$ be a separable metric space. By Lemma 6.1, X is homeomorphic to $D = \{p_x : x \in X\}$. D is a separable metric space, and hence X is also a separable metric space.

The next result is useful in the sense that it yields a specific countable dense subset of $\mathscr{M}(X)$ when X is separable.

Theorem 6.3

Let X be a separable metric space and $E \subseteq X$ dense in X. Then the set of all measures whose supports are finite subsets of E is dense in $\mathscr{M}(X)$.

PROOF. It is obviously enough to prove that the set of all measures whose supports are finite subsets of X is dense in $\mathscr{M}(X)$. Let us denote the class of such measures by $\mathscr{F}(X)$. It is clear that any measure concentrated in a countable subset of X is a weak limit of measures from $\mathscr{F}(X)$. Thus it is sufficient to prove that any measure is a weak limit of measures vanishing outside countable subsets of X.

Choose and fix $\mu \in \mathscr{M}(X)$. Since X is separable we can, for each integer n, write X as $\bigcup_j A_{nj}$, $A_{nj} \cap A_{nk} = \phi$ if $j \neq k$, $A_{nj} \in \mathscr{B}_X$ for all n and j and the diameter of A_{nj} is $\leqslant 1/n$ for all j. Let $x_{nj} \in A_{nj}$ be arbitrary. Let μ_n be the measure with masses $\mu(A_{nj})$ at the points x_{nj}, respectively. Let $g \in U(X)$ be arbitrary, and let

$$\alpha_{nj} = \inf_{x \in A_{nj}} g(x), \qquad \beta_{nj} = \sup_{x \in A_{nj}} g(x)$$

Since g is uniformly continuous and since the diameter of $A_{nj} \to 0$ as $n \to \infty$ uniformly in j, $\sup_j (\beta_{nj} - \alpha_{nj}) \to 0$ as $n \to \infty$. Now

$$\left| \int g \, d\mu_n - \int g \, d\mu \right| = \left| \sum \int_{A_{nj}} (g - g(x_{nj})) \, d\mu \right|$$
$$\leqslant \sup_j (\beta_{nj} - \alpha_{nj}) \to 0$$

as $n \to \infty$. Since $g \in U(X)$ is arbitrary, it follows from Theorem 6.1 that $\mu_n \Rightarrow \mu$. This completes the proof of the theorem.

Theorem 6.4

$\mathscr{M}(X)$ is a compact metric space if and only if X is a compact metric space.

PROOF. Let X be a compact metric space. Then $C(X)$ is a separable Banach space. Hence there exists a sequence $g_1, g_2, \ldots,$ of elements in $C(X)$ such that $g_1 \equiv 1$, $\|g_n\| \leqslant 1$ and $\{g_n\}$ is dense in the unit sphere around 0 in $C(X)$. Let T be the map $\mu \to \{\int g_1 \, d\mu, \int g_2 \, d\mu, \ldots\}$. Then T maps $\mathscr{M}(X)$ into the space I^∞ which is the countable product of the interval $[-1, 1]$. I^∞ is a compact metric space. Exactly as in the proof of Theorem 6.2, T is shown to be a homeomorphism of $\mathscr{M}(X)$ into I^∞. We shall now prove that $T(\mathscr{M}(X))$ is a closed subset of I^∞. Suppose $\{\mu_n\}$ is a sequence of measures such that $T(\mu_n)$ converges to $(\alpha_1, \alpha_2, \ldots)$ in I^∞. Let g be any function in the unit sphere of $C(X)$. Then there exists a sequence g_{k_r} such that $\|g_{k_r} - g\| \to 0$ as $r \to \infty$. Then we have

$$\left| \int g \, d\mu_n - \int g \, d\mu_m \right| \leqslant 2\|g - g_{k_r}\| + \left| \int g_{k_r} \, d\mu_n - \int g_{k_r} \, d\mu_m \right| \cdot$$

Hence

$$\overline{\lim_{m,n\to\infty}} \left| \int g \, d\mu_n - \int g \, d\mu_m \right| \leqslant 2\|g - g_{k_r}\|.$$

Letting $r \to \infty$,

$$\overline{\lim_{m,n\to\infty}} \left| \int g \, d\mu_n - \int g \, d\mu_m \right| = 0.$$

Thus for every g in the unit sphere S_0 of $C(X)$ $\lim \int g \, d\mu_n$ exists. We shall denote this limit by $\Lambda(g)$. For any element $f \in C(X)$ we can find a constant $c \neq 0$ such that $cf \in S_0$. Define $\Lambda(f) = c\Lambda(f/c)$. It is easy to verify that Λ is a nonnegative linear functional on $C(X)$ such that $\Lambda(1) = 1$. Hence, by Theorem 5.8, there exists a unique measure μ such that $\Lambda(g) = \int g \, d\mu$. In particular, $\int g_r \, d\mu = \alpha_r$. Thus $T(\mu) = (\alpha_1, \alpha_2, \ldots)$. In other words, $T(\mathscr{M}(X))$ is closed. The compactness of I^∞ implies that $\mathscr{M}(X)$ is a compact metric space.

Conversely, let $\mathscr{M}(X)$ be a compact metric space. By Lemmas 6.1 and 6.2, X is homeomorphic to a closed subset of $\mathscr{M}(X)$. Hence X is a compact metric space. This completes the proof of the theorem.

We now proceed to prove a theorem on the topological completeness of the space $\mathscr{M}(X)$. We recall that a metric space is called topologically complete if it is homeomorphic to a complete metric space. It is a well-known result of Alexandroff (cf. Kelley [16], pp. 207–208) that a metric space is topologically complete if and only if it is a G_δ in some complete metric space, in which case it is a G_δ in every complete metric space into which it can be topologically imbedded.

Theorem 6.5

Let X be a separable metric space. Then $\mathscr{M}(X)$ is topologically complete if and only if X is so.

Proof. Let X be topologically complete. As in the proof of Theorem 6.2 we may assume X to be totally bounded. Its completion X_1 is compact and X is a G_δ subset of X_1. Let $\mathscr{M}_0 = \{\mu\colon \mu \in \mathscr{M}(X_1), \mu(X_1 - X) = 0\}$. Then $\mathscr{M}_0$ and $\mathscr{M}(X)$ are homeomorphic. By Theorem 6.4, $\mathscr{M}(X_1)$ is a compact metric space and hence complete. Thus in order to establish the topological completeness of $\mathscr{M}(X)$ it is sufficient to prove that

$\mathscr{M}_0$ is a G_δ in $\mathscr{M}(X_1)$. Since X is a G_δ in X_1 we can find open sets G_k, $k = 1, 2, \ldots$, such that $G_1 \supseteq G_2 \supseteq \ldots$ and $\bigcap_k G_k = X$. It is clear that

$$\mathscr{M}_0 = \bigcap_k \{\mu: \mu \in \mathscr{M}(X_1), \mu(X_1 - G_k) = 0\}$$

$$= \bigcap_{k=1}^{\infty} \bigcap_{r=1}^{\infty} \{\mu: \mu \in \mathscr{M}(X_1), \mu(X_1 - G_k) < 1/r\}.$$

We shall now show that $\{\mu: \mu(X_1 - G_k) < 1/r\}$ is open in $\mathscr{M}(X_1)$. In other words, we shall show that $\{\mu: \mu(X_1 - G_k) \geqslant 1/r\}$ is closed. If $\mu_n \Rightarrow \mu$ and $\mu_n(X_1 - G_k) \geqslant 1/r$, then by Theorem 6.1, $\mu(X_1 - G_k) \geqslant \overline{\lim}_n \mu_n(X_1 - G_k) \geqslant 1/r$. Thus $\mathscr{M}_0$ is a G_δ in $\mathscr{M}(X_1)$. In other words, $\mathscr{M}(X)$ is topologically complete.

Conversely, let $\mathscr{M}(X)$ be a complete separable metric space under some metric. Since X is homeomorphic (by Lemma 6.1 and 6.2) to the closed subset D of $\mathscr{M}(X)$, it follows that X is topologically complete. This completes the proof of Theorem 6.5.

The proof of the following theorem is already contained in the proof of Theorem 6.2, but we mention it separately since we will have occasion to use it later.

Theorem 6.6

Let X be a separable metric space. Then we can construct an equivalent metric in X such that there exists a sequence of bounded uniformly continuous functions $\{g_1, g_2, \ldots\}$ with the following property: for any sequence μ_n of measures, $\mu_n \Rightarrow \mu$ if and only if $\int g_k \, d\mu_n \to \int g_k \, d\mu$ as $n \to \infty$ for $k = 1, 2, \ldots$.

We shall now describe the compact subsets of $\mathscr{M}(X)$ in the case when X is a complete separable metric space.

Theorem 6.7

Let X be a complete separable metric space and $\Gamma \subseteq \mathscr{M}(X)$. Then a necessary and sufficient condition that $\bar{\Gamma}$ is compact is that for every $\varepsilon > 0$ there should exist a compact set $K_\varepsilon \subseteq X$ such that $\mu(K_\varepsilon) \geqslant 1 - \varepsilon$ for all $\mu \in \Gamma$. In other words, the family Γ must be uniformly tight.

PROOF. First we shall prove the sufficiency of this condition. It may be remarked that for this part we need only assume that X is a separable metric space. By the Urysohn theorem (as in the proof of Theorem 6.2) there exists a compact metric space $\hat{X}$ containing X as a topological subspace. For any measure μ on X, let $\hat{\mu}$ be the measure on $\hat{X}$ defined by $\hat{\mu}(A) = \mu(A \cap X)$ for all Borel sets $A \subseteq \hat{X}$.

To prove that $\bar{\Gamma}$ is compact we must show that every sequence of elements from Γ possesses a convergent subsequence. Let $\mu_1, \mu_2, \ldots$ be a sequence of measures from Γ. $\hat{\mu}_1, \hat{\mu}_2, \ldots$ is a sequence of measures on $\hat{X}$. Since $\hat{X}$ is compact, by Theorem 6.4, $\{\hat{\mu}_n\}$ possesses a convergent subsequence. Let ν be a limit of $\{\hat{\mu}_n\}$. There exists a sequence $m_1 < m_2 < \ldots$ such that $\hat{\mu}_{m_k} \Rightarrow \nu$ as $k \to \infty$. For each integer r, let $K_r \subseteq X$ be a compact set such that $\mu(K_r) \geqslant 1 - 1/r$ for all $\mu \in \Gamma$. Since K_r is compact in X, it is compact in $\hat{X}$, and hence Borel in $\hat{X}$ and $\mu(K_r) = \hat{\mu}(K_r)$ for all $\mu \in \Gamma$. Hence $\hat{\mu}_{m_k}(K_r) \geqslant 1 - 1/r$. Hence, by Theorem 6.1, we conclude that $\nu(K_r) \geqslant \overline{\lim}_{k\to\infty} \hat{\mu}_{m_k}(K_r) \geqslant 1 - 1/r$. Writing $E = \bigcup_r K_r$ we see that $E \subseteq X$ is a set which is Borel in $\hat{X}$ and $\nu(E) = 1$. In particular, $\nu^*(X) \geqslant \nu(E) = 1$. Therefore, there exists a measure μ on X such that $\hat{\mu} = \nu$ (cf. Halmos [12], p. 75).

Let now C be any closed subset of X. Then there exists a closed subset D of $\hat{X}$ such that $C = X \cap D$. Since $\hat{\mu}_{m_k} \Rightarrow \hat{\mu}$ in $\hat{X}$ we have $\overline{\lim}_k \hat{\mu}_{m_k}(D) \leqslant \hat{\mu}(D)$. This is the same as saying $\overline{\lim}_k \mu_{m_k}(C) \leqslant \mu(C)$. By Theorem 6.1, $\mu_{m_k} \Rightarrow \mu$. This shows that μ_n has a convergent subsequence.

We now turn to the necessity. Let X be a complete separable metric space and Γ a compact set of measures on X. Since X is separable, for each n, we can find open spheres $S_{n1}, S_{n2}, \ldots$ of radius $1/n$ such that $X = \bigcup_j S_{nj}$. For any $n = 1, 2, \ldots$ and any $\eta > 0$ we claim that there is an integer k_n such that

$$\mu\left(\bigcup_1^{k_n} S_{nj}\right) > 1 - \eta$$

for all $\mu \in \Gamma$. If this is not true, then we can find a sequence $\mu_1, \mu_2, \ldots \in \Gamma$ an $\eta_0 > 0$, and a sequence $m_1 < m_2 < \ldots$ of integers such that

$$\mu_k\left(\bigcup_{j=1}^{m_k} S_{nj}\right) \leqslant 1 - \eta_0$$

for $k = 1, 2, \ldots$. Since Γ is compact we may and do assume that $\mu_k \Rightarrow \mu$ where μ is a measure on X. For any fixed l,

$$\bigcup_{j=1}^{m_l} S_{nj} \subseteq \bigcup_{j=1}^{m_k} S_{nj}$$

for all $k > l$, and so

$$\mu_k\left(\bigcup_{j=1}^{m_l} S_{nj}\right) \leqslant 1 - \eta_0$$

for all $k > l$. Since $\mu_k \Rightarrow \mu$ and $\bigcup_{j=1}^{m_l} S_{nj}$ is open, we have by Theorem 6.1,

$$\mu\left(\bigcup_{j=1}^{m_l} S_{nj}\right) \leqslant \varliminf_{k\to\infty} \mu_k\left(\bigcup_{j=1}^{m_l} S_{nj}\right)$$
$$\leqslant 1 - \eta_0.$$

Letting $l \to \infty$ and observing that $\bigcup_{j=1}^{m_l} S_{nj}$ increases to X as $m_l \to \infty$, we have $\mu(X) \leqslant 1 - \eta_0$. This is a contradiction since μ is a measure.

Select now, for each n, an integer k_n such that

$$\mu\left(\bigcup_{j=1}^{k_n} S_{nj}\right) > 1 - \varepsilon/2^n$$

for all $\mu \in \Gamma$. Write $F_n = \bigcup_{j=1}^{k_n} \bar{S}_{nj}$ and $K_\varepsilon = \bigcap_{n=1}^{\infty} F_n$. Since $\mu(F_n) > 1 - \varepsilon/2^n$ for all n and $\mu \in \Gamma$, we have $\mu(K_\varepsilon) > 1 - \varepsilon$ for all $\mu \in \Gamma$. By Lemma 3.1, K_ε is compact. This completes the proof of the theorem.

REMARK. The argument given above shows that the following is a necessary and sufficient condition for compactness.:

Let X be a complete separable metric space and Γ a set of measures on X. In order that $\bar{\Gamma}$ be compact it is necessary and sufficient that for each $\varepsilon > 0$ and $\delta > 0$ there should exist a set $S_{\varepsilon,\delta}$ which is the union of a finite number of spheres of radius $\delta > 0$ such that

$$\mu(S_{\varepsilon,\delta}) > 1 - \varepsilon$$

for all $\mu \in \Gamma$.

Now we shall prove a result which describes the relation between weak convergence of a sequence of measures and uniform convergence of the integrals over certain classes of continuous functions.

Let X be a metric space. A subset $\mathscr{A}_0 \subseteq C(X)$ is said to be *equicontinuous* at a point x if for any $\varepsilon > 0$ there exists a neighborhood N_x of x such that

$$\sup_{f \in \mathscr{A}_0} |f(y) - f(x)| < \varepsilon, \qquad \text{for all } y \in N_x.$$

Definition 6.1

A set $B \in \mathscr{B}_x$ is called a *continuity set* for a measure μ if $\mu(\bar{B} - B^0) = 0$.

Lemma 6.4

Let X be a metric space and μ a measure on X. Then the class $\mathscr{C}_\mu$ of all continuity sets is a field.

PROOF. For any set A, let $\tilde{A}$ denote its boundary. A point x belongs to $\tilde{A}$ if and only if every neighborhood U of x has nonempty intersection with A as well as A'. Thus $\tilde{A} = \tilde{A}'$. Further, for any two sets $A_1, A_2, (A_1 \cup A_2)^{\sim} \subseteq \tilde{A}_1 \cup \tilde{A}_2$. This shows that $\mathscr{C}_\mu$ is a field.

Lemma 6.5

Let X be a separable metric space and μ a measure on X and $\mathscr{A}_0$ be a family of functions equicontinuous at all points $x \in X$. Then for each $\varepsilon > 0$ there exists a sequence of continuity sets $\{A_j\}$ such that (i) $\bigcup_{j=1}^\infty A_j = X$; (ii) $A_i \cap A_j = \phi$, $i \neq j$; *and* (iii) *for any $x, y \in A_j$ and any $f \in \mathscr{A}_0$, $|f(x) - f(y)| < \varepsilon$.*

PROOF. Let d be the metric on X. For each $\delta > 0$ and $x \in X$ we shall denote by $S(x, \delta)$ the open sphere of radius δ with center at x, i.e., $S(x, \delta) = \{y: d(y, x) < \delta\}$. Let $B(x, \delta) = \{y: d(y, x) = \delta\}$. Then $B(x, \delta)$ is the boundary of $S(x, \delta)$. We claim that every sphere $S(x, \delta)$ contains a sphere $S(x, \delta')$, $\delta' \leqslant \delta$ such that $B(x, \delta')$ has μ-measure zero. This is because $S(x, \delta) = \bigcup_{0 \leqslant \delta' < \delta} B(x, \delta')$ is an uncountable disjoint union of Borel sets $B(x, \delta')$, and hence all but a countable number of them must have μ-measure zero.

Since $\mathscr{A}_0$ is an equicontinuous family, for any $x \in X$ we can find a $\delta = \delta(x)$ such that $S(x, \delta)$ is a continuity set and

$$|f(x) - f(y)| < \varepsilon/2$$

for all $y \in S(x, \delta)$ and all $f \in \mathscr{A}_0$. The family $\{S(x, \delta), x \in X\}$ is an open covering of X. Since X is separable, there exists a sequence $\{x_j\}$ such that $\{S(x_j, \delta(x_j)), j = 1, 2, \ldots\}$ is a covering of X. Let $A_1 = S(x_1, \delta(x_1))$, $A_n = S(x_n, \delta(x_n)) \cap S(x_{n-1}, \delta(x_{n-1}))' \cap \ldots \cap S(x_1, \delta(x_1))'$, $n = 2, 3, \ldots$. By Lemma 6.5, all the A_n are continuity sets. They are disjoint and $\bigcup_1^\infty A_n = X$. This completes the proof of the lemma.

Theorem 6.8

Let X be a separable metric space and μ_n be any sequence of measures on X. Then $\mu_n \Rightarrow \mu$ if and only if

$$\lim_{n \to \infty} \sup_{f \in \mathscr{A}_0} \left| \int f \, d\mu_n - \int f \, d\mu \right| = 0$$

for every family $\mathscr{A}_0 \subseteq C(X)$ which is equicontinuous at all the points $x \in X$ and uniformly bounded, i.e., *for some constant M, $|f(x)| \leqslant M$ for all $x \in X$ and $f \in \mathscr{A}_0$.*

Proof. Let A_j be a sequence of sets with the properties stated in Lemma 6.5. Let $x_j \in A_j$ be any fixed sequence of points. For any measure λ on X, let $\tilde{\lambda}$ be the discrete measure concentrated in the set $\{x_j : j = 1, 2, \ldots\}$ in such a way that the mass at x_j is equal to $\lambda(A_j)$. Then by the properties of $\{A_j\}$ for any $f \in \mathscr{A}_0$,

$$\begin{aligned}\left| \int f \, d\lambda - \int f \, d\tilde{\lambda} \right| &\leqslant \sum_{j=1}^{\infty} \left| \int_{A_j} f \, d\lambda - \int_{A_j} f \, d\tilde{\lambda} \right| \\ &\leqslant \sum_{j=1}^{\infty} \int_{A_j} |f(x) - f(x_j)| \, d\lambda \\ &\leqslant \varepsilon.\end{aligned}$$

Thus for any measure λ,

$$\sup_{f \in \mathscr{A}_0} \left| \int f \, d\lambda - \int f \, d\tilde{\lambda} \right| \leqslant \varepsilon.$$

PROOF. By Theorem 2.6, Chapter I, the space X can be written as $Y \cup N$ where N is countable, Y is closed and every open subset of Y has an infinite number of points. Thus Y is a complete separable metric space without isolated points. It is enough to show that there is a nonatomic measure in Y. Let $\mathscr{M}(Y)$, the space of measures on Y be given the weak topology. Then by Theorems 6.2 and 6.5, $\mathscr{M}(Y)$ is a complete separable metric space. For any $\varepsilon > 0$, let $C(\varepsilon)$ be the class of all measures which have at least one atom of mass $\geqslant \varepsilon$. Then the class of all measures with atomic components can be represented as $\bigcup_{r=1}^{\infty} C(1/r)$. If there does not exist any nonatomic measure on Y, then we have

$$\mathscr{M}(Y) = \bigcup_{r=1}^{\infty} C(1/r).$$

We shall now show that $C(\varepsilon)$ is closed. Let $\mu_n \in C(\varepsilon)$ and $\mu_n \Rightarrow \mu$. Since the sequence $\{\mu_n\}$ is conditionally compact by Theorem 6.7, there exists a compact subset K of Y such that $\mu_n(K) > 1 - \varepsilon/2$ for all n. The atoms of μ_n which have mass $\geqslant \varepsilon$ must therefore belong to K. Thus there exists a sequence $\{x_n\}$, $x_n \in K$ for all n, such that $\mu_n(x_n) \geqslant \varepsilon$ and $x_n \to x_0$ as $n \to \infty$. Let V be any closed neighborhood of x_0. Since all the x_n belong to V for all sufficiently large n, it follows that there exists an n_0 such that $\mu_n(V) \geqslant \varepsilon$ for all $n \geqslant n_0$. By Theorem 6.1 $\varepsilon \leqslant \overline{\lim}\, \mu_n(V) \leqslant \mu(V)$. Thus for every closed neighborhood V of x_0, $\mu(V) \geqslant \varepsilon$. Hence $\mu(x_0) \geqslant \varepsilon$. Hence $\mu \in C(\varepsilon)$. This shows that $C(\varepsilon)$ is closed.

Since $\mathscr{M}(Y)$ is a complete metric space and can be expressed as a countable union of closed sets $C(1/r)$, at least one $C(1/r)$ has nonempty interior. Thus we conclude that there exists a measure μ_0 with an atom of positive mass $> \delta > 0$ such that, whenever a sequence of measures μ_n converges weakly to μ_0, μ_n has an atom of mass at least δ for sufficiently large n. Because of Theorem 6.3 we may and do assume that μ_0 has a finite spectrum. Let μ_0 have masses $p_1, p_2, \ldots, p_k$ at the points $x_1, x_2, \ldots, x_k$, respectively, such that $p_i > 0$, $i = 1, 2, \ldots, k$ and $\sum p_i = 1$.

Let $S_n(x_j)$ be the open sphere of radius $1/n$ with center x_j. For sufficiently large n, $S_n(x_i) \cap S_n(x_j) = \phi$, $i \neq j$, $i = 1, 2, \ldots, k$, $j = 1, 2, \ldots, k$. Since the space Y is dense in itself every $S_n(x_j)$ has an infinite number of points belonging to Y. We distribute the mass

p_j among the points of $S_n(x_j)$ such that the mass at each point is less than $\delta/2$. By doing this for every j and every n we obtain a sequence of measures μ_n converging weakly to μ_0 and such that the mass of μ_n at any point is $\leqslant \delta/2$. This contradicts the defining property of μ_0 and shows that $C(1/r)$ has no interior for any r. Hence there exists a nonatomic measure on Y and therefore on X.

Corollary 8.1

Let X be a complete separable metric space which is dense in itself. Then the class of nonatomic measures is an everywhere dense G_δ in $\mathcal{M}(X)$.

PROOF. The proof of this corollary is contained in the proof of the above theorem.

III

PROBABILITY MEASURES IN A METRIC GROUP

1. THE CONVOLUTION OPERATION

Till now we were confined to a study of the properties of the space of probability measures in a general metric space. The two properties which played a dominant role were topological completeness and separability. Now we shall impose a group structure in the basic space and see how far it influences the space of measures which becomes a semigroup under convolution.

Throughout this chapter we shall denote by X a separable metric group. We employ the customary notation of denoting the group operation as xy, x, $y \in X$. e always denotes the identity of X. For any two subsets A, B of X we write $AB = \{z : z = xy,\ x \in A,\ y \in B\}$, and $A^{-1} = \{z : z^{-1} \in A\}$.

By a measure we mean a probability measure defined on $\mathscr{B}_X$. $\mathscr{M}(X)$ will denote the space of all measures on X with the weak topology. $C(X)$ is the space of real-valued, bounded continuous functions. $U(X)$ is the space of real-valued, bounded uniformly continuous functions.

Definition 1.1

For any two measures μ and ν, the *convolution* $\mu * \nu$ is defined as the set function

$$\mu * \nu(A) = \int \mu(Ax^{-1})\, d\nu(x), \qquad A \in \mathscr{B}_X$$

REMARK. That $\mu * \nu$ is a well-defined measure is a consequence of the Fubini theorem. Further,

$$\mu * \nu(A) = \int \nu(x^{-1}A)\, d\mu(x).$$

For any point $x \in X$ we shall denote by x the measure degenerate at the point x. For example, $\mu * x$ is the right translate of the measure μ by x and $(\mu * x)(A) = \mu(Ax^{-1})$ for any Borel set A.

Lemma 1.1

Let Y and Z be separable metric spaces, $\mu_n \in \mathscr{M}(Y)$, $\nu_n \in \mathscr{M}(Z)$ and $\mu_n \Rightarrow \mu$, $\nu_n \Rightarrow \nu$, respectively. Then the product measure $\mu_n \times \nu_n \Rightarrow \mu \times \nu$ as $n \to \infty$ in the space $Y \times Z$.

PROOF. Since Y and Z are separable metric spaces they admit equivalent metrics under which Y and Z are totally bounded. Then their completions $\bar{Y}$ and $\bar{Z}$ are compact. The completion of $Y \times Z$ is $\bar{Y} \times \bar{Z}$. The Banach spaces $U(Y)$, $U(Z)$ and $U(Y \times Z)$ are isomorphic to $C(\bar{Y})$, $C(\bar{Z})$ and $C(\bar{Y} \times \bar{Z})$, respectively (see the proof of Lemma 6.3, Chapter II). Let $\mathscr{A}_0$ be the algebra generated by all the functions of the form $f(y)g(z)$ on $Y \times Z$ where $f \in U(Y)$, $g \in U(Z)$. $\mathscr{A}_0$ separates points and contains constants. Hence by the Stone-Weienstrass theorem ([16], p. 244) $\mathscr{A}_0$ is dense in $U(Y \times Z)$. From the fact that $\mu_n \Rightarrow \mu$, $\nu_n \Rightarrow \nu$ it follows that for every $f \in \mathscr{A}_0$, $\int f\, d\mu_n \times \nu_n \to \int f\, d\mu \times \nu$. Hence for every $f \in U(Y \times Z)$, $\int f\, d\mu_n \times \nu_n \to \int f\, d\mu \times \nu$. Theorem 6.1, Chapter II implies that $\mu_n \times \nu_n \Rightarrow \mu \times \nu$.

Theorem 1.1

Let X be a separable metric group. The space $\mathscr{M}(X)$ is a topological semigroup under the operation $(\mu, \nu) \to \mu * \nu$.

PROOF. That "$*$" is a transitive operation is an easy consequence of the Fubini theorem. The measure e has the property $\mu * e = e * \mu = \mu$. We have to only verify that the operation "$*$" is continuous in the weak topology. From the definition of convolution, it follows that for every continuous function $f \in C(X)$,

$$\int f \, d\mu * \nu = \int f(xy) \, d\mu(x) \, d\nu(y)$$

$$= \int f(xy) \, d\mu \times \nu$$

If $f \in C(X)$ then $f(xy) \in C(X \times X)$. This together with Lemma 1.1 shows that if $\mu_n \Rightarrow \mu$ and $\nu_n \Rightarrow \nu$, then $\mu_n * \nu_n \Rightarrow \mu * \nu$. In other words, the operation "$*$" is continuous.

2. SHIFT COMPACTNESS IN $\mathscr{M}(X)$

In the theory of sums of independent random variables we often come across situations where a sequence of probability measures fails to converge to any limit, but actually does converge when suitably centred. Now we shall make a systematic analysis of this phenomenon in relation to the convolution operation between measures in groups.

Definition 2.1

A set $\mathscr{K} \subseteq \mathscr{M}(X)$ is said to be *right* (*left*) *shift compact* if, for every sequence $\mu_n \in \mathscr{K} (n = 1, 2, \ldots)$, there is a sequence ν_n such that (1) ν_n is a right (left) translate of μ_n, and (2) ν_n has a convergent subsequence.

The main results of this section are the following two theorems which reveal an important structural property of the topological semigroup in relation to the notion of shift compactness.

Theorem 2.1

Let X be a complete separable metric group and let $\{\lambda_n\}$, $\{\mu_n\}$, $\{\nu_n\}$ be three sequences of measures on X such that $\lambda_n = \mu_n * \nu_n$ for each n. If the sequences $\{\lambda_n\}$ and $\{\mu_n\}$ are conditionally compact then so is the sequence $\{\nu_n\}$.

PROOF. Since $\{\lambda_n\}$ and $\{\mu_n\}$ are conditionally compact it follows from Theorem 6.7, Chapter II, that, given $\varepsilon > 0$, there exists a compact set K_ε such that

$$\lambda_n(K_\varepsilon) > 1 - \varepsilon, \qquad \mu_n(K_\varepsilon) > 1 - \varepsilon$$

for all n. Then we have

$$1 - \varepsilon < \lambda_n(K_\varepsilon) = \int \nu_n(x^{-1}K_\varepsilon)\, d\mu_n(x)$$

$$\leqslant \int_{K_\varepsilon} \nu_n(x^{-1}K_\varepsilon)\, d\mu_n(x) + \varepsilon,$$

or

$$\int_{K_\varepsilon} \nu_n(x^{-1}K_\varepsilon)\, d\mu_n(x) > 1 - 2\varepsilon.$$

This implies the existence of a point $x_n \in K_\varepsilon$ such that

$$\nu_n(x_n{}^{-1}K_\varepsilon) > 1 - 3\varepsilon \qquad \text{for} \quad \varepsilon < \tfrac{1}{3}.$$

Since

$$x_n{}^{-1}K_\varepsilon \subseteq K_\varepsilon{}^{-1}K_\varepsilon, \qquad \nu_n(K_\varepsilon{}^{-1}K_\varepsilon) > 1 - 3\varepsilon$$

for all n. Since $K_\varepsilon^{-1} K_\varepsilon$ is compact and ε is arbitrary it follows once more from Theorem 6.7, Chapter II, that $\{\nu_n\}$ is conditionally compact.

Theorem 2.2

Let X be a complete separable metric group and let $\{\lambda_n\}$, $\{\mu_n\}$, $\{\nu_n\}$ be three sequences of measures on X such that $\lambda_n = \mu_n * \nu_n$, $n = 1, 2, \ldots$. If the sequence $\{\lambda_n\}$ is conditionally compact then the sequences $\{\mu_n\}$ and $\{\nu_n\}$ are right- and left-shift compact, respectively.

PROOF. Choose and fix a sequence $\{\varepsilon_n\}$ of positive numbers such that $\sum \varepsilon_n < \infty$. Then it follows from Theorem 6.7, Chapter II, that there exists a sequence of compact sets K_r such that

$$\lambda_n(K_r) > 1 - \varepsilon_r, \qquad r = 1, 2, \ldots$$

for all n. Now choose a positive sequence η_r descending to zero and satisfying

$$\sum_1^\infty \varepsilon_r \eta_r^{-1} \leqslant \tfrac{1}{2}.$$

(One may choose $\varepsilon_r = 1/r^2$ and $\eta_r = c/r^\delta$, $0 < \delta < 1$ where c is a suitable constant).

Let

$$E_{nr} = \{x: \mu_n(K_r x^{-1}) > 1 - \eta_r\},$$

$$F_n = \bigcap_{r=1}^\infty E_{nr}.$$

Then we have

$$1 - \varepsilon_r \leqslant \lambda_n(K_r) = \int_{E_{nr}} \mu_n(K_r x^{-1})\, d\nu_n(x) + \int_{E_{nr}'} \mu_n(K_r x^{-1})\, d\nu_n(x)$$

$$\leqslant \nu_n(E_{nr}) + (1 - \eta_r)\nu_n(E_{nr}'),$$

where E_{nr}' denotes the complement of the set E_{nr}. Thus

$$\nu_n(E_{nr}') \leqslant \varepsilon_r \eta_r^{-1},$$

and consequently

$$\nu_n(F_n') \leqslant \sum_r \varepsilon_r \eta_r^{-1} \leqslant \tfrac{1}{2}.$$

Hence $F_n \neq \phi$. Let x_n be any element of F_n. Then, from the definition of F_n, it follows that for $x_n \in F_n$,

$$\mu_n(K_r x_n^{-1}) > 1 - \eta_r$$

for all n and r. If now we write $\alpha_n = \mu_n * x_n$ and $\beta_n = x_n^{-1} * \nu_n$, then $\lambda_n = \alpha_n * \beta_n$ and

$$\alpha_n(K_r) = \mu_n(K_r x_n^{-1}) \geqslant 1 - \eta_r$$

for all n and r. Once again by Theorem 6.7, Chapter II, α_n is conditionally compact. Since λ_n and α_n are conditionally compact it follows from Theorem 2.1 that β_n is conditionally compact. This completes the proof of the theorem.

3. IDEMPOTENT MEASURES

Definition 3.1

A measure $\mu \in \mathscr{M}(X)$ is said to be *idempotent* if $\mu * \mu = \mu$.

The aim of this section is to show that the only idempotent measures on a complete separable metric group are normalized Haar measures of compact subgroups. We recall that the left invariant Haar measure λ of a locally compact metric group Z is uniquely defined to within a constant multiple by the equation $\lambda(zA) = \lambda(A)$ for all $A \in \mathscr{B}_Z$ and $z \in Z$. If Z is compact or abelian then λ is also right invariant, i.e., $\lambda(Az) = \lambda(A)$ for all $A \in \mathscr{B}_Z$ and $z \in Z$.

Lemma 3.1

Let X be a separable metric group and $\mu \in \mathscr{M}(X)$. Then for any compact set K there exists a point $x_0 \in X$ such that

$$\mu(Kx_0) = \sup_{x \in X} \mu(Kx)$$

PROOF. Let $\delta_K = \sup_{x \in X} \mu(Kx)$. If $\delta_K = 0$, the lemma holds trivially. Suppose $\delta_K > 0$. Let $\{x_n\}$ be a sequence of points in X such that

$$\lim_{n \to \infty} \mu(Kx_n) = \delta_K.$$

We shall first show that $\{x_n\}$ has a convergent subsequence. Suppose this is not true. We may and do assume that $\mu(Kx_n) \geqslant \frac{1}{2}\delta_K$ for all n. If $Kx_1 \cap Kx_n \neq \phi$ for all $n \geqslant 2$, then $x_n \in K^{-1}Kx_1$ for all n. Then the compactness of $K^{-1}Kx_1$ implies that x_n has a convergent subsequence. Since we have assumed to the contrary there exists an n_1 such that $Kx_1 \cap Kx_{n_1} = \phi$. Let $K_1 = Kx_1 \cup Kx_{n_1}$. If $K_1 \cap Kx_n \neq \phi$ for all $n > n_1$ then $x_n \in K^{-1}K_1$ for all $n > n_1$, and once again the compactness of K and K_1 implies that $\{x_n\}$ has a convergent subsequence. Thus there exists an n_2 such that $n_2 > n_1$ and $K_1 \cap Kx_{n_2} = \phi$. Repeating this argument we see that there exists a sequence $\{n_j\}$ such that Kx_{n_1}, $Kx_{n_2}, \ldots$ are mutually disjoint. Further $\mu(Kx_{n_j}) \geqslant \frac{1}{2}\delta_K$, $j = 1, 2, \ldots$. This is a contradiction.

Thus a convergent sequence exists $\{x_n\}$ for which $\lim_{n \to \infty} \mu(Kx_n) = \delta_K$. Let x_0 be the limit of $\{x_n\}$. By Lemma 6.1, Chapter II, and Theorem 1.1, $\mu * x_n^{-1} \Rightarrow \mu * x_0^{-1}$. By Theorem 6.1, Chapter II,

$$\delta_K \geqslant \mu(Kx_0) \geqslant \overline{\lim_{n\to\infty}}\ \mu(Kx_n) = \delta_K.$$

This completes the proof of the lemma.

Theorem 3.1

Let X be a complete separable metric group and μ an idempotent measure on X. Then there exists a compact subgroup $S \subseteq X$ such that μ is the normalized Haar measure of S.

PROOF. We shall first prove that the support of μ (which exists by Theorem 2.1, Chapter II) is compact. Let K be any compact subset of X for which $\mu(K) > 0$. By Theorem 3.2, Chapter II such a K exists. Let $\delta_K = \sup_{x \in X} \mu(Kx)$. By Lemma 3.1 there exists a point x_0 such that $\mu(Kx_0) = \delta_K$. Let $K_0 = Kx_0$. Then

$$\delta_K = \mu(K_0) = \int \mu(K_0 x^{-1})\, d\mu(x).$$

Since the integrand is $\leqslant \delta_K$ it follows that

$$\mu(K_0 x^{-1}) = \delta_K \qquad \text{a.e.} \quad x(\mu).$$

If $\mu(K_0 x_n^{-1}) = \delta_K$ and $x_n \to x$ as $n \to \infty$ then by Theorem 6.1, Chapter II, $\mu(K_0 x^{-1}) = \delta_K$. Thus

$$\mu(K_0 x^{-1}) = \delta_K, \qquad \text{for every} \quad x \in S,$$

where S is the support of μ. This is because, by the definition of S, every set of μ-measure unity is dense in S. If S were not compact, there will exist a sequence $\{x_n\}$ having no convergent subsequences and for which the equation

$$\mu(K_0 x_n^{-1}) = \delta_K$$

holds for all n. By the same argument as in Lemma 3.1 we can arrive at a contradiction. This shows that S is compact.

We shall now prove that the support S of μ is a semigroup. Indeed, we have

$$\int \mu(Sx^{-1})\, d\mu(x) = \mu(S) = 1.$$

Since $\mu(A) \leqslant 1$ for any Borel set A, the above equation implies that

$$\mu(Sx^{-1}) = 1 \qquad \text{a.e.} \quad x(\mu).$$

If $x_n \to x$ as $n \to \infty$ and $\mu(Sx_n^{-1}) = 1$ for all n, then $\mu(Sx^{-1}) = 1$. Hence

$$\mu(Sx^{-1}) = 1, \qquad \text{for every} \quad x \in S.$$

Since S is the smallest closed subset of measure 1, $S \subseteq Sx^{-1}$, $x \in S$. Hence $S \cdot S \subseteq S$, i.e., S is a semigroup.

If now $x \in S$, then $x^n \in S$ for $n = 1, 2, \ldots$. If e is not a limit of the sequence $\{x^n\}$, then this sequence will be discrete. Since S is compact this is a contradiction. Thus e is a limit of the sequence $\{x^n\}$, and hence x^{-1} is also a limit. This shows that $S = S^{-1}$, i.e., S is a group. Thus the support of μ is a compact subgroup.

Let now K be any closed subset of S. Then by Lemma 3.1 there exists an $x_0 \in S$ such that $\mu(Kx_0) = \sup_{x \in S} \mu(Kx) = \delta_K$. If $K_0 = Kx_0$, then

$$\delta_K = \int_S \mu(K_0 x^{-1})\, d\mu(x).$$

This implies once again that

$$\mu(K_0 x^{-1}) = \delta_K \qquad \text{a.e} \quad (\mu),$$

and hence

$$\mu(K_0 x^{-1}) = \delta_K, \qquad \text{for all} \quad x \in S.$$

Thus for every compact set $K \subseteq S$, $\mu(Kx) = \mu(K)$. The regularity of μ implies that $\mu * x = \mu$ for $x \in S$, i.e., μ is right invariant. Hence μ is the normalized Haar measure of S. This completes the proof.

4. INDECOMPOSABLE MEASURES

The main aim of this section is to investigate the properties of the class of all indecomposable measures.

Definition 4.1

A measure λ is said to be *decomposable* if and only if there exist two nondegenerate measures μ and ν such that $\lambda = \mu * \nu$. In the contrary case, λ is said to be *indecomposable.*

Definition 4.2

A nondegenerate measure α is said to be a *factor* of a measure β, $\alpha \prec \beta$ in symbols, if and only if there exists a measure γ such that either $\beta = \alpha * \gamma$ or $\beta = \gamma * \alpha$.

We shall denote by $\mathscr{M}_0(X)$ the set of all decomposable measures and $\mathscr{M}_1(X)$ the set of all indecomposable measures on X.

Lemma 4.1

Let X be a separable metric group. Then there exists an equivalent left (right) invariant metric, i.e., there exists a metric d with the property $d(x, y) = d(zx, zy)$ $(d(x, y) = d(xz, yz))$ for all $x, y, z \in X$.

PROOF. See Kelley [16, Ch. 6, p. 210].

Lemma 4.2

Let X be a separable metric group. Then there exists a sequence $f_1, f_2, \ldots (g_1, g_2, \ldots)$ of real valued bounded functions on X with the following properties:

(a) *for each j, $f_j(x)$ $(g_j(x))$ is left (right) uniformly continuous;*

(b) *the sequence $\{f_j\}$ $(\{g_j\})$ separates points of X.*

PROOF. We shall prove the existence of left uniformly continuous functions (i.e., uniformly continuous in the left invariant metric). The existence of right uniformly continuous functions follows in an exactly same manner.

Since X is a separable metric group there exists a dense sequence of points $\{x_n\}$ in X. Further, there exists a sequence $\{N_i\}$ of neighborhoods of identity descending to the identity, i.e., $N_1 \supseteq N_2 \supseteq \ldots$ and $\bigcap_{i=1}^{\infty} N_i = e$. Let d be a left invariant metric. Let $\varphi_i(x) = d(e, x)/[d(e, x) + d(x, N_i')]$. Then as in the proof of Theorem 1.6, Chapter I, it follows that φ_i are uniformly continuous in the metric d.

Let now $\varphi_{ij}(x) = \varphi_i(x_j x)$. Since d is left invariant it follows that $\varphi_{ij}(x)$ is uniformly continuous. It only remains to show that $\{\varphi_{ij}\}$ separates points of X. Suppose $\varphi_{ij}(a) = \varphi_{ij}(b)$ for all i and j. Then $\varphi_i(x_j a) = \varphi_i(x_j b)$ for all i and j. Since $\{x_n\}$ is dense in X and φ_i are continuous it follows that $\varphi_i(b^{-1}a) = \varphi_i(e) = 0$ for all i. Since $\{N_i\}$ descends to the identity, $b^{-1}a$ is outside N_i for some i if $b \neq a$. Then $\varphi_i(b^{-1}a) = 1$. This is a contradiction and hence $a = b$. If we arrange φ_{ij} in the form of a sequence $\{f_n\}$ the proof of the lemma is complete.

Corollary 4.1

Let $\{f_n\}$ ($\{g_n\}$) be a sequence satisfying properties (a) and (b) in Lemma 4.2. Then the family of functions $\{f_n(ax), a \in X\}$ is equicontinuous for each fixed n. Similarly, the family $\{g_n(xb), b \in X\}$ is equicontinuous for each fixed n.

In what follows we shall choose and fix the sequences $S_l = \{f_j\}$ and $S_r = \{g_j\}$ satisfying properties (a) and (b) of Lemma 4.2.

Lemma 4.3

A measure $\mu \in \mathscr{M}(X)$ is degenerate if and only if $\mu f_j^{-1}(\mu g_j^{-1})$ is degenerate for all j.

Proof. If μ is degenerate then it is clear that μf_j^{-1} is degenerate for all j. Suppose μ is nondegenerate. Then the support of μ consists of at least two points. Let a, b be two distinct points in the support of μ. Since S_l separates points there exists an $f_j \in S_l$ such that $f_j(a) \neq f_j(b)$. Let U and V be disjoint neighborhoods of $f_j(a)$ and $f_j(b)$, respectively, in the real line. Then $f_j^{-1}(U)$ and $f_j^{-1}(V)$ are disjoint neighborhoods of a and b, respectively, and $\mu f_j^{-1}(U) > 0$, $\mu f_j^{-1}(V) > 0$. This shows that μf_j^{-1} is nondegenerate in the real line.

A similar proof can be given for $\{g_j\}$.

Definition 4.3

For any $f \in C(X)$, $\mu \in \mathscr{M}(X)$ we shall write

$$V_l(f, \mu) = \sup_{a \in X} \left[\int f^2(ax)\, d\mu(x) - \left(\int f(ax)\, d\mu(x) \right)^2 \right]$$

$$V_r(f, \mu) = \sup_{a \in X} \left[\int f^2(xa)\, d\mu(x) - \left(\int f(xa)\, d\mu(x) \right)^2 \right]$$

Lemma 4.4

A measure $\mu \in \mathcal{M}(X)$ is degenerate if and only if $V_l(f_j, \mu) = 0$ $(V_r(g_j, \mu) = 0)$ for all $f_j \in S_l (g_j \in S_r)$.

PROOF. This follows from Definition 4.3 and Lemma 4.3.

Lemma 4.5

If $\mu_n \in \mathcal{M}(X)$ and $\mu_n \Rightarrow \mu$ then $\lim_{n\to\infty} V_l(f_j, \mu_n) = V_l(f_j, \mu)$ for all $f_j \in S_l$ and $\lim_{n\to\infty} V_r(g_j, \mu_n) = V_r(g_j, \mu)$ for all $g_j \in S_r$.

PROOF. This is an immediate consequence of Corollary 4.1 and Theorem 6.8, Chapter II.

Lemma 4.6

Let X be a complete separable metric group and let

$$E_{ij}(\varepsilon) = [\mu : \mu \in \mathcal{M}(X), \mu = \alpha * \beta, \quad V_r(g_i, \alpha) \geqslant \varepsilon, V_l(f_j, \beta) \geqslant \varepsilon]$$

where $f_j \in S_l$ and $g_i \in S_r$. Then $E_{ij}(\varepsilon)$ is closed for all i and j.

PROOF. Let $\mu_n \in E_{ij}(\varepsilon)$ and $\mu_n \Rightarrow \mu$. By the definition of $E_{ij}(\varepsilon)$ there exist measures α_n and β_n such that

$$\mu_n = \alpha_n * \beta_n,$$

$$V_r(g_i, \alpha_n) \geqslant \varepsilon, \qquad V_l(f_j, \beta_n) \geqslant \varepsilon,$$

for all n. By Theorem 2.2, there exists a sequence of points $a_n \in X$ such that $\{\alpha_n * a_n\}$ and $\{a_n^{-1} * \beta_n\}$ are conditionally compact. Thus we can choose subsequences $\{\alpha_{n_k} * a_{n_k}\}$ and $\{a_{n_k}^{-1} * \beta_{n_k}\}$ converging to some measures α_0 and β_0, respectively. By the definition of $V_l(f, \mu)$ and $V_r(g, \mu)$ it is clear that

$$V_l(f_j, \beta_n) = V_l(f_j, a_n^{-1} * \beta_n),$$

$$V_r(g_i, \alpha_n) = V_r(g_i, \alpha_n * a_n).$$

Hence by Lemma 4.5,

$$\lim_{k\to\infty} V_l(f_j, \beta_{n_k}) = V_l(f_j, \beta_0),$$

$$\lim_{k\to\infty} V_r(g_i, \alpha_{n_k}) = V_r(g_i, \alpha_0).$$

Thus we have

$$\mu = \alpha_0 * \beta_0,$$
$$V_l(f_j, \beta_0) \geqslant \varepsilon, \qquad V_r(g_i, \alpha_0) \geqslant \varepsilon,$$

i.e., $\mu \in E_{ij}(\varepsilon)$. This completes the proof.

Theorem 4.1

Let X be a complete separable metric group. Then the set $\mathscr{M}_1$ of indecomposable measures is a G_δ in $\mathscr{M}(X)$.

Proof. It is enough to show that the complement of $\mathscr{M}_1$, namely, $\mathscr{M}_0$, the set of all decomposable measures is an F_σ in $\mathscr{M}(X)$. In fact, we shall prove that

$$\mathscr{M}_0 = \bigcup_{j=1}^{\infty} \bigcup_{i=1}^{\infty} \bigcup_{r=1}^{\infty} E_{ij}(r^{-1}),$$

where it is known by Lemma 4.6 that $E_{ij}(r^{-1})$ is closed. It is clear from Lemma 4.4 that any measure belonging to the right-hand side of the above equation is decomposable, and hence belongs to $\mathscr{M}_0$. Let now $\mu \in \mathscr{M}_0$. Then there exist two nondegenerate measures α and β such that $\mu = \alpha * \beta$. By Lemma 4.4 there exist i and j such that

$$V_l(f_j, \beta) > 0, \qquad V_r(g_i, \alpha) > 0.$$

This shows the existence of an r such that $\mu \in E_{ij}(r^{-1})$. The proof of the theorem is now complete.

We shall now proceed to the proof of the fact that the set $\mathscr{M}_1$ is dense in $\mathscr{M}(X)$ whenever X is an infinite group. We need several lemmas.

Definition 4.4

A subset $A \subset X$ is said to be *decomposable* if there exist two sets $A_1, A_2 \subseteq X$ such that (a) each of A_1, A_2 contains at least two elements, and (b) $A_1A_2 = A$; a set $A \subseteq G$ is said to be *indecomposable* if it is not decomposable.

Lemma 4.7

Let A be any countable indecomposable set and μ a measure such that $\mu(A) = 1$ and $\mu(\{g\}) > 0$ for every $g \in A$. Then μ is indecomposable.

PROOF. Suppose μ is decomposable. Then $\mu = \mu_1 * \mu_2$ where μ_1 and μ_2 are nondegenerate. From the definition of convolution it follows that the masses of μ_1 and μ_2 are concentrated in countable subsets. Let

$$A_i = [x : x \in X, \mu_i(\{x\}) > 0], \qquad i = 1, 2.$$

Then it is clear that $A = A_1A_2$ and both A_1 and A_2 have at least two points. This contradicts the fact that A is indecomposable, and hence completes the proof of the lemma.

Lemma 4.8

Let B be an infinite countable set $\{z_1, z_2, \ldots\}$ of distinct elements in X, with the following property: $z_rz_s^{-1} \neq z_tz_u^{-1}$ for every set of four distinct integers r, s, t, u. If F is any finite subset of X then the set $B \cup F$ is indecomposable.

PROOF. Suppose the lemma is not true. Then there exist two sets A_1, A_2, at least one of which contains an infinite number of points and such that $B \cup F = A_1A_2$. Let $A_1 = (x_1, x_2, \ldots)$ and $y_1, y_2 \in A_2$. Since the elements $x_ry_1, r = 1, 2, \ldots$ are all distinct, all but a finite number of them belong to B. Thus there exists a finite set N of integers such that $x_ry_1 \in B$ for $r \notin N$. Take any integer $m \notin N$. For at most one integer s, say $s = k_1$, x_sy_1 can be equal to x_my_2. Similarly, for at most one integer, say $s = k_2$, x_sy_2 can be equal to x_my_1. Choose any integer $n \notin N$ and different from m, k_1, and k_2. Then x_my_1, x_my_2, x_ny_1 and x_ny_2 are all distinct, and belong to B. But

$$(x_my_1)\,(x_ny_1)^{-1} = (x_my_2)\,(x_ny_2)^{-1},$$

which contradicts the defining property of B. Hence $B \cup F$ is indecomposable.

Lemma 4.9

If X is an infinite group, then there exists a set B with the property described in Lemma 4.8.

PROOF. Let z_1, z_2, z_3 be any three distinct elements of X. Suppose $z_1, z_2, \ldots z_n$ have been chosen. Consider the set A_n of all elements of the form $z_{i_1}^{\pm 1}z_{i_2}^{\pm 1}z_{i_3}^{\pm 1}$ where i_1, i_2, i_3 are any three positive integers $\leqslant n$.

Since A_n is finite and X is infinite, A_n' is nonempty. Choose any element z_{n+1} from A_n'. The sequence $z_1, z_2, \ldots$ chosen in this way has the required property.

Theorem 4.2

Let X be an infinite separable metric group. Then the set $\mathcal{M}_1$ of indecomposable measures is dense in $\mathcal{M}(X)$.

PROOF. From Lemmas 4.7–4.9 it is clear that any measure with finite spectrum is a weak limit of indecomposable measures. An application of Theorem 6.3, Chapter II, completes the proof.

Theorem 4.3

Let X be an infinite complete separable metric group. Then the set of indecomposable measures is an everywhere dense G_δ.

PROOF. This is an immediate consequence of Theorems 4.1 and 4.2.

Theorem 4.4

Let X be an uncountable complete separable metric group. Then the set of nonatomic indecomposable measures is an everywhere dense G_δ in $\mathcal{M}(X)$.

PROOF. An uncountable complete separable metric group cannot have isolated points. Hence by Corollary 8.1 to Theorem 8.1, Chapter II, it follows that the set of nonatomic measures is a dense G_δ. Since intersection of two dense G_δ's is a dense G_δ (by Baire category theorem, cf. [16, p. 200]) it follows from Theorem 4.3 that the set of nonatomic indecomposable measures is a dense G_δ.

The situation is exactly the opposite in the case of finite groups.

Theorem 4.5

Let X be a finite group. Then every measure which gives positive mass for every point is decomposable.

PROOF. Let $x_1, x_2, \ldots, x_n$ be the points of the group X. If μ has mass p_i at x_i, $i = 1, 2, \ldots, n$ and $\inf_i p_i > 0$, then μ can be written as $(1 - \theta)h + \theta\nu$, where $0 \leqslant \theta < 1$, h is the measure which has mass

$1/n$ at every x_i and ν is some measure. The measure h has the property $h * \lambda = \lambda * h = h$ for every measure λ. An easy computation shows that

$$\mu = (1 - \theta)h + \theta\nu = [(1 - \sqrt{\theta})h + \sqrt{\theta}\nu] * [\sqrt{\theta}\, e + (1 - \sqrt{\theta})h],$$

where e is the measure degenerate at the identity. Since $0 \leqslant \sqrt{\theta} < 1$, the measures on the right-hand side are nondegenerate. This completes the proof.

5. THE CASE WHEN X IS ABELIAN

Now we shall examine the special case when X is a complete separable metric abelian group. For any two sets $A, B \subseteq X$, we shall write $A + B = \{x + y \colon x \in A, y \in B\}$, where $+$ denotes the operation in the group. $-A$ stands for the set $\{-x \colon x \in A\}$, where $-$ denotes inverse.

First of all, we note that in $\mathscr{M}(X)$, the convolution operation "$*$" is commutative. In particular, the notions of left and right-shift compactness coincide.

Definition 5.1

Two measures α and β are said to be *shift equivalent* ($\alpha \sim \beta$ in symbols) if one is a shift of the other, i.e., there exists a point $x_0 \in X$ such that $\alpha = \beta * x_0$.

For any measure μ, let $F(\mu)$ denote the class of all factors of μ. If $\mathscr{K}$ is a set of measures on X, let $F(\mathscr{K})$ be the set of all factors of all elements belonging to $\mathscr{K}$. As before, we shall write $\alpha \prec \beta$ if α is a factor of β.

We shall denote by $\tilde{\mathscr{M}}(X)$ the collection of all shift equivalence classes in $\mathscr{M}(X)$. For any measure α, let $\tilde{\alpha}$ denote the equivalence class to which α belongs. The space $\tilde{\mathscr{M}}(X)$ endowed with the quotient topology is a topological semigroup and the mapping $\alpha \to \tilde{\alpha}$ is a continuous homomorphism of $\mathscr{M}(X)$ onto $\tilde{\mathscr{M}}(X)$.

Definition 5.2

A subset $\mathscr{K} \subset \mathscr{M}(X)$ is said to be *shift compact* if its image $\tilde{\mathscr{K}}$ in $\tilde{\mathscr{M}}(X)$ is conditionally compact.

The following theorem is an immediate consequence of Theorem 2.2.

Theorem 5.1

Let X be a complete separable metric abelian group and $\mathscr{K}$ be a shift compact subset of $\mathscr{M}(X)$. Then $F(\mathscr{K})$ is shift compact.

For any measure μ we shall write $\bar{\mu}$ for the measure defined by $\bar{\mu}(A) = \mu(-A)$ for any Borel set A. We shall denote by $|\mu|^2$ the measure $\mu * \bar{\mu}$. If $\mu = \bar{\mu}$, then μ is said to be *symmetric.*

Corollary 5.1

A subset $\mathscr{K} \subseteq \mathscr{M}(X)$ is shift compact if and only if the set $|\mathscr{K}|^2$ consisting of all elements $\alpha \in \mathscr{M}$ of the form $|\mu|^2$ with $\mu \in \mathscr{K}$, is conditionally compact.

Corollary 5.2

For any measure μ, $F(\mu)$ is shift compact.

It is clear that the ordering "$\prec$" in $\mathscr{M}(X)$ is carried over to an ordering in $\tilde{\mathscr{M}}(X)$, in a natural way. We shall now prove that "$\prec$" is a linear ordering in $\tilde{\mathscr{M}}(X)$.

Theorem 5.2

Let X be a complete separable metric abelian group. If α and β are two measures on X and $\alpha \prec \beta$ and $\beta \prec \alpha$ then α and β are shift equivalent.

PROOF. Let $\alpha = \beta * \gamma$, $\beta = \alpha * \delta$ and $\eta = \gamma * \delta$. Then we have

$$\alpha = \alpha * \eta = \alpha * \eta^n,$$

$$\beta = \beta * \eta = \beta * \eta^n, \qquad n = 1, 2, \ldots,$$

where η^n denotes the n-fold convolution of η. Hence

$$\begin{aligned} \alpha &= \alpha * \left(\sum_{r=1}^{n} \eta^r / n \right) \\ \beta &= \beta * \left(\sum_{r=1}^{r} \eta^r / n \right) \end{aligned} \tag{5.1}$$

for all n. It follows from Theorem 2.1 that the sequence $\{\sum_{r=1}^{n} \eta^r / n\}$ is compact. An easy computation shows that any limit θ of this sequence has the property $\theta = \theta * \eta = \theta * \theta$. Hence by Theorem 3.1, θ is the normalized Haar measure of a compact subgroup. Further, since $\eta \prec \theta$, it follows that $\gamma \prec \theta$, $\delta \prec \theta$. Hence by the property of Haar measure $(\gamma * \theta) \sim \theta$, $(\delta * \theta) \sim \theta$. We have from (5.1) and the definition of θ,

$$\alpha = \alpha * \theta \sim \alpha * \delta * \theta = \beta * \theta = \beta.$$

This completes the proof.

Theorem 5.3

Let X be a complete separable metric abelian group. Suppose $\alpha_1 \prec \alpha_2 \prec \ldots$ and $\alpha_n \prec \mu$ for all n. Then there is a shift α_n' of α_n for every n such that the sequence $\{\alpha_n'\}$ is weakly convergent.

PROOF. Since $\alpha_n \in F(\mu)$ for all n, it follows from Corollary 5.2 that there exists a sequence $\{x_n\}$ of points in X such that the sequence $\{\alpha_n * x_n\}$ is compact. Let β and γ be any two limits of the sequence $\{\alpha_n * x_n\}$. Since α_n increases in the ordering $\prec$, $\alpha_n * x_n$ also increases. Hence $\beta \prec \gamma$ and $\gamma \prec \beta$. By Theorem 5.2, $\beta \sim \gamma$. This shows that all the limits of $\{\alpha_n * x_n\}$ belong to the same equivalence class. Let α_0 be an element of this equivalence class. Let d be a metric which induces the topology in $\mathscr{M}(X)$. Such a metric exists by Theorem 6.2, Chapter II. Then we have $\lim_{n\to\infty} \inf_{x\in X} d(\alpha_n * x, \alpha_0) = 0$. This shows that we can select a shift α_n' of α_n for every n such that α_n' converges to α_0.

In an exactly similar manner, we have

Theorem 5.4

Let X be a complete separable metric abelian group and $\alpha_1 \succ \alpha_2 \succ \ldots$. Then there exists a shift α_n' of α_n for every n such that the sequence $\{\alpha_n'\}$ converges weakly.

IV

PROBABILITY MEASURES IN LOCALLY COMPACT ABELIAN GROUPS

1. INTRODUCTION

For probability distributions on the real line there are three main theorems on which the entire study of limit theorems for sums of independent random variables is based. These are (a) the Lévy-Khinchine representation of an infinitely divisible distribution; (b) the criteria for weak convergence of such distributions; and (c) Khinchine's theorem on sums of infinitesimal summands, stating that these converge weakly if and only if certain associated infinitely divisible laws converge. For a precise statement of these results we refer to Gnedenko and Kolmogorov [10], Chapters 4 and 5. In this chapter we shall consider the case when X is a locally compact abelian group, and see how far the above-mentioned classical limit theorems on the real line can be generalized.

We shall take for granted the duality theory, as well as the theory of Fourier transforms, for locally compact abelian groups. The reader may refer to the books of Rudin [36], Weil [46], and Pontrjagin [32].

2. PRELIMINARY FACTS ABOUT A GROUP AND ITS CHARACTER GROUP

Let X be a locally compact second countable abelian group and Y its character group. Y consists of all continuous homomorphisms from X into the circle group in the complex plane. Under the topology of uniform convergence in compacta Y is also a locally compact second countable abelian group. For $x \in X$ and $y \in Y$, let $\langle x, y\rangle$ denote the value of the character y at x and $R\langle x, y\rangle$ its real part. By duality theory the relation between X and Y is perfectly symmetric, i.e., X is the character group of Y. Further, if G is a closed subgroup of X and H is the annihilator of G in Y, i.e., the set

$$H = \{y : \langle x, y\rangle = 1 \quad \text{for all} \quad x \in G\},$$

then G and Y/H are character groups of each other. If X is compact, then Y is discrete, and vice versa. If X is generated by a compact neighborhood of the identity, then X has the structure $V \oplus C \oplus Z_0^r$, where V is a finite dimensional real vector space, C is a compact group, and Z_0^r is the cartesian product of r copies of the additive group of all integers. These and some other well-known facts about locally compact abelian groups will be used in the sequel.

3. MEASURES AND THEIR FOURIER TRANSFORMS

By a measure on X we shall mean a nonnegative, completely additive set function on the Borel subsets of X. By a probability measure we mean a measure with total mass $= 1$. Note that in the earlier chapters by a measure we always meant a probability measure. The necessity of considering both measures and probability measures arises in this chapter, and hence we make this distinction now. As before $\mathcal{M}(X)$ will denote the space of probability measures. Since a locally compact second countable group is a topologically complete space (i.e., homeomorphic to a complete metric space), all the results of Chapter III hold good for $\mathcal{M}(X)$. For any two elements λ, $\mu \in \mathcal{M}(X)$, and any Borel set E, we write

$$(\lambda * \mu)(E) = \int \mu(E - x)\, d\lambda.$$

$\lambda * \mu \in \mathcal{M}(X)$. If $\lambda_1, \lambda_2, \ldots, \lambda_n \in \mathcal{M}(X)$ we shall denote $\lambda_1 * \lambda_2 * \ldots * \lambda_n$ by $\prod_{i=1}^{n} \lambda_i$. As before, $\bar{\mu}$ denotes the measure defined by $\bar{\mu}(A) = \mu(-A)$ and $|\mu|^2 = \mu * \bar{\mu}$. By convergence in $\mathcal{M}(X)$ we shall mean weak convergence, unless otherwise stated.

For each $\mu \in \mathcal{M}(X)$ its *characteristic function* $\hat{\mu}(y)$ is a function on the character group Y, defined as follows:

$$\hat{\mu}(y) = \int_X \langle x, y \rangle \, d\mu(x).$$

The basic properties of characteristic functions are given by the following theorem.

Theorem 3.1

(1) *$\hat{\mu}(y)$ is a uniformly continuous function of Y;*

(2) *if $\hat{\mu}_1(y) = \hat{\mu}_2(y)$ for all $y \in Y$ then $\mu_1 = \mu_2$;*

(3) *$(\mu * \lambda)\hat{}\,(y) = \hat{\mu}(y)\hat{\lambda}(y)$ for all $y \in Y$ and $\mu, \lambda \in \mathcal{M}(X)$*

(4) *$\hat{\bar{\mu}}(y) = \overline{\hat{\mu}(y)}$.*

Definition 3.1

A function φ defined on Y is said to be *positive definite* if and only if for any n complex numbers $a_1, a_2, \ldots, a_n$, any n points $y_1, y_2, \ldots, y_n \in Y$ and any n,

$$\sum_{i,j} a_i \bar{a}_j \varphi(y_i - y_j) \geqslant 0.$$

Theorem 3.2

A function φ defined on Y is the characteristic function of a measure $\mu \in \mathcal{M}(X)$ if and only if the following conditions hold: (1) $\varphi(e) = 1$; (2) φ is continuous; and (3) φ is positive definite.

For the proof of Theorems 3.1–3.2 the reader may refer to Rudin [36, Chap. 1].

Theorem 3.3

Let $\{\mu_n\}$ be a sequence of measures in $\mathscr{M}(X)$. Then $\mu_n \Rightarrow \mu$ if and only if $\hat{\mu}_n(y) \to \hat{\mu}(y)$ uniformly over compact subsets of Y. Moreover if $\hat{\mu}_n(y)$ converges to a limit uniformly on each compact subset of Y, then there is a $\mu \in \mathscr{M}(X)$ such that

(i) $\hat{\mu}(y) = \lim_{n\to\infty} \hat{\mu}_n(y)$;

(ii) $\mu_n \Rightarrow \mu$.

PROOF. Suppose $\mu_n \Rightarrow \mu$. The family of functions $\{\langle x, y\rangle \ y \in K\}$, where K is any compact subset of Y, is uniformly bounded and equicontinuous at all points $x \in X$. Hence by Theorem 6.8, Chapter II it follows that $\hat{\mu}_n(y) \to \hat{\mu}(y)$ uniformly over K.

Now suppose that $\hat{\mu}_n(y)$ converges to a function $\varphi(y)$ uniformly over every compact set in Y as $n \to \infty$. Since $\hat{\mu}_n(y)$ is continuous, it follows that $\varphi(y)$ is continuous. Since $\hat{\mu}_n(e) = 1$ and $\hat{\mu}_n(y)$ is positive definite, $\varphi(e) = 1$ and $\varphi(y)$ is positive definite. Hence by Theorem 3.2 there exists a measure $\mu \in \mathscr{M}(X)$ such that $\hat{\mu}(y) = \varphi(y)$.

If X is a finite dimensional vector space Theorem 3.3 is nothing but the well-known Lévy-Cramér continuity theorem (cf. Cramér [4], p. 102).

If X is a discrete group then for any $\mu \in \mathscr{M}(X)$ and any point $x \in X$, we have

$$\mu(\{x\}) = \int_Y \overline{\langle x, y\rangle} \hat{\mu}(y)\, dy,$$

where dy is the normalized Haar measure of the compact group Y. Hence the uniform convergence of $\hat{\mu}_n(y)$ to $\hat{\mu}(y)$ implies the weak convergence of μ_n to μ.

Suppose Theorem 3.3 holds good in X_1 and X_2, where X_1 and X_2 are two locally compact second countable abelian groups. Let μ_n be a sequence of measures on $X_1 \oplus X_2$, $\mu_n^{(1)}$ and $\mu_n^{(2)}$ be the marginal measures of μ_n on X_1 and X_2, respectively (induced by the projections on X_1 and X_2), and $\hat{\mu}_n(y)$ converge uniformly over compact sets to $\hat{\mu}(y)$. Then it is clear that $\hat{\mu}_n^{(1)}$ and $\hat{\mu}_n^{(2)}$ converge uniformly over compact subsets to $\hat{\mu}^{(1)}$ and $\hat{\mu}^{(2)}$, respectively, where $\mu^{(1)}$ and $\mu^{(2)}$ are the marginal measures of μ on X_1 and X_2, respectively. Since the theorem holds on

X_1 and X_2, it follows that $\mu_n^{(1)} \Rightarrow \mu^{(1)}$ and $\mu_n^{(2)} \Rightarrow \mu^{(2)}$. Let $\varepsilon > 0$ be arbitrary and $K_1 \subseteq X_1$ and $K_2 \subseteq X_2$ be compact subsets such that $\mu_n^{(1)}(K_1) > 1 - \varepsilon/2$, $\mu_n^{(2)}(K_2) > 1 - \varepsilon/2$ for all n. Such sets K_1 and K_2 exist by Theorem 6.7, Chapter II. Let $K = K_1 \oplus K_2$. K is a compact subset of $X_1 \oplus X_2$. Further $\mu_n(K) = 1 - \mu_n(K') \geqslant 1 - \mu_n^{(1)}(K_1') - \mu_n^{(2)}(K_2') \geqslant 1 - \varepsilon$ for all n. Hence by Theorem 6.7, Chapter II, it follows that $\{\mu_n\}$ is conditionally compact. But by property (2) of Theorem 3.1 all the limits must coincide with μ. Thus the theorem holds for $X_1 \oplus X_2$.

Suppose H is a compact subgroup of X and the theorem holds on the group X/H. Then we claim that the theorem holds on X. Let $\mu_n \in \mathscr{M}(X)$ and $\hat{\mu}_n(y)$ converge uniformly over compact subsets of Y to $\hat{\mu}(y)$. Let τ be the canonical homomorphism from X to X/H. Since the character group of X/H is a closed subgroup Z of Y, $\hat{\nu}(y) = \widehat{\nu\tau^{-1}}(y)$ for any $y \in Z$, $\nu \in \mathscr{M}(X)$, and hence $\widehat{\mu_n\tau^{-1}}$ converges to $\widehat{\mu\tau^{-1}}$ uniformly over compact subsets of Z, it follows that $\mu_n\tau^{-1} \Rightarrow \mu\tau^{-1}$. Hence by Theorem 6.7, Chapter II, for any $\varepsilon > 0$, there exists a compact subset $K \subseteq X/H$ such that $(\mu_n\tau^{-1})(K) > 1 - \varepsilon$ for all n. Since H is compact, $\tau^{-1}(K)$ is also compact in X and hence by Theorem 6.7, Chapter II, it follows that μ_n is compact in X. Once again property (2) of Theorem 3.1 implies that $\mu_n \Rightarrow \mu$.

By the structure theory of locally compact abelian groups, there always exists a compact subgroup H of X such that X/H is of the form $V \oplus D$ where V is a vector space and D is a discrete group. From what has been proved in the earlier paragraphs it follows that Theorem 3.3 holds in any X.

4. INFINITELY DIVISIBLE DISTRIBUTIONS

By a distribution in X we mean a probability measure. We shall now introduce the definition of infinitely divisible distributions and study some of their elementary properties.

Definition 4.1

A distribution μ is said to be *infinitely divisible* if, for each n, there are elements $x_n \in X$ and $\lambda_n \in \mathscr{M}(X)$ such that $\mu = \lambda_n^n * x_n$.

We note that the above definition is slightly different from the classical one in the case of the real line (cf. Gnedenko and Kolmogorov [10]). Such a modification is necessary if we want to avoid the role of divisibility of elements from the group. As yet it is not clear whether there exists a single element x of the group X with the property $\mu = \lambda_n^n * x$ for every n. That such is the case will be clear from the results of a later section.

Theorem 4.1

The infinitely divisible distributions form a closed subsemigroup of $\mathscr{M}(X)$.

PROOF. If λ and μ are infinitely divisible, it is obvious from the definition that $\lambda * \mu$ is also infinitely divisible. Let now μ_k, $k = 1, 2, \ldots$ be a sequence of infinitely divisible distributions weakly converging to μ. For any fixed integer n, let

$$\mu_k = \lambda_{kn}^n * x_{kn}.$$

From Theorem 5.1, Chapter III it is clear that there exists a subsequence of λ_{kn} which after a suitable shift converges to a distribution λ_n as $k \to \infty$. Since $\mu_k \Rightarrow \mu$, it is clear from the above equation that there exists an element x_n such that $\mu = \lambda_n^n * x_n$. This completes the proof.

The normalized Haar measure of a compact subgroup of X is an example of an infinitely divisible distribution. This follows from the fact that such a measure is idempotent (cf. Definition 3.1 and Theorem 3.1, Chapter III). We shall now prove a result concerning the absence of zeros for the characteristic function of an infinitely divisible distribution without idempotent factors.

Theorem 4.2

Let $\hat{\mu}(y)$ be the characteristic function of an infinitely divisible distribution μ. If $\hat{\mu}(y_0) = 0$ for some character y_0, then μ has an idempotent factor.

PROOF. From the definition of infinite divisibility it follows that, for each n, there exist an element $x_n \in X$ and a distribution λ_n such that $\mu = \lambda_n^n * x_n$. Since $\hat{\mu}(y_0) = 0$, $\hat{\lambda}_n(y_0) = 0$ for every n. By Theorem 5.1, Chapter III, λ_n is shift compact. Let λ be a limit of shifts of λ_n.

Then $\hat{\lambda}(y_0) = 0$, and hence λ is a nondegenerate distribution. It is also clear that $\lambda^n \prec \mu$. Thus by Theorem 5.3, Chapter III, there exists a sequence x_n' of elements in X such that $\lambda^n * x_n' \Rightarrow \lambda_0$. Then $\hat{\lambda}_0(y_0) = 0$. Further, there exists a point x_0 such that $\lambda_0{}^2 = \lambda_0 * x_0$. Hence $\lambda_0 * (-x_0)$ is idempotent. Obviously, $\lambda_0 * (-x_0)$ is a nondegenerate factor of μ. In other words, μ has an idempotent factor.

Conversely, let μ have a nondegenerate idempotent factor λ. Then $\hat{\lambda}(y)^2 = \hat{\lambda}(y)$. Thus $\hat{\lambda}(y)$ takes only two values 0 and 1. If $\hat{\lambda}(y) \equiv 1$, then λ is degenerate. Hence there exists a y_0 such that $\hat{\lambda}(y_0) = 0$. Then $\hat{\mu}(y_0) = 0$. This completes the proof.

Definition 4.2

If F is any totally finite measure on X the distribution $e(F)$ associated with F is defined as follows:

$$e(F) = e^{-F(X)}\left[1 + F + \frac{F^2}{2!} + \dots + \frac{F^n}{n!} + \dots\right],$$

where 1 is used to denote the measure with unit mass which is degenerate at the identity.

It is clear that the characteristic function of $e(F)$ is given by

$$\widehat{e(F)}(y) = \exp \int [\langle x, y\rangle - 1]\, dF(x).$$

From this equation it follows that, for any two totally finite measures F and G,

$$e(F) * e(G) = e(F + G).$$

In particular, $e(F) = (e(F/n))^n$. Thus $e(F)$ is an infinitely divisible distribution. Distributions of the type $e(F)$ are called elementary infinitely divisible distributions. From Theorem 4.1, it is clear that limits of shifts of elementary infinitely divisible distributions are also infinitely divisible. From theorems to be proved later it will follow that this is the only way of constructing infinitely divisible distributions.

Suppose F_n is a sequence of totally finite measures and we form the sequence $e(F_n)$. We shall now obtain a necessary condition (which will be shown to be sufficient later) for the shift compactness of $e(F_n)$.

Theorem 4.3

Let $\mu_n = e(F_n)$ where F_n is a sequence of totally finite measures. Then, in order that

(a) *μ_n be shift compact;*

(b) *if μ is any limit of shifts of $\{\mu_n\}$, then μ have no idempotent factor;*

the following conditions are necessary:

(i) *For each neighborhood N of the identity the family $\{F_n\}$ restricted to $X - N$ is weakly conditionally compact.*

(ii) *For each $y \in Y$,*

$$\sup_n \int [1 - R\langle x, y\rangle]\, dF_n < \infty.$$

PROOF. Let N be any symmetric open neighborhood of the identity. We shall first show that the sequence $F_n(N')$ is bounded. Suppose this is not true. Then we can choose a subsequence for which

$$F_{n_k}(N') \geqslant 2k, \qquad k = 1, 2, \ldots .$$

Let L_k, $k = 1, 2, \ldots$, be measures such that

$$L_k(A) \leqslant \frac{1}{k} F_{n_k}(A) \qquad \text{for every Borel set } A,$$

$$L_k(N) = 0,$$

$$L_k(N') = 1.$$

The distribution $\lambda_k = e(L_k)$ is a factor of $e(F_{n_k})$, and the shift compactness of $e(F_n)$ implies the shift compactness of $\{\lambda_k\}$ by Theorem 5.1, Chapter III. Let λ be any limit of shifts of λ_k. From the above equations it is clear that every power of λ is a factor of μ. Thus the sequence λ^n is shift compact. As was shown in the proof of Theorem 4.2, it follows that any limit of shifts of λ^n is a shift of an idempotent distribution. Since μ has no idempotent factors it follows that any limit of shifts of λ^n is degenerate. Since λ^n increases (under $\prec$), λ itself must be degenerate. Thus the sequence $|\lambda_k|^2$ converges to the distribution degenerate at the identity. Hence

$$\lim_{k\to\infty} e(L_k + \bar{L}_k)(N') = 0.$$

But

$$e(L_k + \bar{L}_k)(N') = \exp\,[-(L_k + \bar{L}_k)(X)]\left[\sum \frac{(L_k + \bar{L}_k)^r}{r!}(N')\right]$$
$$\geqslant e^{-2}L_k(N') = e^{-2}$$

which is a contradiction. Hence $\sup_n F_n(N') < \infty$. Since every neighborhood of e contains a symmetric open neighborhood, it follows that for all neighborhoods N of e, $\sup_n F_n(N') < \infty$.

Let $k = \sup_n F_n(N')$, where N is a fixed neighborhood of e. Let now G_n denote the restriction of F_n to N', i.e., for any Borel set A, $G_n(A) = F_n(A \cap N')$. Then $e(G_n)$ is a factor of $e(F_n)$. Since $e(F_n)$ is shift compact, it follows that $\{e(G_n)\}$ is shift compact and hence $\{e(H_n)\}$ is compact where $H_n = G_n + \bar{G}_n$. Hence by Theorem 6.7, Chapter II, for any $\varepsilon > 0$, there exists a compact set C such that $e(H_n)(C') < \varepsilon$ for all n. Since $e(H_n) = e^{-H_n(X)}[\sum_{r=0}^{\infty} H_n^r/r!]$, we have

$$\varepsilon > e(H_n)(C') \geqslant e^{-H_n(X)}H_n(C')$$
$$\geqslant e^{-2k}G_n(C'),$$

for all n. Since k is a constant not depending on n, and ε is arbitrary, it follows that the sequence G_n is uniformly tight (cf. Definition 3.1, Chapter II). A slight modification of the proof of Theorem 6.7, Chapter II shows that G_n is weakly conditionally compact. This completes the proof of (i).

In order to prove the necessity of (ii) we observe that $e(F_n + \bar{F}_n) = |e(F_n)|^2$ is a compact sequence, and an application of Theorems 4.1 and 4.2 shows that any limit of $|e(F_n)|^2$ has a nonvanishing characteristic function. Thus for any y,

$$\lim_{n\to\infty} \exp\left\{\int [R\langle x, y\rangle - 1]\, d(F_n + \bar{F}_n)\right\} \neq 0,$$

which implies condition (ii). The proof is complete.

5. GENERAL LIMIT THEOREMS FOR SUMS OF INFINITESIMAL SUMMANDS

The aim of this section is to introduce the notion of infinitesimal distributions in a group and prove a generalized version of the classical limit theorems due to Khinchin in the case of the real line (cf. [10]).

Definition 5.1

A triangular sequence $\{\alpha_{nj}\}$, $j = 1, 2, \ldots, k_n$ of distributions is said to be *uniformly infinitesimal* if

$$\lim_{n\to\infty} \sup_{1\leqslant j\leqslant k_n} \sup_{y\in K} |\hat{\alpha}_{nj}(y) - 1| = 0$$

for each compact set $K \subset Y$.

REMARK. Since the correspondence between characteristic functions and distributions is one-one and continuous (cf. Theorems 3.1 and 3.3) it is clear that $\{\alpha_{nj}\}$ is uniformly infinitesimal if and only if for every neighborhood N of the identity,

$$\lim_{n\to\infty} \sup_{1\leqslant j\leqslant k_n} |\alpha_{nj}(N')| = 0.$$

Before proceeding to state and prove the main results of this section, we shall establish several lemmas.

Lemma 5.1

For each compact set $C \subseteq Y$ there exists a neighborhood N_C of the identity in X and a finite set $E \subseteq C$ such that

$$\sup_{y\in C} [1 - R\langle x, y\rangle] \leqslant M \cdot \sup_{y\in E} [1 - R\langle x, y\rangle]$$

for all $x \in N_C$, where M is a finite constant depending on C.

PROOF. From the inequality

$$1 - \cos(\alpha + \beta) \leqslant 2[(1 - \cos\alpha) + (1 - \cos\beta)], \qquad 0 \leqslant \alpha, \quad \beta \leqslant 2\pi$$

it follows that

$$1 - R\langle x_1 + x_2, y\rangle \leqslant 2[(1 - R\langle x_1, y\rangle) + (1 - R\langle x_2, y\rangle)]. \tag{5.0}$$

This shows that if the lemma is valid in two groups X_1 and X_2, it is valid for their direct sum $X_1 \oplus X_2$. Let now Y' denote the closed subgroup generated by C, and Φ its annihilator in X. If τ denotes the canonical homomorphism from X onto $X' = X/\Phi$, it is obvious that $R\langle x, y\rangle = R\langle \tau(x), y\rangle$ for all $x \in X$ and $y \in Y'$. It is thus sufficient to prove the lemma when the groups concerned are X' and Y' instead of X and Y. Since Y' is generated by a compact neighborhood of e, it is of the form $V \oplus C \oplus Z_0^r$, where V is a finite dimensional vector space, C is a compact group, and Z_0^r is the product of r copies of the integer group. Hence X' is of the form $V \oplus D \oplus K^r$ where D is a discrete group and K^r is the product or r copies of the circle group. Since the lemma is trivially valid in the case of the real line, discrete group, and compact group, the proof of the lemma is complete.

Lemma 5.2

For any $y \in Y$, there is a continuous function $h_y(x)$ on X with the following properties:

(1) $|h_y(x)| \leqslant \pi$ *for all* $x \in X$, *and* $h_y(-x) = -h_y(x)$;

(2) $\langle x, y\rangle = \exp(ih_y(x))$ *for all* $x \in N_y$ *where*

$$N_y = [x: |\langle x, y\rangle - 1| \leqslant \tfrac{1}{2}].$$

PROOF. Let $\langle x, y\rangle = \exp(i\varphi(X))$ where $-\pi \leqslant \varphi(x) < \pi$. Then it is not difficult to verify that $\varphi(x)$ is a continuous function of x in the closed set N_y. Now choose any continuous extension of $\varphi(x)$ to X such that the first condition is fulfilled. Such an extension exists by Tietze's theorem (cf. Kelley [16], p. 242). This will serve the purpose.

Lemma 5.3

There is a function $g(x, y)$ defined on the product space $X \times Y$ possessing the following properties:

(1) $g(x, y)$ *is a continuous function of both the variables x and y;*

(2) $\sup_{x \in X} \sup_{y \in C} |g(x, y)| < \infty$ *for each compact set* $C \subseteq Y$;

(3) $g(x, y_1 + y_2) = g(x, y_1) + g(x, y_2)$ *for each* $x \in X$, *and* $y_1, y_2 \in Y$, *and* $g(-x, y) = -g(x, y)$;

(4) *If* C *is any compact subset of* Y, *then there is a neighborhood* N_C *of the identity in* X *such that* $\langle x, y\rangle = \exp\,[ig(x, y)]$ *for all* $x \in N_C$ *and* $y \in C$.

(5) *If* C *is any compact subset of* Y, *then* $g(x, y)$ *tends to zero uniformly in* $Y \in C$ *as* x *tends to the identity of the group* X.

PROOF. We shall reduce the proof of the proposition to the case of certain simple groups by making use of the structure theory. Suppose that the proposition is true for an open subgroup G of X. Let H and Y be the character groups of G and X, respectively. Since H can be obtained as a quotient group of Y by taking the quotient with respect to the annihilator of G in Y, there is a canonical homomorphism τ from Y to H. Suppose $g(x, h)$ has been defined for $x \in G$ and $h \in H$ with the required properties. We extend the definition of g as follows. For $x \in G$ and $y \in Y$, we define

$$g(x, y) = g(x, \tau(y)).$$

For $x \notin G$, we define

$$g(x, y) = 0 \qquad \text{for all} \quad y \in Y.$$

Since an open subgroup is also closed, the continuity of $g(x, y)$ follows immediately. The rest of the properties of $g(x, y)$ is an immediate consequence of their validity in $G \times H$.

In the case of a general group X, we take G to be the group generated by a compact neighborhood of the identity. This is both open and closed in X. This group G has the simple structure, $V \oplus C \oplus Z_0^r$ where V is a finite dimensional vector group, C is a compact group, and Z_0^r is the product of the integer group taken r times. We now observe that if functions $g_1(x, y)$ and $g_2(u, v)$ with the properties mentioned in the lemma exist in groups X and U with character groups Y and V, respectively, then a function $g(\xi, \eta)$ with the same properties exists for $\xi \in X \oplus U$ and $\eta \in Y \oplus V$. We have only to define

$$g(\xi, \eta) = g_1(x, y) + g_2(u, v)$$

where x and u are projections of ξ into X and U, respectively, and y and v are projections of η into Y and V, respectively. Thus it is enough to construct $g(x, y)$ in the case of real line, a compact group, and the integer group. In the case of the integer group we can take $g(x, y)$ to be identically zero. In the case of the real line we can take $g(x, y) = \theta(x)y$ where

$$\begin{aligned} \theta(x) &= x, & x &\in [-1, 1], \\ &= 1, & x &> 1, \\ &= -1, & x &< -1. \end{aligned}$$

(Note that the character group of the real line is itself.) Thus, in order to complete the proof of the lemma it is enough to consider the case of a compact group X.

Let X be a compact group with Y as the character group. Let X_0 be the connected component of the identity in X, Y_1 the annihilator of X_0 in Y, $X_1 = X/X_0$, and $Y_0 = Y/Y_1$. Y_0 is the character group of X_0 and Y_1 is the character group of X_1. Since X_0 is connected and compact, Y_0 is a discrete group in which every element is of infinite order. By Zorn's lemma we choose a maximal family of elements $\{d_\alpha\}$ with the following property: if $\sum_{i=1}^{r} n_{\alpha_i} d_{\alpha_i} = 0$ for some positive integer r, integers $n_{\alpha_1}, \ldots, n_{\alpha_r}$ and elements $d_{\alpha_1}, \ldots, d_{\alpha_r}$ from this family, then $n_{\alpha_i} = 0$ for $i = 1, 2, \ldots, r$. Then for any $d \in Y_0$, there exist elements $d_{\alpha_1}, \ldots, d_{\alpha_k}$ from this family and integers $n, n_1, n_2, \ldots, n_k$, $(n > 0)$ such that

$$n\, d = n_1 d_{\alpha_1} + \ldots + n_k d_{\alpha_k}. \tag{5.1}$$

This representation is unique except for multiplication by an integer on both sides.

Each element of Y_0 is a coset of Y_1 in Y. We take the coset d_α and pick out an element y_α of Y from this coset. We fix the elements y_α. We define

$$g(x, y_\alpha) = h_{y_\alpha}(x)$$

for every α where $h_{y_\alpha}(x)$ is as in Lemma 5.2. Let now $y \in Y$ be arbitrary. Then y belongs to some coset of Y_1 which is an element of Y_0. If this element is denoted by d, then there exist integers $n, n_1, \ldots, n_k (n > 0)$ and elements $d_{\alpha_1}, \ldots, d_{\alpha_k}$ from the collection $\{d_\alpha\}$ such that Eq. (5.1) is satisfied. We define

$$g(x, y) = \frac{n_1}{n} g(x, y_{\alpha_1}) + \ldots + \frac{n_k}{n} g(x, y_{\alpha_k}).$$

We shall now prove that the function constructed in this way has all the required properties.

Since $g(x, y)$ is continuous in x for each fixed $y \in Y$ and Y is discrete, the continuity of $g(x, y)$ in both the variables follows immediately. Properties (2) and (3) are obvious from the nature of the construction.

Since compact sets in Y are finite sets, it is enough to prove property (4) for each $y \in Y$. For any $y \in Y$, let $[y]$ denote the coset of Y_1 to which y belongs. Then $[y] \in Y_0$. If we write $[y]$ for d and $[y_\alpha]$ for d_α, then (5.1) can be written as

$$n[y] = n_1[y_{\alpha_1}] + \ldots + n_k[y_{\alpha_k}]. \tag{5.2}$$

For any two elements $y_1, y_2 \in [y]$ it is clear that $y_1 - y_2 \in Y_1$. Since Y_1 is the character group of X/X_0 which is totally disconnected, every element of Y_1 is of finite order. Hence for any $y \in Y_1$, there exists a neighborhood of the identity in X where $\langle x, y\rangle = 1$. Thus for any two elements $y_1, y_2 \in [y]$ there exists a neighborhood of the identity in X where $\langle x, y_1\rangle = \langle x, y_2\rangle$.

Making use of the remarks made in the previous paragraph we shall complete the proof of the lemma. From the construction of $g(x, y)$ and Lemma 5.2, it is clear that, for each y_α, there exists a neighborhood of the identity in X where $e^{ig(x, y_\alpha)} = \langle x, y_\alpha\rangle$. Let now $y \in Y$ be arbitrary. From (5.2) it is clear that there exist elements $y_{\alpha_j 1}, \ldots, y_{\alpha_j n_j}$ in $[y_{\alpha_j}]$ for $j = 1, 2, \ldots, k$, such that

$$ny = \sum_{j=1}^{k} (y_{\alpha_j 1} + \ldots + y_{\alpha_j n_j}). \tag{5.3}$$

From the remarks made in the previous paragraph it follows that there exists a neighborhood of the identity in X (depending on $y_{\alpha_j r}$'s and y_{α_j}) where

$$\langle x, y_{\alpha_j r}\rangle = \langle x, y_{\alpha_j}\rangle.$$

Denoting by N the intersection of all the neighborhoods corresponding to $y_{\alpha_j r}$ $(r = 1, 2, \ldots, n_j,\ j = 1, 2, \ldots, k)$ we have

$$\langle x, y_{\alpha_j r}\rangle = \langle x, y_{\alpha_j}\rangle \qquad \text{for} \quad x \in N, r = 1, 2, \ldots, n_j$$
$$j = 1, 2, \ldots, k. \tag{5.4}$$

Hence from (5.3) and (5.4)

$$\langle x, y\rangle^n = \prod_{j=1}^{k} \langle x, y_{\alpha_j}\rangle^{n_j} \qquad \text{for} \quad x \in N.$$

Since there are neighborhoods of the identity where $\langle x, y_{\alpha_j}\rangle = \exp \{ig(x, y_{\alpha_j})\}$, it follows that there exists a neighborhood of the identity where

$$\langle x, y\rangle^n = e^{ing(x, y)}.$$

Since $\langle x, y\rangle$ and $e^{ig(x, y)}$ are continuous and nonvanishing at the identity of X, there exists a neighborhood of the identity where

$$\langle x, y\rangle = e^{ig(x, y)}.$$

Property (5) is obvious from the property (1) and the fact that $g(x, y)$ vanishes when either x or y is the identity of the corresponding group. This completes the proof of the lemma.

In the following paragraphs we give examples of the function $g(x, y)$ for some particular groups.

EXAMPLE 1. Let $X = Y = R^n$. If $x = (x_1, \ldots, x_n) \in X$ and $y = (y_1, \ldots, y_n) \in Y$, then

$$g(x, y) = \sum_{i=1}^{n} \varphi_i(x_i) y_i,$$

where $\varphi_i(t)$ $(i = 1, 2, \ldots, n)$ are bounded continuous functions on the real line such that $\varphi_i(t) = t$ in a neighborhood of $t = 0$ and $\varphi_i(-t) = -\varphi_i(t)$.

EXAMPLE 2. Let K denote the circle group, and let $X = K^n$ and $Y = Z_0^{\,n}$, Z_0 being the integer group. Let

$$X = [(x_1, \ldots, x_n) : -1 < x_i \leqslant 1 \qquad \text{for} \quad i = 1, 2, \ldots, n]$$

addition being taken modulo 2. Then if $y = (y_1, \ldots, y_n) \in Z_0^{\,n}$,

$$g(x, y) = \sum_{i=1}^{n} \varphi_i(x_i)y_i,$$

where φ_i are as in Example 1.

EXAMPLE 3. Let Y be the additive group of rationals, and X be its character group. Let $\varphi(x)$ be a bounded continuous function on X such that $\exp(i\,\varphi(x)) = \langle x, y_0 \rangle$ for x in a neighborhood of the identity in X, where y_0 is a fixed element of Y different from the identity. Then

$$g(x, y) = \varphi(x) \frac{y}{y_0}.$$

EXAMPLE 4. If X is totally disconnected, then every homomorphism of Y into the real line is trivial, so that in this case $g(x, y) = 0$ for all $x \in X$ and $y \in Y$.

Lemma 5.4

Let $\mu_n = \prod_{j=1}^{k_n} \alpha_{nj}$ where $\{\alpha_{nj}\}$ is a uniformly infinitesimal triangular array of distributions on X. If the distribution μ is a limit of shifts of μ_n, then the set of characters $[y\colon \hat{\mu}(y) \neq 0]$ is an open subgroup of Y, and consequently the normalized Haar measure of the annihilator of this subgroup in X is a factor of μ.

PROOF. Since μ is a limit of shifts of μ_n, it is clear that for a subsequence (which we shall denote by μ_n itself) $|\mu_n|^2 \Rightarrow |\mu|^2$, and hence

$$\lim_{n\to\infty} \prod_{j=1}^{k_n} |\hat{\alpha}_{nj}(y)|^2 = |\hat{\mu}(y)|^2.$$

If $\hat{\mu}(y) \neq 0$, it is obvious that $\hat{\mu}(-y) \neq 0$. The above equation implies that $\hat{\mu}(y) \neq 0$ if and only if

$$\sup_n \sum_{j=1}^{k_n} (1 - |\hat{\alpha}_{nj}(y)|^2) < \infty.$$

From the inequality used in the proof of Lemma 5.1, it follows that

$$1 - \varphi(y_1 + y_2) \leqslant 2[(1 - \varphi(y_1)) + (1 - \varphi(y_2))]$$

for any real valued characteristic function φ. In particular,

$$\sum_{j=2}^{k_n}(1-|\hat{\alpha}_{nj}(y_1+y_2)|^2)\leqslant 2\left[\sum_{j=1}^{k_n}(1-|\hat{\alpha}_{nj}(y_1)|^2)+\sum_{j=1}^{k_n}(1-|\hat{\alpha}_{nj}(y_2)|^2)\right].$$

This inequality together with the earlier remark implies that $\hat{\mu}(y_1+y_2)\neq 0$ if $\hat{\mu}(y_1)\neq 0$ and $\hat{\mu}(y_2)\neq 0$. The continuity of $\hat{\mu}(y)$ implies that $[y: \hat{\mu}(y)\neq 0]$ is an open subgroup of Y. This completes the proof.

We choose and fix a function $g(x, y)$ defined on $X \times Y$ and satisfying all the properties mentioned in Lemma 5.3. The main result of this section can now be stated as follows:

Theorem 5.1

Let $\{\alpha_{nj}\}$, $j = 1, 2, \ldots, k_n$, be a uniformly infinitesimal sequence of distributions, and let

$$\mu_n=\prod_{j=1}^{k_n}\alpha_{nj}.$$

Let

$$\beta_{nj}=e(\alpha_{nj} * x_{nj})$$

where x_{nj} is that element of the group X defined by the equation

$$\langle x_{nj}, y\rangle=\exp\left[-i\int g(x, y)\, d\alpha_{nj}(x)\right].$$

Let $\lambda_n = (\prod_{j=1}^{k_n}\beta_{nj}) * x_n$, where $x_n = -\sum_j x_{nj}$. If one of the sequences $\{\lambda_n\}$ and $\{\mu_n\}$ is shift compact and no limit of its shifts has an idempotent factor, then

$$\lim_{n\to\infty}\sup_{y\in K}|\hat{\lambda}_n(y)-\hat{\mu}_n(y)|=0$$

for each compact set K of Y.

PROOF. During the course of the proof of the theorem we shall adopt the following conventions: We denote by $c_1, c_2, \ldots,$ constants depending on the compact set K (and not on n). All the statements we make are for sufficiently large n. By N we denote any arbitrarily small neighborhood of the identity in X.

Turning to the proof of the theorem, we observe that the elements x_{nj} are well defined, since, from the properties of $g(x, y)$, it follows that $\exp [-i \int g(x, y)\, d\alpha(x)]$ is a character on Y for any distribution α. Further, for any neighborhood N of the identity in X, all the points x_{nj} are in N for sufficiently large n. Therefore, the uniform infinitesimality of $\{\alpha_{nj}\}$ implies the uniform infinitesimality of the sequence $\{\beta_{nj}\}$. Thus $\hat{\lambda}_n(y)$ and $\hat{\mu}_n(y)$ are nonvanishing in K, and hence we use the logarithmic notation freely. Suppose that μ_n is shift compact. Since no limit of shifts of μ_n has an idempotent factor, it follows from Lemma 5.4 that the sequence $\hat{\mu}_n(y)$ is uniformly bounded away from zero for all $y \in K$. Thus it is enough to prove that

$$\lim_{n \to \infty} \sup_{y \in K} |\log \hat{\lambda}_n(y) - \log \hat{\mu}_n(y)| = 0.$$

We have

$$\begin{aligned}\log \hat{\lambda}_n(y) &= \sum_j \log \hat{\beta}_{nj}(y) - \sum_j \log \langle x_{nj}, y \rangle \\ &= \sum_j \log \hat{\beta}_{nj}(y) + i \sum_j \int g(x, y)\, d\alpha_{nj}(x) \\ &= \sum_j [(\alpha_{nj} * x_{nj})\hat{\ }(y) - 1] + i \sum_j \int g(x, y)\, d\alpha_{nj}(x),\end{aligned}$$

and

$$\log \hat{\mu}_n(y) = \sum_j \log \hat{\alpha}_{nj}(y).$$

Writing $\theta_{nj} = \alpha_{nj} * x_{nj}$, and observing that $|\log (1 - z) + z| \leqslant |z|^2$ whenever $|z| \leqslant \frac{1}{2}$, we obtain

$$\begin{aligned}&|\log \hat{\lambda}_n(y) - \log \hat{\mu}_n(y)| \\ &= \left| \sum_j (\hat{\theta}_{nj}(y) - 1) + i \sum_j \int g(x, y)\, d\alpha_{nj} - \sum_j \log \hat{\theta}_{nj}(y) + \sum_j \log \langle x_{nj}, y \rangle \right| \\ &= \left| \sum_j (\hat{\theta}_{nj}(y) - 1) - \sum_j \log \hat{\theta}_{nj}(y) \right|\end{aligned}$$

$$\leqslant c_1\left(\sum_j |1-\hat{\theta}_{nj}(y)|\right)\sup_j |1-\hat{\theta}_{nj}(y)|.$$

Since $\{\theta_{nj}\}$ is uniformly infinitesimal, it is clear from the above inequality that it is enough to prove that

$$\sup_n \sup_{y\in K}\left[\sum_j |1-\hat{\theta}_{nj}(y)|\right] < \infty. \tag{5.5}$$

We have, for any neighborhood N of the identity in X,

$$\begin{aligned}|1-\hat{\theta}_{nj}(y)| &\leqslant \left|\int_N [1-\langle x,y\rangle]\,d\theta_{nj}\right| + \left|\int_{N'} [1-\langle x,y\rangle]\,d\theta_{nj}\right| \\ &\leqslant \left|\int_N [1-\langle x,y\rangle]\,d\theta_{nj}\right| + 2\theta_{nj}(N'). \end{aligned}\tag{5.6}$$

From property (4) of $g(x, y)$ in Lemma 5.3, it follows that there exists a neighborhood of the identity in X where

$$\langle x, y\rangle = e^{ig(x,y)} \qquad \text{for} \quad y \in K.$$

In such a neighborhood we have, for $y \in K$,

$$|1-\langle x,y\rangle + ig(x,y)| \leqslant c_2 g^2(x,y). \tag{5.7}$$

(5.6) and (5.7) imply

$$|1-\hat{\theta}_{nj}(y)| \leqslant \left|\int_N g(x,y)\,d\theta_{nj}\right| + c_2\int_N g^2(x,y)\,d\theta_{nj} + 2\theta_{nj}(N') \tag{5.8}$$

for all $y \in K$. By property (2) of $g(x, y)$ in Lemma 5.3, we have

$$\begin{aligned}\left|\int_X g(x,y)\,d\theta_{nj}\right| &= \left|\int_X g(x+x_{nj},y)\,d\alpha_{nj}\right| \\ &\leqslant \left|\int_N g(x+x_{nj},y)\,d\alpha_{nj}(x)\right| + c_3\alpha_{nj}(N'). \end{aligned}\tag{5.9}$$

Since all the x_{nj} will be in any small neighborhood of the identity after a certain stage, and since $e^{ig(x,y)} = \langle x, y\rangle$ for $x \in N$ and $y \in K$, we conclude by making use of property (5) of $g(x, y)$ in Lemma 5.3, that

$$g(x+x_{nj},y) = g(x,y) + g(x_{nj},y) \tag{5.10}$$

for all $x \in N$ and $y \in K$. Further,

$$e^{ig(x_{nj}, y)} = \langle x_{nj}, y\rangle = \exp\left\{-i\int g(x, y)\, d\alpha_{nj}(x)\right\}$$

for all $y \in K$ and all sufficiently large n. By property (5) of $g(x, y)$ in Lemma 5.3, we get

$$g(x_{nj}, y) = -\int g(x, y)\, d\alpha_{nj}. \tag{5.11}$$

Equations (5.10) and (5.11) imply that for all $y \in K$,

$$\begin{aligned}\left|\int_N g(x + x_{nj}, y)\, d\alpha_{nj}\right| &= \left|\int_N [g(x, y) + g(x_{nj}, y)]\, d\alpha_{nj}(x)\right| \\ &= \left|\int_N g(x, y)\, d\alpha_{nj} - \alpha_{nj}(N)\int g(x, y)\, d\alpha_{nj}\right| \\ &= \left|\alpha_{nj}(N')\int_N g(x, y)\, d\alpha_{nj} - \alpha_{nj}(N)\int_{N'} g(x, y)\, d\alpha_{nj}\right| \\ &\leqslant c_4\alpha_{nj}(N').\end{aligned}$$

The above inequality and (5.9) imply

$$\left|\int g(x, y)\, d\theta_{nj}\right| \leqslant c_5\alpha_{nj}(N') \qquad \text{for} \quad y \in K. \tag{5.12}$$

Equations (5.8), (5.12), and property (2) of Lemma 5.3 give

$$|1 - \hat{\theta}_{nj}(y)| \leqslant c_2\int g^2(x, y)\, d\theta_{nj} + c_6\theta_{nj}(N') + c_7\alpha_{nj}(N')$$

for $y \in K$. Thus in order to complete the proof of the theorem we have only to show that

$$\limsup_n \sum_j \theta_{nj}(N') < \infty, \tag{5.13}$$

$$\limsup_n \sum_j \alpha_{nj}(N') < \infty, \tag{5.14}$$

$$\limsup_n \sup_{y \in K} \sum_j \int_N g^2(x, y)\, d\theta_{nj}(x) < \infty. \tag{5.15}$$

To this end we consider the distribution

$$|\mu_n|^2 = \prod_{j=1}^{k_n} |\alpha_{nj}|^2.$$

Since $|\mu_n|^2$ is compact and no limit of $|\mu_n|^2$ has an idempotent factor, according to Lemma 5.4, $|\hat{\mu}_n(y)|^2$ is bounded away from zero uniformly for $y \in K$ and in n. Thus

$$\overline{\lim_{n\to\infty}} \sup_{y\in K} \sum_j (1 - |\hat{\alpha}_{nj}(y)|^2) < \infty.$$

This is the same as (5.5) with $|\alpha_{nj}|^2$ replacing θ_{nj}, and hence

$$\lim_{n\to\infty} \sup_{y\in K} \left| \exp\left[\sum_j (|\hat{\alpha}_{nj}(y)|^2 - 1)\right] - |\hat{\mu}_n(y)|^2 \right| = 0.$$

Thus the sequence $e(\sum |\alpha_{nj}|^2)$ is compact. We now appeal to Theorem 4.3. Then for any neighborhood N of e in X,

$$\overline{\lim_{n\to\infty}} \sum_j |\alpha_{nj}|^2(N') < \infty, \tag{5.16}$$

$$\overline{\lim_{n\to\infty}} \sum_j \int (1 - R\langle x, y\rangle)\, d|\alpha_{nj}|^2 < \infty. \tag{5.17}$$

We now choose a neighborhood V of the identity such that $V + V \subseteq N$. Then

$$\begin{aligned}
\sum_j \alpha_{nj}(N') &\leqslant \sum_j \alpha_{nj}((V+V)') \\
&\leqslant \sum_j \inf_{x\in V} \alpha_{nj}((V+x)') \\
&= \sum_j \inf_{x\in V} \alpha_{nj}(V'+x) \\
&\leqslant \sum_j \,[\alpha_{nj}(V)]^{-1} \int_V \alpha_{nj}(V'+x)\, d\alpha_{nj} \\
&\leqslant \sum_j \,[\alpha_{nj}(V)]^{-1} \int_X \alpha_{nj}(V'+x)\, d\alpha_{nj} \\
&\leqslant \sup_j \,[\alpha_{nj}(V)]^{-1} \sum_j |\alpha_{nj}|^2(V').
\end{aligned}$$

By the remark after Definition 5.1, it follows that for any $\varepsilon > 0$ there exists an n_0 such that for all $n \geqslant n_0$, $\sup_j [\alpha_{nj}(V)]^{-1} < 1 + \varepsilon$. The above inequality and the validity of (5.16) for any neighborhood N of the identity imply (5.14). Since $|\alpha_{nj}|^2 = |\theta_{nj}|^2$ and $\{\theta_{nj}\}$ is uniformly infinitesimal the same argument leads to (5.13).

From (5.17) and Lemma 5.1, it follows that

$$\overline{\lim_{n\to\infty}} \sup_{y\in K} \sum_j \int [1 - R\langle x, y\rangle]\, d|\theta_{nj}|^2 < \infty.$$

The above inequality and (5.16) imply

$$\overline{\lim_{n\to\infty}} \sup_{y\in K} \sum_j \iint_{V\times V} [1 - R\langle x_1 - x_2, y\rangle]\, d\theta_{nj}(x_1)\, d\theta_{nj}(x_2) < \infty \tag{5.18}$$

for any neighborhood V of the identity. We now choose V such that $V - V \subset N$. Then

$$R\langle x_1 - x_2, y\rangle = \cos g(x_1 - x_2, y), \qquad x_1, x_2 \in V.$$

Since $1 - \cos\theta > \theta^2/4$ for sufficiently small θ, we have from property (5) of $g(x, y)$ in Lemma 5.3,

$$1 - R\langle x_1 - x_2, y\rangle \geqslant \tfrac{1}{4} g^2(x_1 - x_2, y)$$

for $y \in K$. Since $e^{ig(x,y)} = \langle x, y\rangle$ for $x \in N$, $y \in K$, the same property of $g(x, y)$ gives

$$g(x_1 - x_2, y) = g(x_1, y) - g(x_2, y), \qquad x_1, x_2 \in V, y \in K.$$

Thus, for $x_1, x_2 \in V, y \in K$,

$$1 - R\langle x_1 - x_2, y\rangle \geqslant \tfrac{1}{4}[g^2(x_1, y) + g^2(x_2, y) - 2g(x_1, y)\, g(x_2, y)] \tag{5.19}$$

(5.18) and (5.19) imply

$$\overline{\lim_{n\to\infty}} \sup_{y\in K} \left\{ \sum_j \left[\int_V g^2(x, y)\, d\theta_{nj}(x) - \left(\int_V g(x, y)\, d\theta_{nj}(x) \right)^2 \right] \right\} < \infty. \tag{5.20}$$

Equations (5.12), (5.14), and (5.20) imply (5.15).

Now suppose that λ_n is shift compact and no limit of its shifts has an idempotent factor. Then by Theorem 4.3 and Lemma 5.1 we have, for every neighborhood N of the identity and every compact set $K \subset Y$,

$$\sum_{j=1}^{k_n} \theta_{nj}(N') < \infty,$$

$$\sup_n \sup_{y \in K} \sum_j \int [1 - R\langle x, y \rangle] \, d\theta_{nj} < \infty.$$

Let now N be any neighborhood of the identity in X, and V be another neighborhood such that $V - V \subset N$. Since all the x_{nj} belong to V for all sufficiently large n, we have

$$V' - x_{nj} \supseteq N',$$

$$\sum_j \alpha_{nj}(N') \leqslant \sum_j \alpha_{nj}(V' - x_{nj})$$

$$= \sum_j \theta_{nj}(V'),$$

and therefore

$$\sup_n \sum_j \alpha_{nj}(N') < \infty.$$

Since, for any compact set $K \subseteq Y$, there exists a sufficiently small neighborhood N of the identity in X such that

$$1 - R\langle x, y \rangle \geqslant \tfrac{1}{4} g^2(x, y), \qquad x \in N, y \in K,$$

it follows that

$$\overline{\lim_{y \to \infty}} \sup_{y \in K} \sum_j \int_N g^2(x, y) \, d\theta_{nj}(x) < \infty.$$

Thus (5.13)–(5.15) hold good. This implies (5.5) and therefore

$$\lim_{n \to \infty} \sup_{y \in K} |\hat{\lambda}_n(y) - \hat{\mu}_n(y)| = 0.$$

The proof of the theorem is complete.

Lemma 5.5

Let $H \subseteq Y$ be an open subgroup of Y and $\varphi(y)$, $y \in H$ be a continuous positive definite function defined on H. Let

$$\tilde{\varphi}(y) = \varphi(y) \qquad \text{if} \quad y \in H,$$
$$= 0 \qquad \text{if} \quad y \notin H.$$

Then $\tilde{\varphi}$ is a continuous positive definite function on Y.

PROOF. Since an open subgroup is also closed, it follows that $\tilde{\varphi}$ is continuous. Let $a_1, a_2, \ldots, a_n$ be any n complex constants and $y_1, y_2, \ldots, y_n$ any n points in Y. Each y_i belongs to some coset of H in Y. Let $H_1, \ldots, H_k$ be the distinct cosets to which $y_1, \ldots, y_n$ belong. Let $w_1, w_2, \ldots, w_k$ be some elements from $H_1, H_2, \ldots, H_k$, respectively. Then

$$\sum_{i,j} a_i \bar{a}_j \tilde{\varphi}(y_i - y_j) = \sum_i \left\{ \sum_{(r,s):\, y_r, y_s \in H_i} a_r \bar{a}_s \tilde{\varphi}(y_r - y_s) \right\}$$

$$= \sum_i \left\{ \sum_{(r,s):\, y_r, y_s \in H_i} a_r \bar{a}_s \tilde{\varphi}\left[(y_r - w_i) - (y_s - w_i)\right] \right\}$$

Since $y_r - w_i \in H$ for all r such that $y_r \in H_i$ and $\tilde{\varphi} = \varphi$ on H, it follows that every term within brackets on the right-hand side of the above equation is nonnegative. Thus $\tilde{\varphi}$ is positive definite.

Theorem 5.2

If $\{\alpha_{nj}\}$ is uniformly infinitesimal, $\mu_n = \prod_j \alpha_{nj}$, and $\mu_n \Rightarrow \mu$, then μ is infinitely divisible.

PROOF. If μ has no idempotent factor, then it is also a limit of λ_n where λ_n is constructed as in Theorem 5.1. Then Theorem 4.1 implies that μ is infinitely divisible.

Now let us consider the general case. By Lemma 5.4, the set $[y: \hat{\mu}(y) \neq 0]$ is an open subgroup H of Y. If G is the annihilator of this subgroup in X, then the normalized Haar measure of the compact group G is a factor of μ. Let τ be the canonical homomorphism from X to X/G. Then the sequence $\{\alpha_{nj}\tau^{-1}\}$ is uniformly infinitesimal in X/G, and $\mu_n\tau^{-1} \Rightarrow \mu\tau^{-1}$. $\mu\tau^{-1}$ has no idempotent factors, and hence is infinitely divisible. For $y \in H$, $\hat{\mu}(y) = (\widehat{\mu\tau^{-1}})(y)$. For $y \notin H$, $\hat{\mu}(y) = 0$. Let k be any positive integer and ν be a measure on X/G such that $\mu\tau^{-1} = \nu^k * z$, where $z \in X/G$. By Lemma 5.5 and Theorem 3.2, there exists a measure $\tilde{\nu}$ on X such that $\tilde{\nu}\tau^{-1} = \nu$ and $\hat{\tilde{\nu}}(y) = \hat{\nu}(y)$ for $y \in H$ and $\hat{\tilde{\nu}}(y) = 0$ for $y \notin H$. If x is any point in the G-coset of z, it is clear that $\mu = \tilde{\nu}^k * x$. This shows that μ is infinitely divisible.

REMARK. In the statement of Theorem 5.2 we have assumed that $\{\alpha_{nj}\}$ is uniformly infinitesimal. However, it is enough to assume the existence of a sequence $\{x_{nj}\}$ of elements from the group with the property that $\{\alpha_{nj} * x_{nj}\}$ is uniformly infinitesimal.

6. GAUSSIAN DISTRIBUTIONS

We shall now give an algebraic definition of a Gaussian distribution and obtain its representation. This definition is also consistent with the classical definition of Gaussian laws in the case of the finite dimensional vector spaces.

From the point of view of limit theorems, the Gaussian laws arise very naturally as follows. Suppose F_n is a sequence of finite measures on the group X such that (1) outside each neighborhood of the identity $F_n \to 0$ as $n \to \infty$, and (2) $e(F_n)$ converges to a limit after a suitable shift. If the total mass of F_n is not uniformly bounded, $e(F_n)$ may actually converge to a nondegenerate distribution. These are precisely the Gaussian laws.

Definition 6.1

A distribution μ is said to be *Gaussian* if it has the following properties: (i) μ is infinitely divisible; and (ii) if $\mu = e(F) * \alpha$ where α is infinitely divisible, then F is degenerate at the identity.

Theorem 6.1

A function on Y is the characteristic function of a Gaussian distribution on X if and only if it has the form

$$\langle x, y \rangle \exp [- \varphi(y)]$$

where x is a fixed point of X and $\varphi(y)$ is a continuous, nonnegative function on Y satisfying the equality

$$\varphi(y_1 + y_2) + \varphi(y_1 - y_2) = 2[\varphi(y_1) + \varphi(y_2)] \tag{6.1}$$

for all y_1, y_2 in Y.

PROOF. Let μ be Gaussian. Then μ cannot have a nondegenerate idempotent factor. For, otherwise, the Haar measure of some compact subgroup will be a factor of μ, and hence if F is any measure concentrated in that subgroup, then $\mu = e(F) * \mu$. This contradicts property (ii) of Definition 6.1. From the definition of infinite divisibility it follows that, for each n, there exist a distribution α_n and an element g_n of X such that $\mu = \alpha_n^n * g_n$.

Since μ has no idempotent factors, any limit of shifts of α_n is degenerate. In fact if a limit of shifts of α_n is a nondegenerate α, then every power of α will be a factor of μ. Then by the argument used in the proof of Theorem 4.2 it will follow that μ has an idempotent factor. This is a contradiction.

Without loss of generality we may assume that α_n converges to the distribution degenerate at the identity. Because otherwise α_n may be shifted suitably to behave in this manner and g_n too can be altered accordingly. We now write

$$\theta_n = \alpha_n * x_n, \qquad \beta_n = e(\theta_n), \qquad \lambda_n = \beta_n^n * (-nx_n) * g_n,$$

where the element x_n is determined by the equation

$$\langle x_n, y\rangle = \exp\left[-i\int g(x, y)\, d\alpha_n\right].$$

Since μ has no idempotent factors, an application of Theorem 5.1 shows that

$$\overline{\lim_{n\to\infty}} \sup_{y\in K} |\hat{\lambda}_n(y) - \hat{\mu}(y)| = 0$$

for any compact set $K \subseteq Y$. Thus

$$|\hat{\mu}(y)| = \lim_{n\to\infty} \exp\left\{n\int [R\langle x, y\rangle - 1]\, d\theta_n\right\}$$

We shall first prove that

$$\varphi(y) = \lim_{n\to\infty} n\int [1 - R\langle x, y\rangle]\, d\theta_n$$

satisfies (6.1). We write $P_n = n\theta_{n'}$. Then $e(P_n)$ is a shift of $\lambda_{n'}$, and hence $e(P_n)$ is shift compact. By Theorem 4.3 [condition (i)], P_n restricted to N' is weakly conditionally compact for every neighborhood N of the identity. But any limit P of P_n restricted to N' will be such that $\mu = e(P) * \alpha$ where α is also infinitely divisible. From condition

(ii) of Definition 6.1 it follows that the mass of P_n outside every neighborhood of the identity tends to zero. Thus

$$\varphi(y) = \lim_{n \to \infty} \int_N [1 - R\langle x, y\rangle] \, dP_n \tag{6.2}$$

for every neighborhood N of the identity. From the property of the function $\cos \theta$, $0 \leqslant \theta \leqslant 2\pi$, it follows that for any $\varepsilon > 0$, and any two elements $y_1, y_2 \in Y$, there exists a neighborhood N (depending on ε, y_1, y_2) of the identity in X such that

$$\begin{aligned} &2(1 - \varepsilon) \, [(1 - R\langle x, y_1\rangle) + (1 - R\langle x, y_2\rangle)] \\ &\leqslant [(1 - R\langle x, y_1 + y_2\rangle) + (1 - R\langle x, y_1 - y_2\rangle)] \\ &\leqslant 2(1 + \varepsilon) \, [(1 - R\langle x, y_1\rangle) + (1 - R\langle x, y_2\rangle)], \end{aligned}$$

for all $x \in N$. Hence by (6.2) we have

$$\begin{aligned} &2(1 - \varepsilon) [\varphi(y_1) + \varphi(y_2)] \\ &\leqslant \varphi(y_1 + y_2) + \varphi(y_1 - y_2) \leqslant 2(1 + \varepsilon) [\varphi(y_1) + \varphi(y_2)]. \end{aligned}$$

Since ε is arbitrary we have

$$\varphi(y_1 + y_2) + \varphi(y_1 - y_2) = 2[\varphi(y_1) + \varphi(y_2)].$$

Thus, in order to complete the proof of the theorem it is enough to show that $\hat{\mu}(y)/|\hat{\mu}(y)|$ is a character on Y. Let us denote this by $\chi(y)$. It is not difficult to verify that, for every neighborhood N of the identity,

$$\begin{aligned} &\chi(y_1 + y_2) [\chi(y_1)\chi(y_2)]^{-1} \\ &= \exp\left(\lim_{n \to \infty} \int [I\langle x, y_1 + y_2\rangle - I\langle x, y_1\rangle - I\langle x, y_2\rangle] \, dP_n \right), \end{aligned} \tag{6.3}$$

where $I\langle x, y\rangle$ denotes the imaginary part of $\langle x, y\rangle$. For any given $\varepsilon > 0$, we choose a neighborhood N of the identity such that

$$|I\langle x, y_1\rangle| < \varepsilon, \qquad |I\langle x, y_2\rangle| < \varepsilon$$

for $x \in N$. Since

$$\begin{aligned} &|I\langle x, y_1 + y_2\rangle - I\langle x, y_1\rangle - I\langle x, y_2\rangle| \\ &\leqslant |I\langle x, y_1\rangle| \, |1 - R\langle x, y_2\rangle| + |I\langle x, y_2\rangle| \, |1 - R\langle x, y_1\rangle| \end{aligned}$$

and

$$\overline{\lim_{n\to\infty}} \int [1 - R\langle x, y\rangle]\, dP_n < \infty$$

(by Theorem 4.3), we have

$$\left| \int_N [I\langle x, y_1 + y_2\rangle - I\langle x, y_1\rangle - I\langle x, y_2\rangle]\, dP_n \right| < c\varepsilon$$

where c is a constant depending only on y_1 and y_2. Since ε is arbitrary the right-hand side of (6.3) is equal to unity. The continuity of $\chi(y)$ is obvious. This shows that χ is a character on Y. Thus there exists an element $x \in X$ such that

$$\hat{\mu}(y) = \langle x, y\rangle \exp [-\varphi(y)].$$

This proves necessity.

Conversely, let $\hat{\mu}(y) = \langle x, y\rangle \exp(-\varphi(y))$, where $\varphi(y)$ is a non-negative continuous function of y satisfying (6.1). Let $y_1, \ldots, y_k$ be some k characters. Then it is easily verified that $\exp[-\varphi(n_1 y_1 + \ldots + n_k y_k)]$ considered as a function of integers $n_1, n_2, \ldots, n_k$, is positive definite in the product of integer group taken k times. This implies the positive definiteness of $\exp[-\varphi(y)]$, and hence by Theorem 3.2, this function is the characteristic function of a measure μ. Since $\hat{\mu}(y) = 1$ at the identity of Y, the measure μ is a distribution. The infinite divisibility of μ is obvious. We shall now prove property (ii) of Definition 6.1. Let, if possible, $\hat{\mu}(y) = \hat{\mu}_1(y)\hat{\mu}_2(y)$, where $\mu_1 = e(F)$ and μ_2 is infinitely divisible. Since $\hat{\mu}(y)$ does not vanish for any y, $\hat{\mu}_2(y)$ also does not vanish, and hence by Theorem 5.1, μ_2 is a limit of shifts of distributions of the type $e(H)$. From the inequality (5.0) it is clear that for any finite measure H,

$$\begin{aligned} &-\log |e(H)\,\hat{}\,(y_1 + y_2)| - \log |e(H)\,\hat{}\,(y_1 - y_2)| \\ &\leqslant 2[-\log |(e(H))\,\hat{}\,(y_1)| - \log |e(H)\,\hat{}\,(y_2)|]. \end{aligned} \tag{6.4}$$

Thus (6.4) is also valid when $e(H)$ is replaced by either μ_1 or μ_2. Substituting μ_1 and μ_2 for $e(H)$ and adding, we get

$$\varphi(y_1 + y_2) + \varphi(y_1 - y_2) \leqslant 2[\varphi(y_1) + \varphi(y_2)].$$

Since equality holds good in this case, we must have

$$\int([1 - R\langle x, y_1 + y_2\rangle] + [1 - R\langle x, y_1 - y_2\rangle])\, dF$$

$$= 2\int([1 - R\langle x, y_1\rangle] + [1 - R\langle x, y_2\rangle])\, dF$$

for each $y_1, y_2 \in Y$, i.e.,

$$\int [1 - R\langle x, y_1\rangle]\,[1 - R\langle x, y_2\rangle]\, dF = 0.$$

Since F is a finite measure, this implies that F must be degenerate at the origin. This completes the proof.

REMARK 1. Consider real valued continuous functions $\psi(y_1, y_2)$ defined for $y_1, y_2 \in Y$ possessing the following properties:

(i) $\psi(y_1, y_2) = \psi(y_2, y_1)$;

(ii) $\psi(y_1 + y_2, y_3) = \psi(y_1, y_3) + \psi(y_2, y_3)$;

(iii) $\psi(y, y) \geqslant 0$.

Clearly for any such function ψ, $\varphi(y) = \psi(y, y)$ satisfies the identity (6.1). Conversely, any nonnegative continuous function satisfying (6.1) can be obtained in this way. In fact $\psi(y_1, y_2)$ can be recovered from $\varphi(y)$ by the relation

$$\psi(y_1, y_2) = \tfrac{1}{2}[\varphi(y_1 + y_2) - \varphi(y_1) - \varphi(y_2)].$$

REMARK 2. If X_0 is the connected component of the identity in X, then its annihilator Y_0 is the smallest closed subgroup containing all compact subgroups of Y. Let $y_1, y_2 \in Y_0$. If ψ satisfies the properties (i), (ii) and (iii) above, then $\psi(ny_1, y_2) = n\psi(y_1, y_2)$. Since the group generated by y_1 is compact and ψ is continuous, it follows that $\psi(y_1, y_2) = 0$. Thus if μ is a symmetric (i.e., $\mu = \bar{\mu}$) Gaussian distribution on X, then $\hat{\mu}(y) = 1$ for $y \in Y_0$. This implies that μ must be concentrated in X_0. Theorem 6.1 and Remark 1 also show that every connected locally compact group has nontrivial Gaussian measures defined on it.

REMARK 3. It is quite possible that the spectrum of a Gaussian distribution may be the whole group but it need not be absolutely continuous with respect to the Haar measure. Let K be the circle group and K^∞ the product of a countable number of copies of K. Let μ be the Gaussian distribution on K whose characteristic function $\hat{\mu}(n)$ is given by

$$\hat{\mu}(n) = \exp(-n^2)$$

for every integer n. Let μ^∞ be the product measure $\mu \times \mu \times \ldots$. The Haar measure of K^∞ is the product measure $\lambda^\infty = \lambda \times \lambda \times \ldots$, where λ is the Haar measure of K. Then it follows from certain well-known results in measure theory that two such measures λ^∞ and μ^∞ must be orthogonal.

7. REPRESENTATION OF INFINITELY DIVISIBLE DISTRIBUTIONS

The purpose of this section is to obtain a canonical representation for the characteristic function of an infinitely divisible distribution.

Definition 7.1

An infinitely divisible distribution λ is said to be a *proper factor* of another infinitely divisible distribution μ, if $\mu = \lambda * \alpha$ and α is infinitely divisible.

Lemma 7.1

The set of proper factors of an infinitely divisible distribution is closed.

PROOF. This is an immediate consequence of Theorem 5.1, Chapter III and Theorem 4.1.

Lemma 7.2

If $e(F_n)$ converges to the distribution degenerate at the identity, then $F_n(N') \to 0$ as $n \to \infty$ for every neighborhood N of the identity.

PROOF. This is an immediate consequence of Theorem 5.1, Chapter III and Theorem 4.3.

Theorem 7.1

If μ is an infinitely divisible distribution without idempotent factors, then $\hat{\mu}(y)$ has a representation

$$\hat{\mu}(y) = \langle x_0, y\rangle \exp\left[\int [\langle x, y\rangle - 1 - ig(x, y)]\, dF(x) - \varphi(y)\right], \quad (7.0)$$

where x_0 is a fixed point of X, $g(x, y)$ is a function on $X \times Y$ which is independent of μ and has the properties mentioned in Lemma 5.3, F is a σ-finite measure with finite mass outside every neighborhood of the identity in X which satisfies

$$\int [1 - R\langle x, y\rangle]\, dF < \infty \qquad \text{for every} \quad y \in Y,$$

and $\varphi(y)$ is a nonnegative continuous function satisfying

$$\varphi(y_1 + y_2) + \varphi(y_1 - y_2) = 2[\varphi(y_1) + \varphi(y_2)]$$

for each $y_1, y_2 \in Y$. Conversely, any function of the type (7.0) is the characteristic function of an infinitely divisible distribution without idempotent factors.

PROOF. Let μ be any infinitely divisible distribution without an idempotent factor. Choose and fix a sequence $\{N_k\}$ of neighborhoods of the identity in X descending to the identity. Let μ_1 be that proper factor of μ which is of the type $e(F)$ and for which $F(N_1) = 0$ and $F(N_1')$ is maximum. Such an $e(F)$ exists by Theorem 5.1, Chapter III, Theorem 4.3 and Lemma 7.1. Let the F at which the maximum is attained be F_1, and let $\mu = \mu_1 * \lambda_1$ and $\mu_1 = e(F_1)$. Since λ_1 is infinitely divisible and without idempotent factors, the same argument can be applied to λ_1 and the neighborhood N_2. Thus there exists a measure F_2 for which $F_2(N_2) = 0$, $F_2(N_2')$ is a maximum, $\mu_2 = e(F_2)$, $\lambda_1 = \mu_2 * \lambda_2$, and λ_2 is infinitely divisible. Repeating this procedure we can write

$$\mu = \mu_1 * \mu_2 * \dots * \mu_n * \lambda_n, \quad (7.1)$$

$$\lambda_{n-1} = \mu_n * \lambda_n, \quad (7.2)$$

$$\mu_n = e(F_n), \qquad F_n(N_n) = 0, \quad (7.3)$$

where λ_n is infinitely divisible, and $F_n(N_n')$ is a maximum in the sense explained above. Thus by Theorem 5.1, Chapter III there exist shifts of $\mu_1 * \ldots * \mu_n$ and λ_n converging to ν and λ, respectively, and $\mu = \nu * \lambda$. We now assert that λ cannot have a proper factor of the type $e(F)$. Suppose, on the contrary, $e(F)$ is a proper factor of λ. Then it will have a positive mass outside some N_k. Further, since the sequence λ_n is descending (in the order $\prec$), $e(F)$ is a proper factor of λ_k. $\lambda_k = e(F) * \theta$ where θ is infinitely divisible. If F' is the restriction of F to N_k', then (7.2) and (7.3) imply that

$$\lambda_{k-1} = e(F_k + F') * e(F - F') * \theta.$$

This is a contradiction since the total mass of $F_k + F'$ exceeds that of F_k. Thus λ has no proper factor of the type $e(F)$, and is therefore a Gaussian distribution. An application of Theorem 6.1 leads to the existence of a function $\varphi(y)$ and an element $x \in X$ for which

$$\hat{\lambda}(y) = \langle x, y \rangle \exp[-\varphi(y)] \tag{7.4}$$

and

$$\varphi(y_1 + y_2) + \varphi(y_1 - y_2) = 2[\varphi(y_1) + \varphi(y_2)], \qquad y_1, y_2 \in Y.$$

Now we write $H_n = F_1 + F_2 + \ldots + F_n$. From the construction of the distributions $\nu_n = \mu_1 * \ldots * \mu_n$, it is clear that

$$\hat{\nu}_n(y) = \exp\left[\int [\langle x, y \rangle - 1]\, dH_n(x)\right].$$

Since $\exp[i \int g(x, y)\, dH_n(x)]$ is a character on Y, it can be considered as an element of X. Thus there exists an element $x_n \in X$ such that

$$\hat{\nu}_n(y) = \langle x_n, y \rangle \exp\left[\int [\langle x, y \rangle - 1 - ig(x, y)]\, dH_n(x)\right]. \tag{7.5}$$

Since $e(H_n)$ is a factor of μ and H_n increases as $n \to \infty$, it follows from the shift compactness of $e(H_n)$, Theorem 4.3 and Lemma 5.1, that H_n increases to a σ-finite measure H for which $H(N') < \infty$ for every neighborhood N of the identity and

$$\int \sup_{y \in K} [1 - R\langle x, y \rangle]\, dH < \infty$$

for every compact $K \subseteq Y$. Since $[\langle x, y\rangle - 1 - ig(x, y)]$ is bounded uniformly in $y \in K$, by property (2) of $g(x, y)$ in Lemma 5.3, we have, for every neighborhood N of the identity,

$$\lim_{n\to\infty} \int_{N'} [\langle x, y\rangle - 1 - ig(x, y)]\, dH_n = \int_{N'} [\langle x, y\rangle - 1 - ig(x, y)]\, dH$$

uniformly in $y \in K$. When N is sufficiently small, we have by the properties (4) and (5) of $g(x, y)$ in Lemma 5.3,

$$\langle x, y\rangle = e^{ig(x,y)}, \qquad \text{for } x \in N, \quad y \in K,$$

$$g^2(x, y) \leqslant c_1[1 - R\langle x, y\rangle], \qquad \text{for } x \in N, \quad y \in K,$$

where c_1 is a constant depending on K only. Thus

$$|\langle x, y\rangle - 1 - ig(x, y)| \leqslant c_2[1 - R\langle x, y\rangle], \qquad x \in N, \quad y \in K, \tag{7.6}$$

where c_2 is a constant depending on K only. Thus

$$\int_N \sup_{y\in K} |\langle x, y\rangle - 1 - ig(x, y)|\, dH_n \leqslant c_2 \int_N \sup_{y\in K} [1 - R\langle x, y\rangle]\, dH.$$

The above inequality implies the convergence of $\{\int [\langle x, y\rangle - 1 - ig(x, y)]\, dH_n\}$ to $\int [\langle x, y\rangle - 1 - ig(x, y)]\, dH$, uniformly in $y \in K$. Now (7.5) implies that $\hat{\nu}_n(y)$, after a suitable shift converges uniformly over compact sets to $\exp \int [\langle x, y\rangle - 1 - ig(x, y)]\, dH$. This completes the proof of the first part since ν_n converges to ν after a suitable shift, $\mu = \nu * \lambda$ and λ satisfies (7.4).

To prove the converse, we first observe that if F is a totally finite measure, then $\exp [i \int g(x, y)\, dF]$ is a character, and hence $\hat{\mu}(y)$ given by (7.0) is the characteristic function of an infinitely divisible distribution. In the general case we consider a sequence F_n of totally finite measures increasing to F. If K is any compact subset of Y, then by Lemma 5.1, $1 - R\langle x, y\rangle$ is uniformly integrable with respect to F for $y \in K$. (7.6) implies the uniform integrability of $[\langle x, y\rangle - 1 - ig(x, y)]$ for $y \in K$. This shows that the function

$$\langle x_0, y\rangle \exp\left(\int [\langle x, y\rangle - 1 - ig(x, y)]\, dF_n - \varphi(y)\right)$$

converges uniformly over compact sets to $\hat{\mu}(y)$. Thus by Theorems 3.3 and 4.1, $\hat{\mu}(y)$ is the characteristic function of an infinitely divisible distribution. This completes the proof.

Theorem 7.2

Let μ be an infinitely divisible distribution on X. Then μ can be expressed as $\lambda * \nu$ where λ is the normalized Haar measure of a compact subgoup and ν is an infinitely divisible distribution without idempotent factors.

PROOF. As in Lemma 5.4, it follows from the infinite divisibility of μ that the set $[y: \hat{\mu}(y) \neq 0]$ is an open subgroup Y_0 of Y. Let H_0 be the annihilator of Y_0 in X. Then H_0 is a compact subgroup of X. Let λ be the normalized Haar measure of H_0.

$\hat{\mu}(y)$ is a continuous positive definite function without zeros in Y_0. It is the characteristic function of an infinitely divisible distribution without idempotent factors in the group X/H_0. Hence by Theorem 7.1, $\hat{\mu}(y)$ admits a representation

$$\hat{\mu}(y) = \langle x_0, y\rangle \exp\left[\int_{X/H_0} [\langle x, y\rangle - 1 - ig_0(x, y)]\, dF_0 - \varphi_0(y)\right], \tag{7.7}$$

where $g_0(x, y)$ is a function on $(X/H_0) \times Y_0$ satisfying the properties (1)–(5) of Lemma 5.3, F_0 is a measure in X/H_0 with finite mass outside every compact neighborhood of the identity, $\int_{X/H_0} [1 - R\langle x, y\rangle]\, dF_0(x) < \infty$ for every $y \in Y_0$, $x_0 \in X/H_0$, and φ_0 is a continuous function on Y_0 satisfying the equation $\varphi_0(y_1 + y_2) + \varphi_0(y_1 - y_2) = 2[\varphi_0(y_1) + \varphi_0(y_2)]$ for all $y_1, y_2 \in Y_0$.

Let now y_1 be any element outside Y_0. Then one of the following cases can arise:

(i) $ry_1 \notin Y_0$ for any integer $r \neq 0$,

(ii) There exists a least positive integer $r_0 > 0$ such that $r_0 y_1 \in Y_0$.

We shall now consider case (i). Let Y_1 be the group generated by Y_0 and y_1. Any element of Y_1 admits a unique representation $y + ry_1$ for some integer r and $y \in Y_0$. Hence $Y_1 = Y_0 \oplus D$ where D is the discrete group generated by y_1. We shall now write

$$\psi_1(y + ny_1) = \hat{\mu}(y) \tag{7.8}$$

for all r. Then ψ_1 is a well-defined continuous positive definite function on Y_1.

Now let us consider case (ii). Once again let Y_1 be the group generated by Y_0 and y_1. For any $y \in Y_1$, we have $r_0 y \in Y_0$. Let

$$\varphi_1(y) = \frac{1}{r_0^2} \varphi_0(r_0 y), \qquad y \in Y_1, \tag{7.9}$$

where φ_0 is as in (7.7). Then φ_1 is a well-defined continuous nonnegative function on Y_1, satisfying the equation

$$\varphi_1(y_1 + y_2) + \varphi_1(y_1 - y_2) = 2[\varphi_1(y_1) + \varphi_1(y_2)], \qquad y_1, y_2 \in Y_1.$$

Let H_1 be the annihilator of Y_1 in X. Then $H_1 \subseteq H_0$ and there is a canonical homomorphism τ_1 from X/H_1 onto X/H_0. Let x_1 be any point of X/H_1 such that $\tau_1(x_1) = x_0$. By Lemma 5.1, Chapter I, there exists a Borel set B_1 in X/H_1 such that τ_1 maps B_1 onto X/H_0 in a one–one fashion. Further, B_1 can be so chosen that for every compact set $K \subseteq X/H_1$, $B_1 \cap \tau_1^{-1}(\tau_1(K))$ is also compact. Let F_1 be the measure on X/H_1 defined by

$$F_1(A) = F_0(\tau_1(A \cap B_1)) \tag{7.10}$$

for every Borel set A of X/H_1, where F_0 is as in (7.7). Then F_1 is a measure in X/H_1 which gives finite mass for the complement of every neighborhood of the identity. Let now $y \in Y_1$. Then we have

$$\begin{aligned}
&\int_{X/H_1} [1 - R\langle x, y\rangle^{r_0}]\, dF_1(x) \\
&= \int_{X/H_1} [1 - R\langle x, r_0 y\rangle]\, dF_1(x) \\
&= \int_{X/H_1} [1 - R\langle \tau_1(x), r_0 y\rangle]\, dF_1(x) \\
&= \int_{X/H_0} [1 - R\langle x, r_0 y\rangle]\, dF_0(x) < \infty.
\end{aligned}$$

Since $1 - R\langle x, y\rangle \leqslant c[1 - R\langle x, y\rangle^{r_0}]$ for some constant depending on r_0 and some neighborhood of the identity depending on y, it follows that

$$\int_{X/H_1} [1 - R\langle x, y\rangle]\, dF_1(x) < \infty$$

for every $y \in Y_1$.

Let us now define

$$g_1(x, y) = \frac{1}{r_0} g_0(\tau_1(x), r_0 y), \qquad y \in Y_1, \quad x \in X/H_1.$$

Then it is easy to verify that the function g_1 is well defined on $(X/H_1) \times Y_1$ and has all the properties stated in Lemma 5.3. Let

$$\psi_1(y) = \langle x_1, y\rangle \exp\left[\int [\langle x, y\rangle - 1 - ig_1(x, y)]\, dF_1(x) - \varphi_1(y)\right] \quad (7.11)$$

where φ_1 and F_1 are given by (7.9) and (7.10), respectively, and x_1 satisfies equation $\tau_1(x_1) = x_0$. Then ψ_1 is a well-defined, nonvanishing positive definite function on Y_1 and $\psi_1(y) = \hat{\mu}(y)$ for every $y \in Y_0$.

Equations (7.8) and (7.11) give an extension of $\hat{\mu}(y)$ to Y_1 in cases (i) and (ii), respectively. We can now choose an element y_2 outside Y_1, and repeat the same construction for the group Y_2 generated by Y_1 and y_2. Then we get an extension ψ_2 on Y_2. Since Y_0 is open, we have

$$Y_0 \subseteq Y_1 \subseteq Y_2 \subseteq \ldots$$

and Y_n increases to the group Y. We can define ψ on Y by the equation

$$\psi(y) = \psi_n(y), \qquad y \in Y_n$$

for all n. Then $\psi(y)$ is continuous, positive definite, nonvanishing, and Theorem 7.1 implies that it is the characteristic function of an infinitely divisible distribution without idempotent factors on X. We can now write $\hat{\mu}(y) = \psi(y)\hat{\lambda}(y)$, $y \in Y$. This completes the proof.

Corollary 7.1

Let μ be an infinitely divisible distribution on X. Then $\hat{\mu}(y)$ admits the representation

$$\hat{\mu}(y) = \langle x_0, y\rangle\hat{\lambda}(y) \exp\left[\int [\langle x, y\rangle - 1 - ig(x, y)]\, dF(x) - \varphi(y)\right], \quad (7.12)$$

where x_0 is a point in X, λ is the Haar measure of a (probably trivial) compact subgroup, and F and φ satisfy the same conditions as in Theorem 7.1.

REMARK 1. If the group X is totally disconnected, then the representation takes a simpler form. For in such groups $\varphi(y) = 0$ (see Remark 2 following Theorem 6.1), and $g(x, y) = 0$ (see Example 4 following Lemma 5.3). Thus every infinitely divisible distribution has the representation

$$\hat{\mu}(y) = \langle x_0, y\rangle \hat{\lambda}(y) \exp\left[\int [\langle x, y\rangle - 1]\, dF\right],$$

where $x_0 \in X$, λ is the Haar measure of a (probably trivial) compact subgroup, and F is a σ-finite measure which has finite mass outside every neighborhood of the identity and $\int [1 - R\langle x, y\rangle]\, dF(x) < \infty$ for every y.

8. UNIQUENESS OF THE REPRESENTATION

We shall now obtain conditions for the uniqueness of the representation. First of all, we note that the representation cannot be unique if the distribution concerned has a nontrivial idempotent factor λ. This is because for any measure ν concentrated in the support of λ, $\lambda * \nu = \lambda$. We shall therefore consider the case of distributions without idempotent factors.

Before proceeding to the statement of the main result we shall prove an elementary lemma. If μ is any infinitely divisible distribution without idempotent factors, we shall say that μ has the representation (x_0, F, φ) where x_0, F, and φ are as in Theorem 7.1. If F is any signed measure, we denote by F_y the measure given by

$$F_y(A) = \int_A [1 - R\langle x, y\rangle]\, dF(x).$$

Lemma 8.1

Let μ be a totally finite signed measure. If $\hat{\mu}(y)$ is constant on the cosets of a closed subgroup Y_0 of Y, then μ vanishes identically on the complement of the annihilator of Y_0 in X.

PROOF. Let $Y_1 = Y/Y_0$, and let X_1 be the annihilator of Y_0 in X. $\hat{\mu}(y)$, being constant on cosets of Y_0, can be considered as a function on Y_1. Then $\hat{\mu}(y_1), y_1 \in Y_1$ is the characteristic function of a signed measure λ on X_1. Since, for $x \in X_1$, $\langle x, y \rangle$ remains constant on cosets of Y_1 and $\hat{\mu}(y)$ has the same property, we can write

$$\hat{\mu}(y) = \int_{X_1} \langle x, y_1 \rangle \, d\lambda = \int_{X_1} \langle x, y \rangle \, d\lambda,$$

where y_1 denotes that coset of Y_1 to which y belongs. This shows that $\mu = \lambda$, and hence μ vanishes identically on the complement of X_1.

Theorem 8.1

If (x_1, F_1, φ_1) and (x_2, F_2, φ_2) are two representations of the same infinitely divisible distribution without idempotent factors, then (i) $\varphi_1 = \varphi_2$, *and* (ii) *the signed measure $F_1 - F_2$ vanishes identically on the complement of the annihilator of the component of the identity of the character group Y.*

PROOF. Writing $F = F_1 - F_2$, $\varphi = \varphi_1 - \varphi_2$, and $x_0 = x_2 - x_1$, we have

$$\exp \int [\langle x, y \rangle - 1 - ig(x, y)] \, dF = \langle x_0, y \rangle \exp \varphi(y), \tag{8.1}$$

$$\varphi(y_1 + y_2) + \varphi(y_1 - y_2) - 2[\varphi(y_1) + \varphi(y_2)] = 0, \qquad y_1, y_2 \in Y. \tag{8.2}$$

Equating the logarithm of the absolute value on both sides of (8.1) we obtain

$$\varphi(y) = \int [R\langle x, y \rangle - 1] \, dF. \tag{8.3}$$

Substituting the values of the above expression at $y_1 + y_2, y_1 - y_2$, y_1 and y_2 in (8.2), we get

$$\int [1 - R\langle x, y_1 \rangle][1 - R\langle x, y_2 \rangle] \, dF = 0. \tag{8.4}$$

(8.4) can be rewritten as

$$\int [1 - R\langle x, y_1 \rangle] \, dF_{y_2} = 0, \qquad y_1, y_2 \in Y.$$

Since F_{y_2} is totally finite, we have

$$\int \langle x, y\rangle \, d(F_{y_2} + \bar{F}_{y_2}) = 2F_{y_2}(X), \qquad y \in Y. \tag{8.5}$$

Since the right-hand side of (8.5) is a constant when y_2 is fixed, we conclude that the signed measure $F_{y_2} + \bar{F}_{y_2}$ is degenerate at the identity. But the mass of F_{y_2} at the identity is zero. Thus $F_{y_2} + \bar{F}_{y_2} = 0$. In particular, $F_{y_2}(X) = 0$, i.e.,

$$\int [1 - R\langle x, y_2\rangle] \, dF = 0, \qquad y_2 \in Y. \tag{8.6}$$

Equations (8.3) and (8.6) imply the equality of φ_1 and φ_2.

In order to prove the second part of the theorem we make use of the equality of φ_1 and φ_2 and rewrite (8.1) as

$$\exp \int [\langle x, y\rangle - 1 - ig(x, y)] \, dF = \langle x_0, y\rangle, \qquad y \in Y. \tag{8.7}$$

Substituting $y = y_1 + y_2, y_1 - y_2$, and y_1 successively in (8.7), and dividing the product of the first two by the square of the third, we obtain

$$\exp \int 2\langle x, y_1\rangle [1 - R\langle x, y_2\rangle] \, dF = 1, \qquad y_1, y_2 \in Y, \tag{8.8}$$

or equivalently

$$\int \langle x, y_1\rangle [1 - R\langle x, y_2\rangle \, dF = i\pi n(y_1, y_2)$$

where $n(y_1, y_2)$ is an integer valued continuous function of y_1 and y_2. We fix y_2 for the present. Then $n(y_1, y_2)$ remains constant on every connected subset of Y and, in particular, on the cosets of the component of the identity in Y. This implies, by Lemma 8.1, that the signed measure F_{y_2} vanishes identically outside the annihilator of the component of the identity in Y. Since this is true for each y_2, it follows that F itself vanishes identically outside this annihilator. This completes the proof of the theorem.

REMARK 1. It is not difficult to show that the annihilator of the component of the identity of Y is the smallest closed subgroup containing all compact subgroups of X. This reflects the role of compact subgroups in making the representations nonunique. In particular, if the group has no compact subgroups, then the representation is unique.

REMARK 2. It was shown in the course of the proof of Theorem 8.1 that the measure F_y is antisymmetric for each character y, i.e., $F_y(A) = -F_y(-A)$ for every Borel set. But if every element in the group were of order two, then such a measure would be identically zero. Coupling this with Remark 1 we can say that if the group X is such that every compact subgroup of X consists only of elements of order two, then the representation is unique.

REMARK 3. Conversely, if X is a compact group such that not all elements of X are of order two, then the representation is not unique as can be seen from the following example. We take an element y_0 in the character group which is not of order two, and consider the function

$$f(x) = 2\pi i [\overline{\langle x, y_0 \rangle} - \langle x, y_0 \rangle],$$

where $f(x)$ is real and not identically zero. If h denotes the normalized Haar measure of X, we have

$$\begin{aligned} \int \langle x, y \rangle f(x)\, dh(x) &= 2\pi i && \text{if } \ y = y_0, \\ &= -2\pi i && \text{if } \ y = -y_0, \\ &= 0 && \text{otherwise.} \end{aligned}$$

Writing f^+ and f^- for the positive and negative parts of $f(x)$, we define two measures

$$F_1(A) = \int_A f^+(x)\, dh(x), \qquad F_2(A) = \int_A f^-(x)\, dh(x).$$

Then $F_1 \neq F_2$, but

$$\exp \int [\langle x, y \rangle - 1 - ig(x, y)]\, dF_1$$

$$= \langle x_0, y \rangle \int [\langle x, y \rangle - 1 - ig(x, y)]\, dF_2(x),$$

where $\langle x_0, y\rangle = \exp [i \int g(x, y)\, d(F_2 - F_1)]$ is a character on Y, and hence an element of X. Thus $(e, F_1, 0)$ and $(x_0, F_2, 0)$ are two representations of the same infinitely divisible distribution.

9. COMPACTNESS CRITERIA

We shall now obtain conditions for the compactness of a family of infinitely divisible distributions in terms of their representations.

Before proceeding to state the main result of this section we shall investigate what happens to the representation when we pass over from a group to its quotient group. Let $G \subset X$ be some closed subgroup of X and $X' = X/G$ the quotient group. Let τ denote the canonical homomorphism from X to X'. If Y' is the character group of X', we choose and fix a function $g'(x', y')$ defined on $X' \times Y'$ and satisfying all the properties of Lemma 5.3. We observe that Y' is the annihilator of G in Y. Any infinitely divisible distribution μ' on X' without idempotent factors has a representation (x', F', φ') (with g replaced by g') according to Theorem 7.1.

Lemma 9.1

Let μ be an infinitely divisible distribution on X with a representation (x, F, φ). If $\mu' = \mu\tau^{-1}$, $x' = \tau x$, $F' = F\tau^{-1}$, and φ' is the restriction of φ to Y', then μ' is an infinitely divisible distribution on X' and is a shift of the distribution represented by (x', F', φ').

PROOF. Let $\mu = \mu_1 * \mu_2$ where μ_2 is the unique Gaussian component of μ. Clearly $\mu' = \mu_1\tau^{-1} * \mu_2\tau^{-1}$. Since $e(\alpha)\tau^{-1} = e(\alpha\tau^{-1})$ for every finite measure α, it follows easily that $\mu_1\tau^{-1}$ and the distribution represented by $(x', F', 0)$ are shifts of each other. Thus $\mu_2\tau^{-1}$ is the Gaussian component of μ'. This completes the proof.

Theorem 9.1

Let $\{\mu_\alpha\}$ be a family of infinitely divisible distributions without idempotent factors and with representations $\{(x_\alpha, F_\alpha, \varphi_\alpha)\}$. The necessary and sufficient conditions that $\{\mu_\alpha\}$ be shift compact and any limit of shifts of $\{\mu_\alpha\}$ be devoid of idempotent factors, are

(1) *The family* $\{F_\alpha\}$ *of measures is conditionally compact when restricted to* N' *for every neighborhood* N *of the identity.*

(2) $\sup_\alpha [\int [1 - R\langle x, y\rangle]\, dF_\alpha + \varphi_\alpha(y)] < \infty$ *for all* y.

PROOF. The necessity of the above two conditions is obvious in view of Theorem 4.3. Regarding sufficiency we first observe that if $\{\mu_\alpha\}$ is a shift compact family, then condition (2) is sufficient to ensure the absence of idempotent factors in any limit of shifts of $\{\mu_\alpha\}$. We shall now prove shift compactness.

We have only to prove the compactness of the family $\{|\mu_\alpha|^2\}$. We now observe that if (x, F, φ) is a representation of an infinitely divisible distribution μ in a group X and τ is a continuous homomorphism of X onto another group X', then $\mu\tau^{-1}$ is a shift of the distribution represented by $(\tau x, F\tau^{-1}, \varphi')$, where φ' is the restriction of φ to the character group of X' (which is a subgroup of Y). Further, if $\{(x_\alpha, F_\alpha, \varphi_\alpha)\}$ satisfies conditions (1) and (2), so does the family $\{(\tau x_\alpha, F_\alpha\tau^{-1}, \varphi_\alpha')\}$. Making use of these remarks we shall reduce the proof of the general case to that of certain simple groups.

In order that a family of measures be conditionally compact, it is necessary and sufficient that the family be uniformly tight (see Theorem 6.7, Chapter II). If C is a compact subgroup of X, and if the family of measures induced by the canonical homomorphism on X/C is uniformly tight, then the original family itself is uniformly tight. We now choose the group C in such a manner that X/C has the structure $V \oplus D \oplus K^r$ where V is a vector group, D a discrete group, and K^r the r-dimensional torus. But a family of measures in the product of two topological spaces is uniformly tight as soon as the two marginal families are so. Thus it is enough to prove the sufficiency of (1) and (2) in the case of the real line, discrete groups, and compact groups. In the case of the real line the boundedness of $\int [1 - R\langle x, y\rangle]\, dF_\alpha$ implies the boundedness of $\int_{|x|<\varepsilon} x^2\, dF_\alpha$ for a suitable ε which, together with condition (1), implies the equicontinuity of the family of functions $\exp\{-\int [1 - R\langle x, y\rangle]\, dF_\alpha\}$. Since $\phi_\alpha(y)$ assumes the form $\sigma_\alpha^2 y^2$, and hence σ_α^2 is dounded, it is clear that $\{|\hat{\mu}_\alpha(y)|^2\}$ is equicontinuous. But by Ascoli theorem (cf. Kelley [16], p. 234), equicontinuity and uniform boundedness of the family imply the compactness of $\{|\hat{\mu}_\alpha(y)|^2\}$ in the topology of uniform convergence on compacta. Theorem 3.3 implies the compactness of $\{|\mu_\alpha|^2\}$. In the case of a discrete group, identity itself is an open set, and hence the family $\{F_\alpha\}$ is compact outside the identity. This, together with the fact that every infinitely divisible distribution without idempotent factor is a shift of $e(F)$ for some F with zero mass at the identity, implies the required result.

Corollary 9.1

In addition to the conditions (1) and (2) of Theorem 9.1, the condition that $\{x_\alpha\}$ be a conditionally compact set is necessary and sufficient to ensure the conditional compactness of $\{\mu_\alpha\}$ with representations $\{(x_\alpha, F_\alpha, \varphi_\alpha)\}$.

PROOF. From (7.6) we have

$$|\langle x, y\rangle - 1 - ig(x, y)| \leqslant c[1 - R\langle x, y\rangle]$$

for all $x \in N$, $y \in K$ where c is a constant depending on K only, N is a sufficiently small neighborhood of the identity in X, and K is a compact subset of Y. This implies the equicontinuity of the family of functions

$$\exp\left[\int [\langle x, y\rangle - 1 - ig(x, y)]\, dF_\alpha - \varphi_\alpha(y)\right].$$

Hence $\{x_\alpha\}$ is conditionally compact if and only if $\{\mu_\alpha\}$ is so.

The proof of Theorem 5.1 and Corollary 9.1 yields the standard limit theorems for sums of infinitesimal summands. In particular, we have the following generalization of central limit theorem.

Corollary 9.2

Let $\{\alpha_{nj}\}$, $j = 1, 2, \ldots, k_n$, be a uniformly infinitesimal sequence of distributions, and let

$$\mu_n = \prod_1^{k_n} \alpha_{nj}.$$

Let

$$F_n = \sum_{j=1}^{k_n} \alpha_{nj} * x_{nj},$$

where

$$\langle x_{nj}, y\rangle = \exp\left\{-i\int g(x, y)\, d\alpha_{nj}(x)\right\}.$$

In order that all the limits of shifts of μ_n be Gaussian, it is necessary and sufficient that

$$\lim_{n\to\infty} F_n(N') = 0,$$

for every neighborhood N of the identity and

$$\overline{\lim_{n\to\infty}} \int [1 - R\langle x, y\rangle]\, dF_n < \infty,$$

for every $y \in Y$.

10. REPRESENTATION OF CONVOLUTION SEMIGROUPS

We have observed earlier that the representation of an infinitely divisible distribution need not be unique. We shall now consider the problem for a one-parameter convolution semigroup of distributions. By such a semigroup we mean a family $\{\mu_t\}$ of distributions indexed by $t \geqslant 0$ such that $\mu_t * \mu_s = \mu_{t+s}$. We shall further assume that μ_t converges weakly to the distribution degenerate at the identity when $t \to 0$. Obviously, for such semigroups $\hat{\mu}_t(y) \neq 0$ for any $t > 0$ and $y \in Y$. That such a semigroup has a unique canonical representation is the content of the following theorem.

Theorem 10.1

Let $\{\mu_t\}$ be a one-parameter convolution semigroup of distributions such that μ_t converges weakly to the distribution degenerate at the identity as $t \to 0$. Then $\hat{\mu}_t(y)$ has the canonical representation

$$\hat{\mu}_t(y) = \langle x_t, y\rangle \exp\left\{t\int [\langle x, y\rangle - 1 - ig(x, y)]\, dF - t\varphi(y)\right\},$$

where F and φ are as in Theorem 7.1 and $\{x_t\}$ is a continuous one-parameter semigroup in X. Moreover $\{x_t\}$, F, and φ are uniquely determined by $\{\mu_t\}$.

PROOF. Since $\mu_t = (\mu_{t/n})^n$, μ_t is infinitely divisible. As remarked at the beginning, $\hat{\mu}_t(y)$ is nonvanishing at any point, and hence has no idempotent factors. Thus by Theorem 7.1, μ_t has a representation (z_t, F_t, φ_t). The uniqueness of φ_t implies that $\varphi_t = t\varphi_1$. We write $\varphi = \varphi_1$ and $\hat{\lambda}_t(y) = \hat{\mu}_t(y)e^{t\varphi}$. Then $\{\lambda_t\}$ is a weakly continuous convolution semigroup, and λ_t has neither idempotent nor Gaussian factors. For any σ-finite measure F which has finite mass outside every neighborhood of the identity and integrates the function $1 - R\langle x, y\rangle$ for every $y \in Y$, we define the distribution $E(F)$ through its characteristic function

$$E(F)\hat{\ } (y) = \exp \int [\langle x, y\rangle - 1 - ig(x, y)]\, dF(x).$$

We observe that the distribution $E(n!F_{1/n!})$ is a shift of λ_1 for every n. By Theorem 4.3 the sequence of measures $n!F_{1/n!}$ is compact outside every neighborhood of the identity. Thus we can choose a subsequence $n_k!F_{1/n_k!}$, which converges to a measure F outside every neighborhood of the identity. Proceeding along the same lines as in the proof of Theorem 9.1, we see that λ_1 has a representation $(z, F, 0)$ for some $z \in X$. We now define

$$\hat{P}_t(y) = \exp \left\{ t \int [\langle x, y\rangle - 1 - ig(x, y)]\, dF \right\}.$$

If $t = p/q$ is rational then $E((p/q)n!F_{1/n!})$ is a shift of $\lambda_{p/q}$ for all sufficiently large n. Since $(p/q)n_k!F_{1/n_k!}$ converges to $(p/q)F$ outside every neighborhood of the identity, the proof of Theorem 9.1 shows that $\lambda_{p/q}$ is a shift of $P_{p/q}$. By the continuity of the semigroups it is clear that, for every t, λ_t is a shift of P_t. Thus $\hat{\lambda}_t(y)$ can be written as $\langle x_t, y\rangle \hat{P}_t(y)$. Then x_t automatically becomes a continuous one-parameter semigroup in X.

If now $(x_t, tF, t\varphi)$ and $(x_t', tF', t\varphi)$ are two representations of the semigroup $\{\mu_t\}$, then by proceeding in the same way as in the proof of Theorem 8.1 we obtain

$$\exp \left[t \int \langle x, y_1\rangle [1 - R\langle x, y\rangle]\, d(F - F') \right] = 1, \qquad y_1, y \in Y,$$

for every t. But this can happen if and only if $F - F' = 0$. Thus the representation of the semigroup is always unique.

11. A DECOMPOSITION THEOREM

Theorem 11.1

Let μ be any distribution on X. Then it can be written as $\lambda_G * \lambda$ where λ is a distribution without any idempotent factor and λ_G is the maximal idempotent factor of μ.

Proof. Let H be the group generated by the set of all characters y at which $\hat{\mu}(y) \neq 0$. H is open and hence its annihilator G in X is compact. The normalized Haar measure λ_G of G is the required maximal idempotent factor. If we denote by τ the canonical homomorphism from X to X/G, then the distribution $\mu\tau^{-1}$ in X/G has no idempotent factors. We now choose a Borel set $B \subset X$ such that τ restricted to B maps B onto X/G in a one-one manner (see Lemma 5.1, Chapter I). By Corollary 3.3, Chapter I, τ^{-1} is measurable. Let λ be a measure defined on X as follows:

$$\lambda(A) = \mu\tau^{-1}(\tau(A \cap B))$$

for every Borel set A. It is easy to see that $\mu = \lambda_G * \lambda$, and λ has no idempotent factors.

We shall now introduce a function $\theta(\alpha)$ defined for all factors of a distribution μ. Let μ be a distribution without any idempotent factors. Then there is a sequence $y_1, y_2, \ldots$ of characters in Y such that $\hat{\mu}(y_i) \neq 0$ for $i = 1, 2, \ldots,$ and the smallest closed subgroup generated by this sequence is Y. Since $-\log|\hat{\mu}(y_i)|$ is well defined, we can choose a sequence $\varepsilon_n > 0$ such that

$$-\sum_{n=1}^{\infty} \varepsilon_n \log|\hat{\mu}(y_n)| < \infty.$$

This implies at once that, for every factor α of μ, the function

$$\theta(\alpha) = -\sum_{n=1}^{\infty} \varepsilon_n \log|\hat{\alpha}(y_n)|$$

is well defined and has the following properties:

(i) $\theta(\alpha) \geqslant 0.$

(ii) $\theta(\alpha) = 0$ if and only if α is degenerate.

(iii) $\theta(\alpha_1 * \alpha_2) = \theta(\alpha_1) + \theta(\alpha_2).$ (11.1)

(iv) If $\alpha_n \Rightarrow \alpha$, then $\theta(\alpha_n) \to \theta(\alpha)$.

(v) $\theta(\alpha) = \theta(\beta)$ if α is a shift of β.

Theorem 11.2

Let μ be a distribution without any indecomposable or idempotent factors. Then μ is infinitely divisible.

PROOF. In view of the remark following Theorem 5.2, it is enough to factorize μ in the form

$$\mu = \alpha_{n1} * \alpha_{n2} * \dots * \alpha_{n2^n}, \tag{11.2}$$

where $\{\alpha_{nj}\}$ is such that any limit of their shifts is degenerate. From the properties (i)–(v) of the θ-function it is clear that it is sufficient to factorize μ in the form (11.2) with $\theta(\alpha_{nj}) = 2^{-n}\theta(\mu)$. If μ satisfies the conditions stated in the theorem, then any factor of μ also satisfies them. Thus it suffices to prove that μ can be written as $\mu_1 * \mu_2$ with $\theta(\mu_1) = \theta(\mu_2) = \frac{1}{2}\theta(\mu)$. A repetition of this argument will then complete the proof. In order to do this we observe that

$$\inf_{\alpha \in F(\mu),\, \theta(\alpha) \neq 0} \theta(\alpha) = 0,$$

where $F(\mu)$ is the class of all factors of μ. For otherwise, the class $F(\mu)$ being shift compact, the infimum would be attained at an indecomposable distribution. But this is a contradiction. Thus there are factors of μ with arbitrarily small θ-values. We now take two distributions μ_1, μ_2, for which $\mu = \mu_1 * \mu_2$ and $|\theta(\mu_1) - \theta(\mu_2)|$ is minimum. From the shift compactness of $F(\mu)$ it follows that the minimum is attained. This minimum has to be zero. For otherwise, by transferring a factor of μ_1 or μ_2 with an arbitrarily small θ-value to μ_2 or μ_1 we can make $|\theta(\mu_1) - \theta(\mu_2)|$ smaller. This completes the proof of the theorem.

Theorem 11.3

Any distribution μ on X can be written as $\lambda_H * \lambda_1 * \lambda_2$ where λ_H is the maximal idempotent factor of μ, λ_1 is the convolution of a finite or a countable number of indecomposable distributions, and λ_2 is an infinitely divisible distribution without indecomposable or idempotent factors.

PROOF. An application of Theorem 11.1 shows that μ can be written as $\lambda_H * \lambda$ where λ_H is the maximal idempotent factor of μ, and λ has no idempotent factors. Thus we can define a θ-function on $F(\lambda)$ satisfying properties (i)–(v) of (11.1). Let now δ_1 be the maximum of $\theta(\alpha)$ as α varies over the indecomposable factors of λ. If $\delta_1 > 0$, we write $\lambda = \alpha_1 * P_1$ where α_1 is indecomposable and $\theta(\alpha_1) \geqslant \frac{1}{2}\delta_1$. We now denote by δ_2 the maximum of $\theta(\alpha)$ as α varies over the indecomposable factors of P_1. If $\delta_2 > 0$, then we write $P_1 = \alpha_2 * P_2$, where α_2 is indecomposable and $\theta(\alpha_2) \geqslant \frac{1}{2}\delta_2$. We repeat this argument. If the process terminates at the nth stage, $\lambda = \alpha_1 * \ldots * \alpha_n * P_n$ and $\delta_{n+1} = 0$, which means that P_n has no indecomposable factors. Otherwise, the process continues *ad infinitum*. Since $\sum_1^\infty \theta(\alpha_i)$ is convergent, $\theta(\alpha_n) \to 0$ as $n \to \infty$. The sequence $\alpha_1 * \ldots * \alpha_n$ being increasing in the order $\prec$ converges after a suitable shift (see Theorem 5.3, Chapter III). Absorbing this shift in α_n we can assume that $\alpha_1 * \ldots * \alpha_n$ converges to a distribution λ_1. Automatically, P_n will converge to a distribution λ_2. If λ_2 has an indecomposable factor α, then it is a factor of P_n. Thus $\theta(\alpha) \leqslant \delta_n$ for each n. But $\delta_n \leqslant 2\theta(\alpha_n)$, and hence tends to zero. Therefore $\theta(\alpha) = 0$, or equivalently λ_2 has no indecomposable factors.

12. ABSOLUTELY CONTINUOUS INDECOMPOSABLE DISTRIBUTIONS IN X

In Chapter III we investigated the properties of the class of all indecomposable distributions in a complete separable metric group and showed that it is a dense G_δ in the weak topology if the group is infinite. If the group has no isolated points we also established that the class of nonatomic indecomposable distributions is a dense G_δ.

Now we consider the case of a locally compact abelian group X, and the space $\mathscr{A}^*$ of all distributions which are absolutely continuous with respect to the Haar measure. Let $\mathscr{A}_I^*$ be the subset of indecomposable distributions in $\mathscr{A}^*$. We shall give $\mathscr{A}^*$ the norm topology. By norm we mean the L_1-norm with respect to the Haar measure. Since the norm topology is stronger than the weak topology it follows that $\mathscr{A}_I^*$ is a G_δ subset of $\mathscr{A}^*$. We shall prove in this section that if X is noncompact then $\mathscr{A}_I^*$ is dense in $\mathscr{A}^*$ (in the norm topology). To this end we need several lemmas.

Lemma 12.1

Let μ be a distribution with support contained in a bounded interval. If μ is not degenerate at the identity, then the function

$$\hat{\mu}(z) = \int e^{izx}\, d\mu(x) \tag{12.1}$$

is an integral function of order one in the complex variable z and admits a unique factorization

$$\hat{\mu}(z) = \prod_{n=1}^{\infty} (1 - z/a_n)e^{z/a_n}. \tag{12.2}$$

PROOF. This follows from the inequality

$$|\hat{\mu}(z)| \leqslant \int e^{|z||x|}\, d\mu(x),$$

and the Hadamard factorization theorem (cf. [3], p. 174).

Lemma 12.2

Let μ_1, μ_2 denote the uniform distributions on the intervals $[a, b]$ and $[c, d]$, respectively. If $(b - a)/(d - c)$ is irrational, then μ_1 and μ_2 have no nondegenerate common factor.

PROOF. We have from (12.1),

$$\begin{aligned}
\hat{\mu}_1(z) &= (e^{ibz} - e^{iaz})/iz(b - a) \\
&= \exp\left[i\left(\frac{a+b}{2}\right)z\right] \cdot \sin\left[\tfrac{1}{2}(b - a)z\right]/\tfrac{1}{2}(b - a)z \\
&= \exp\left[i\left(\frac{a+b}{2}\right)z\right] \cdot \prod_{r=1}^{\infty}\left\{1 - \frac{[\frac{1}{2}(b - a)z]^2}{r^2\pi^2}\right\}, \\
\hat{\mu}_2(z) &= \exp\left[i\left(\frac{c+d}{2}\right)z\right] \cdot \prod_{r=1}^{\infty}\left\{1 - \frac{[\frac{1}{2}(d - c)z]^2}{r^2\pi^2}\right\}.
\end{aligned}$$

If $(b - a)/(d - c)$ is irrational it is clear that $\hat{\mu}_1(z)$ and $\hat{\mu}_2(z)$ have no common zeros. If μ_1 and μ_2 have a nondegenerate common factor ν, then the support of ν is contained in a bounded interval, and hence by Lemma 12.1, $\hat{\nu}(z)$ admits a representation of the form (12.2). The zeros of $\hat{\nu}$ are common zeros of $\hat{\mu}_1$ and $\hat{\mu}_2$. This shows that μ_1 and μ_2 cannot have a common factor.

Let Z be any real valued random variable taking values in a bounded interval. We denote by $[Z]$ the integral part of Z and the conditional distribution of Z given that $[Z] = n$, by μ_n.

Lemma 12.3

Let Z be any nonnegative real valued bounded random variable satisfying the following conditions:

(a) *$[Z]$ is even with probability one;*
(b) *the interval $[0, \varepsilon]$ has positive probability for every $\varepsilon > 0$;*
(c) *the distribution of $[Z]$ is indecomposable;*
(d) *the family of distributions μ_n, n running over the possible values of $[Z]$ has no nondegenerate common factor.*

Then the distribution of Z is indecomposable.

PROOF. Suppose that the distribution of Z is decomposable. Then $Z = X + Y$ where X and Y are nondegenerate independent random variables. Since Z is nonnegative condition (b) implies that both X and Y must be nonnegative. Let $Z = z + \zeta$, $X = x + \xi$, $Y = y + \eta$ where z, x and y are $[Z]$, $[X]$, and $[Y]$, respectively. The origin is in the spectrum of the distributions of X, Y, and Z. Hence x and y can assume only even integral values. Further, $\xi + \eta$ must be strictly less than one with probability one. For otherwise, condition (a) will be contradicted. Thus we have

$$z = x + y, \qquad \zeta = \xi + \eta.$$

Now condition (c) implies that the distribution of x or y must be degenerate. The nonnegativity of the random variables x and y and (b) imply that x or y must be degenerate at 0. Let us suppose that x is so. Then we have $z = y$ and $\zeta = X + \eta$. Since the condition $[Z] = n$ is the same as $y = n$, we see that X and η are independent whenever y is fixed. Thus all the μ_n have a common factor which is the distribution of X. This contradicts (d), and therefore completes the proof.

Lemma 12.4

Let A_1, A_2, A_3 be three closed subsets of the group X satisfying the following conditions:

$$(1)\quad (A_i - A_i) \cap (A_j - A_k) = \phi \quad for \quad i = 1, 2, 3 \quad and \quad j \neq k;$$

$$(2)\quad (A_1 - A_2) \cap (A_2 - A_3) = (A_2 - A_3) \cap (A_3 - A_1)$$
$$= (A_3 - A_1) \cap (A_1 - A_2) = \phi.$$

Let μ_1, μ_2, μ_3, be three distributions with $\mu_i(A_i) = 1$ and $\lambda = p_1\mu_1 + p_2\mu_2 + p_3\mu_3$, where $p_i > 0$ $(i = 1, 2, 3)$ and $p_1 + p_2 + p_3 = 1$. If λ is decomposable, then μ_1, μ_2, μ_3 have a nondegenerate common factor.

PROOF. Let $\lambda = \alpha * \beta$ where α and β are nondegenerate distributions. Let C and D denote the spectra of α and β, respectively. It is obvious that

$$C + D \subseteq A_1 \cup A_2 \cup A_3 = A. \tag{12.3}$$

For each $c \in C$, we write

$$D_i(c) = [d; d \in D \text{ and } c + d \in A_i] = D \cap (A_i - c) \tag{12.4}$$

for $i = 1, 2, 3$. The rest of the proof depends on an analysis of the nature of the decomposition $\{D_i(c)\}$ of D. We shall divide it into three steps:

1. The sets $D_i(c)$ possess the following properties:

(i) $\bigcup_{i=1}^{3} D_i(c) = D$ for each c;
(ii) $D_i(c) \cap D_j(c) = \phi$ for $i \neq j$;
(iii) if $c_1 \neq c_2$, $D_i(c_1) \cap D_j(c_2) \neq \phi$ implies that $D_i(c_1) = D_j(c_2)$;
(iv) for any two distinct c_1 and c_2, $D_i(c_1) = D_i(c_2) \neq \phi$ for some i, implies that $D_j(c_1) = D_j(c_2)$ for $j = 1, 2, 3$.

Property (i) is obvious from (12.3) and (12.4). If (ii) were not true there is a point common to A_i and A_j, $i \neq j$. This means that the identity of the group belongs to $A_i - A_i$ and $A_i - A_j$. This contradicts condition (1) of the lemma. In order to prove (iii) we shall suppose that $D_i(c_1)$ and $D_j(c_2)$ have a common point d and $D_i(c_1) \neq D_j(c_2)$. Then we may assume that there exists a point $d' \in D_i(c_1)$ which is not in $D_j(c_2)$. From (i) it follows that there is a $k(\neq j)$ such that $d' \in D_k(c_2)$. Hence

$$c_1 + d \in A_i, \qquad c_1 + d' \in A_i$$

$$c_2 + d \in A_j, \qquad c_2 + d' \in A_k, \qquad k \neq j.$$

Consequently, $d - d' \in (A_i - A_i) \cap (A_j - A_k)$. This contradicts condition (1) of the lemma. In order to prove (iv), suppose that $D_i(c_1) = D_i(c_2) \neq \phi$ for some i and $c_1 \neq c_2$ and $D_j(c_1) \neq D_j(c_2)$ for $j \neq i$.. Then there exist $d, d' \in D$ such that

$$c_1 + d \in A_i, \qquad c_2 + d \in A_i$$

$$c_1 + d' \in A_j, \qquad c_2 + d' \in A_k, \qquad k \neq j.$$

Then $c_1 - c_2 \in (A_i - A_i) \cap (A_j - A_k)$ which contradicts condition (1).

2. One of the following relations is always satisfied. Either

(a) for each $c \in C$, all but one of the $D_i(c)$ are empty, i.e., $D_i(c) = D$ for some i, or

(b) for any two $c_1, c_2 \in C, D_i(c_1) = D_i(c_2)$ for $i = 1, 2, 3$.

First of all we note that property (iii) of step 1 implies that for any two c_1 and c_2, the partitions $\{D_i(c_1)\}$ and $\{D_j(c_2)\}$ are permutations of one another.

Suppose now that (a) does not hold. Then we may assume that there exists a $c_1 \in C$ such that $D_i(c_1) \neq \phi$, $D_j(c_1) \neq \phi$, $i \neq j$. Let $D_k(c_1) \neq \phi$, where k is different from i and j. Because of property (iv) of step 1 we may assume that for $c_2 \neq c_1$, $D_i(c_1) = D_j(c_2)$, $D_j(c_1) = D_k(c_2)$, and $D_k(c_1) = D_i(c_2)$. This implies that there exist $d, d' \in D$ such that

$$c_1 + d \in A_i, \qquad c_2 + d \in A_j,$$

$$c_1 + d' \in A_j, \qquad c_2 + d' \in A_k.$$

Hence $d - d' \in (A_i - A_j) \cap (A_j - A_k)$. This contradicts condition (2) of the lemma.

Let now $D_k(c_1) = \phi$. We may and do assume that $D_i(c_1) = D_j(c_2)$, $D_j(c_1) = D_i(c_2)$. There exists a c_3 such that $D_k(c_3) \neq \phi$. We may assume without loss of generality that $D_i(c_1) = D_j(c_2) = D_k(c_3)$ and $D_j(c_1) = D_i(c_2) = D_i(c_3)$. This implies that there exist $d, d' \in D$ such that

$$c_1 + d \in A_i, \qquad c_1 + d' \in A_j,$$

$$c_3 + d \in A_k, \qquad c_3 + d' \in A_i.$$

Hence $c_1 - c_3 \in (A_i - A_k) \cap (A_j - A_i)$, which contradicts condition (2) of the lemma. This proves step 2.

3. Now suppose that case (a) obtains. Let $C_i = [c: D_i(c) \neq \phi]$. It is then easy to verify that (1) C_i's are mutually disjoint and their union is C; (2) $C_i + D \subset A_i$ for each i. Let the measures $\alpha_i (i = 1, 2, 3)$ be defined as follows:

$$\alpha_i(E) = \alpha(E \cap C_i)/\alpha(C_i), \qquad E \in \mathscr{B}_X.$$

Note that $\alpha(C_i) > 0$. Then $\alpha * \beta = \sum \alpha(C_i) \cdot (\alpha_i * \beta)$. Since $\alpha_i * \beta(A_i) = 1$ and $A_i \cap A_j = \phi$ for $i \neq j$, it follows that $\alpha_i * \beta = \mu_i$. Thus β is a factor of μ_1, μ_2, and μ_3.

In case (b), let $D_i = D_i(c)$. Obviously, the D_i's are mutually disjoint and $C + D_i \subseteq A_i$ for each i. Writing $\beta_i(E) = \beta(E \cap D_i)/\beta(D_i)$ we get, as before, $\alpha * \beta_i = \mu_i$ for each i. In this case α is the required common factor. This completes the proof of the lemma.

Lemma 12.5

Let X be a noncompact group. Then for any given compact set K, there exist elements $g, h \in X$ such that $K, K + g, K + h$ satisfy the conditions (1) *and* (2) *of Lemma* 12.4.

PROOF. It may be verified that conditions (1) and (2) of Lemma 12.4 reduce to choosing g and h so that none of the elements $g, h, g - h, g + h, 2g - h, 2h - g$ belong to the compact set $C = (K - K) - (K - K)$. Let

$$F = \{x: x = 2x', \quad x' \in X\}.$$

Then there are two possibilities.

CASE 1. F has compact closure. In this case we can choose an element g such that $g \notin C$ and $\bar{F} \cap (C + g) = \phi$. Since X is noncompact, such elements exist. Let h be any element such that $h \notin C \cup (C+g) \cup (C-g) \cup (C+2g)$. The pair g, h satisfies our requirements.

CASE 2. The closure of F is not compact. Let $g \notin C$ be arbitrary. Since $\bar{F}$ is not compact we can find an $h \in X$ such that $2h \notin C + g$ and $h \notin C \cup (C+g) \cup (C-g) \cup (C-2g) \cup (C+2g)$. As is easily verified the pair g, h serves the purpose. This completes the proof.

Lemma 12.6

Let X be an infinite compact metric abelian group. Let A be a subset such that

(i) $0 < \lambda(A) < 1$;

(ii) $\displaystyle\int_A \langle x, y\rangle \, d\lambda(x) \neq 0$ *for every* $y \in Y$,

where λ is the normalized Haar measure of X. If λ_1, λ_2 are defined by

$$\lambda_1(E) = \lambda(E \cap A)/\lambda(A),$$

$$\lambda_2(E) = \lambda(E \cap A')/\lambda(A'),$$

then λ_1 and λ_2 do not have a common factor.

PROOF. Since for the Haar measure $\int \langle x, y\rangle \, d\lambda = 0$, if y is not equal to identity and $0 < \lambda(A) < 1$, we have

$$\int_{A'} \langle x, y\rangle \, d\lambda \neq 0 \quad \text{for every} \quad y \in Y. \tag{12.5}$$

Suppose λ_1 and λ_2 have a common factor μ. Then there exist α_1 and α_2 such that

$$\lambda_1 = \alpha_1 * \mu, \qquad \lambda_2 = \alpha_2 * \mu. \tag{12.6}$$

From the definitions of λ_1 and λ_2 and (12.6), we have

$$\lambda(A)\lambda_1 + \lambda(A')\lambda_2 = \lambda = (\lambda(A)\alpha_1 + \lambda(A')\alpha_2) * \mu. \tag{12.7}$$

Hence

$$\left.\begin{aligned} \hat{\lambda}_1(y) &= \hat{\alpha}_1(y)\hat{\mu}(y), \\ \hat{\lambda}_2(y) &= \hat{\alpha}_2(y)\hat{\mu}(y), \\ [\lambda(A)\hat{\alpha}_1(y) + \lambda(A')\hat{\alpha}_2(y)]\hat{\mu}(y) &= 0 \qquad \text{for} \quad y \neq e. \end{aligned}\right\} \tag{12.8}$$

From condition (ii) of the lemma and Eq. (12.8) we have

$$\int \langle x, y \rangle \, d\mu \neq 0$$

for every $y \in Y$, and

$$\lambda(A)\hat{\alpha}_1(y) + \lambda(A')\hat{\alpha}_2(y) = 0$$

for $y \neq e$. Thus

$$\lambda(A)\alpha_1 + \lambda(A')\alpha_2 = \lambda. \tag{12.9}$$

Equation (12.6) and the definition of λ_1 and λ_2 imply

$$\int \alpha_1(A' - x) \, d\mu(x) = \lambda_1(A') = 0,$$

$$\int \alpha_2(A - x) \, d\mu(x) = \lambda_2(A) = 0.$$

Consequently,

$$\alpha_1(A' - x) = 0 \qquad \text{a.e.} \quad (\mu).$$

$$\alpha_2(A - x) = 0 \qquad \text{a.e.} \quad (\mu).$$

Thus there exists a point x_0 such that

$$\alpha_1(A' - x_0) = \alpha_2(A - x_0) = 0. \tag{12.10}$$

Equations (12.9) and (12.10) imply that

$$\alpha_1(E) = \frac{\lambda(E \cap [A - x_0])}{\lambda(A)} = [\lambda_1 * (-x_0)](E),$$

$$\alpha_2(E) = \frac{\lambda(E \cap [A' - x_0])}{\lambda(A')} = [\lambda_2 * (-x_0)](E),$$

and therefore

$$\lambda_1 = \lambda_1 * (-x_0) * \mu, \qquad \lambda_2 = \lambda_2 * (-x_0) * \mu.$$

Since $\hat{\mu}(y) \neq 0$, $\hat{\lambda}_1(y) \neq 0$ and $\hat{\lambda}_2(y) \neq 0$,

$$\int \langle x, y \rangle \, d((-x_0) * \mu) = 1, \qquad \text{for every} \quad y \in Y.$$

Hence μ is degenerate at x_0. This completes the proof of the lemma.

Lemma 12.7

In any infinite compact group X there exists a set A possessing the properties (i) *and* (ii) *of Lemma* 12.6.

PROOF. Let $S(\lambda)$ be the measure ring obtained by considering the space of Borel subsets of X modulo λ-null sets. This is a complete metric space under the distance $d(E, F) = \lambda(E \Delta F)$, where E and F belong to $S(\lambda)$ (cf. Halmos [12], pp. 165–169). Let $y_0 = e, y_1, y_2, \ldots$ be the characters of X. Consider the following mapping from $S(\lambda)$ to the complex plane. For any $E \in S(\lambda)$, we write

$$f_j(E) = \int_E (x, y_j) \, d\lambda.$$

The mapping f_j is obviously continuous. Hence the sets

$$V_j = \{E : f_j(E) \neq 0\}$$

are open in $S(\lambda)$. We shall now prove that each V_j is dense in $S(\lambda)$. Let $A \in S(\lambda)$ and $f_j(A) = 0$. Let $\lambda(A) = c > 0$. Since λ is nonatomic, for any $0 < \varepsilon < c$ there exists a set $B \subset A$ such that $\varepsilon/2 < \lambda(B) < \varepsilon$. Let C be any subset of B for which $f_j(C) \neq 0$. Such a C exists, for otherwise $\langle x, y_j \rangle = 0$, almost everywhere in B but at the same time $|\langle x, y_j \rangle| = 1$. The set $A \cap C'$ has the property

$$d(A \cap C', A) = \lambda((A \cap C') \Delta A) = \lambda(C) < \varepsilon.$$

Since this is true for any sufficiently small ε it is possible to get A as a limit of elements in V_j. Since the class of sets A with $\lambda(A) > 0$ is dense in the ring $S(\lambda)$ it follows that the sets V_j are dense in $S(\lambda)$. By the Baire category theorem it follows that $\bigcap_1^\infty V_j$ is a dense G_δ in $S(\lambda)$. Thus there exist Borel sets with the required properties.

Lemma 12.8

In any uncountable locally compact separable metric abelian group X there exist two absolutely continuous measures with compact supports which do not have a common factor.

We shall prove this lemma in two steps. First of all let us assume that X is a finite dimensional vector space. Let A_1 and A_2 be two cubes in X such that the ratio of the lengths of their sides is irrational.

Then the uniform distributions μ_1 and μ_2, concentrated in A_1 and A_2, respectively, cannot have a common factor. For, if they have, then at least one of the one dimensional marginal distributions of μ_1 must have a common factor with the corresponding marginal distribution of μ_2. This contradicts Lemma 12.2. This proves the lemma in the case of a vector space.

If X is an infinite compact group, Lemmas 12.6 and 12.7 yield two absolutely continuous measures which do not have a common factor.

In any group X satisfying the conditions of the lemma there exists an open subgroup H such that $H = V \oplus Z$, where V is a vector group and Z a compact group. In V we take any two absolutely continuous measures μ_1 and μ_2 without any common factor. If Z is infinite we take two absolutely continuous measures ν_1 and ν_2 in Z without common factor. If Z is finite we take ν_1 and ν_2 to be any two degenerate measures. If Z is finite V can be taken to be nontrivial. Now we form the product measures

$$\lambda_1 = \mu_1 \times \nu_1, \qquad \lambda_2 = \mu_2 \times \nu_2$$

in H. Since H is open in X, λ_1 and λ_2 are absolutely continuous with respect to the Haar measure of X. Since none of the marginals have a common factor, we conclude that λ_1 and λ_2 do not have a common factor.

Theorem 12.1

In any locally compact noncompact complete separable metric abelian group X the set of all absolutely continuous indecomposable distributions is a dense G_δ in $\mathscr{A}^*$, in the norm topology.

PROOF. The G_δ part of the theorem has been proved at the beginning of this section. We have only to show the density.

If the group is discrete the theorem is contained already in Theorem 4.3, Chapter III. Suppose the group is nondiscrete. First of all we observe that any absolutely continuous measure can be approximated in norm by a sequence of absolutely continuous measures with compact supports. Hence it is enough to prove that an absolutely continuous measure μ with compact support is a limit in the norm of absolutely continuous indecomposable distributions. Let the support of μ be K_0. Let μ_1 and μ_2 be two absolutely continuous measures with compact supports K_1 and K_2, and having no common factor. Such measures exist by Lemma 12.8. Let

$$K = K_0 \cup K_1 \cup K_2.$$

By using Lemma 12.5 we choose two points $g, h \in X$ such that K, $K + g$, $K + h$ satisfy conditions (1) and (2) of Lemma 12.4. We write

$$\alpha_1 = \mu, \qquad \alpha_2 = \mu_1 * g, \qquad \alpha_3 = \mu_2 * h$$

and

$$\mu_n = \left(1 - \frac{2}{n}\right)\alpha_1 + \frac{1}{n}\alpha_2 + \frac{1}{n}\alpha_3, \qquad n > 2.$$

By Lemma 12.4, μ_n is indecomposable. It obviously converges in norm to μ as $n \to \infty$. This completes the proof.

V

THE KOLMOGOROV CONSISTENCY THEOREM AND CONDITIONAL PROBABILITY

1. STATEMENT OF THE FIRST PROBLEM

In probability theory one of the most important questions is the existence of random variables with preassigned joint distributions. In abstract language the problem can be described as follows: Let $(X_1, \mathscr{S}_1), (X_2, \mathscr{S}_2), \ldots$ be a sequence of Borel spaces. For each n let $(X_{(n)}, \mathscr{S}_{(n)})$ denote the cartesian product $\prod_{i=1}^{n} (X_i, \mathscr{S}_i)$. Let $(X, \mathscr{S})$ be the cartesian product of all the $(X_i, \mathscr{S}_i)$. Given $(x_1, x_2, \ldots) = x$ in X let $\pi_n\colon x \to (x_1, x_2, \ldots, x_n)$ and for $1 \leqslant m \leqslant n$, let $\pi_{nm}\colon (x_1, \ldots, x_n) \to (x_1, \ldots, x_m)$. Clearly π_n is a measurable map of X onto $X_{(n)}$ and π_{nm} is a measurable map of $X_{(n)}$ onto $X_{(m)}$. Throughout this chapter, by a measure we shall always mean a probability measure. A sequence $\mu_1, \mu_2, \ldots$ of measures is said to be *consistent* if (1) μ_n is a measure on $\mathscr{S}_{(n)}$; and (2) if $1 \leqslant m \leqslant n$; then for any $A \in \mathscr{S}_{(m)}$, $\mu_m(A) = \mu_n(\pi_{nm}^{-1}(A))$. The problem is then to investigate whether there exists a measure μ on $\mathscr{S}$ such that for each n we have $\mu_n(A) = \mu(\pi_n^{-1}(A))$ for all $A \in \mathscr{S}_{(n)}$. In his celebrated book on the foundations of probability theory, Kolmogorov [19] proved that if each $X_n = R$ (the real line), then for any consistent sequence of measures $\mu_1, \mu_2, \ldots$, there exists a unique measure μ on $\mathscr{S}$ satisfying the equations $\mu_n(A) = \mu(\pi_n^{-1}(A))$ for all $A \in \mathscr{S}_{(n)}$ and each $n = 1, 2, \ldots$.

In many applications, theorems similar to this intervene. In order to obtain a general result which is powerful enough to apply to diverse situations it is necessary to generalize the setting of the above-mentioned extension problem. To motivate this generalization we look at the above set up. If we write $\{\mathscr{B}_n = \pi_n^{-1}(A) : A \in \mathscr{S}_{(n)}\}$ then $\mathscr{B}_n \subseteq \mathscr{S}$ and is a σ-algebra. Moreover, $\mathscr{B}_1 \subseteq \mathscr{B}_2 \subseteq \ldots$. The class of sets $\mathscr{F} = \bigcup_n \mathscr{B}_n$ is clearly a Boolean algebra and $\mathscr{S}$ is the σ-algebra generated by $\mathscr{F}$. For any $n = 1, 2, \ldots$, write $\nu_n(\pi_n^{-1}(A)) = \mu_n(A)$, $A \in \mathscr{S}_{(n)}$. Then ν_n is a measure on $\mathscr{B}_n$ and the measures $\mu_1, \mu_2, \ldots$, are consistent if and only if whenever $1 \leqslant m \leqslant n$, $\nu_n(A) = \nu_m(A)$ for $A \in \mathscr{B}_m$. The problem is then to investigate whether there exists a measure μ on $\mathscr{S}$ such that $\mu(A) = \nu_n(A)$ whenever $A \in \mathscr{B}_n$.

The fact that if $m \leqslant n$, ν_n and ν_m agree on $\mathscr{B}_m$ implies that the definition $\mu'(A) = \nu_n(A)$ whenever $A \in \mathscr{B}_n$ leads to a well-defined set function μ' on $\mathscr{F}$. $\mu'(X) = 1$, $\mu'(\phi) = 0$, and obviously μ' is finitely additive. It is then clear that there exists a measure μ on $\mathscr{S}$ such that $\mu = \nu_n$ on $\mathscr{B}_n$ if and only if μ' is countably additive on $\mathscr{F}$ and that then μ is unique. The uniqueness follows from the fact that $\mathscr{F}$ generates $\mathscr{S}$. The essential difficulty is to establish the countable additivity of μ'.

The general setting in which we shall attempt to solve this problem involves the notion of standard Borel spaces and the next section is devoted to a study of the properties of standard Borel spaces.

2. STANDARD BOREL SPACES

Definition 2.1

A Borel space $(X, \mathscr{B})$ is said to be *countably generated* if there exists a denumerable class $\mathscr{D} \subseteq \mathscr{B}$ such that $\mathscr{D}$ generates $\mathscr{B}$. $(X, \mathscr{B})$ is called *separable* if it is countably generated and for each $x \in X$, the single point set $\{x\} \in \mathscr{B}$. An *atom* of a Borel space $(X, \mathscr{B})$ is a set $A_0 \in \mathscr{B}$ such that the relations $A \subseteq A_0$, $A \in \mathscr{B}$ imply that $A = A_0$ or $A = \phi$.

Theorem 2.1

Let $(X, \mathscr{B})$ be countably generated. Then for each $x \in X$, there exists a unique atom e_x containing x. If A is any set in $\mathscr{B}$, $A = \bigcup_{x \in A} e_x$.

PROOF. Let $\{A_1, A_2, \ldots\}$ be a subclass of $\mathscr{B}$ generating $\mathscr{B}$. For each $x \in X$, write $\tau(x) = \{\chi_{A_1}(x), \chi_{A_2}(x), \ldots\}$, where χ_A denotes the characteristic function of A. We write M for the space of sequences $(a_1, a_2, \ldots)$ where each a_j is either 0 or 1. M is the underlying set of a Borel space whose σ-algebra $\mathscr{B}_M$ is generated by the sets $M_j = \{(a_1, a_2, \ldots) : a_j = 1\}$, $j = 1, 2, \ldots$. Since $\tau^{-1}(M_j) = A_j$, it is clear that τ is measurable. Moreover, $\{\tau^{-1}(A) : A \in \mathscr{B}_M\} = \mathscr{B}$, since the left-hand member of this equation is a σ-algebra contained in $\mathscr{B}$ and containing all the A_j.

We write $e_x = \tau^{-1}(\{\tau(x)\})$ for any $x \in X$. Clearly, $e_x \in \mathscr{B}$. If $B \in \mathscr{B}$ and $B \subseteq e_x$, then $B = \tau^{-1}(A)$ for some $A \in \mathscr{B}_M$, and $A \subseteq \{\tau(x)\}$. It thus follows that $B = e_x$ or $B = \phi$. In other words, e_x is an atom. It is obviously the unique atom containing x. The second assertion follows trivially from the fact that every point of X is included in a unique atom. This completes the proof.

We write X^0 for the set of all atoms of X and define π as the map $x \to e_x$. We define $\mathscr{B}^0$ as the collection of all subsets $A^0 \subseteq X^0$ such that $\pi^{-1}(A^0) \in \mathscr{B}$. $\mathscr{B}^0$ is a σ-algebra so that $(X^0, \mathscr{B}^0)$ is a Borel space. It is obviously countably generated. If $e^0 \in X^0$, $\pi^{-1}(\{e^0\})$ is an element of $\mathscr{B}$ so that the single point set $\{e^0\} \in \mathscr{B}^0$. $(X^0, \mathscr{B}^0)$ is thus a separable Borel space and the σ-algebras $\mathscr{B}^0$ and $\mathscr{B}$ are isomorphic. $(X^0, \mathscr{B}^0)$ is called the *canonical separable Borel space associated with* $(X, \mathscr{B})$. The mapping $A^0 \to \pi^{-1}(A^0)$ is a σ-isomorphism between $\mathscr{B}^0$ and $\mathscr{B}$, i.e., maps $\mathscr{B}^0$ onto $\mathscr{B}$ in a one-one manner, and preserves countable set operations.

As in Chapter I we shall write M for the space of all sequences $(a_1, a_2, \ldots)$, where each a_j is either 0 or 1. Considered as the cartesian product of countably many copies of the discrete space consisting of 0 and 1, M is a compact metric space. $\mathscr{B}_M$ is the class of Borel subsets of M. We shall adopt the notations of Chapter I in the case of metric spaces.

Definition 2.2

A countably generated Borel space $(X, \mathscr{B})$ is called *standard* if there exists a complete separable metric space Y such that the σ-algebras $\mathscr{B}$ and $\mathscr{B}_Y$ are σ-isomorphic.

Theorem 2.2

If $(X, \mathscr{B})$ is countably generated, then there exists a separable metric space Y such that $\mathscr{B}$ and $\mathscr{B}_Y$ are σ-isomorphic. If X is a separable metric *space and $\mathscr{B}$ the class of Borel subsets of X, then $(X, \mathscr{B})$ is standard if and only if X is a Borel set in some complete separable metric space $\tilde{X}$ in which X can be imbedded as a topological subspace. In this case X is a Borel set in every complete separable metric space in which it is a topological subspace.*

PROOF. Let $(X, \mathscr{B})$ be countably generated and $(X^0, \mathscr{B}^0)$ be the canonical separable Borel space associated with $(X, \mathscr{B})$. Let $\{A_1, A_2, \ldots\}$ generate $\mathscr{B}^0$ and define, for $x^0 \in X^0$, $\tau(x^0) = (\chi_{A_1}(x^0), \chi_{A_2}(x^0), \ldots)$. Using the argument of Theorem 2.1 we conclude that τ is a measurable map of X^0 into M. Since the same argument shows that for each $x^0 \in X^0$, $\tau^{-1}(\{\tau(x^0)\})$ is the atom of X^0 containing x^0, and since the atoms of X^0 are points, it is clear that τ is one-one. Let $Y = \tau[X^0]$. Y is a separable metric space in the relative topology. τ is a one-one measurable map of X^0 onto Y. τ^{-1} is measurable since $\tau[A_j] = M_j \cap Y$ where $M_j = \{(a_1, a_2, \ldots): a_j = 1\}$ for $j = 1, 2, \ldots$. We may thus conclude that $\mathscr{B}^0$ and $\mathscr{B}_Y$ are σ-isomorphic, and hence that $\mathscr{B}$ and $\mathscr{B}_Y$ are σ-isomorphic.

For the rest of the proof we shall assume that X is a separable metric space and $\mathscr{B} = \mathscr{B}_X$. Suppose X is a topological subspace of a complete separable metric space $\tilde{X}$ and suppose that X is a Borel set in $\tilde{X}$. If X is countable, $\mathscr{B}$ is obviously isomorphic to the class of all subsets of the integers so that $(X, \mathscr{B})$ is standard. If X is finite then it is also trivially seen that $(X, \mathscr{B})$ is standard. If X is uncountable, it follows from Theorems 2.8 and 2.12, Chapter I, that $\mathscr{B}_X$ and $\mathscr{B}_{\tilde{X}}$ are isomorphic. This proves that $(X, \mathscr{B})$ is standard.

Conversely, suppose $(X, \mathscr{B})$ is standard and $X \subseteq \tilde{X}$ where $\tilde{X}$ is a complete separable metric space. Since $(X, \mathscr{B})$ is standard, there exists a complete separable metric space Y such that $\mathscr{B}_Y$ and $\mathscr{B}_X$ are σ-isomorphic. Let τ be a σ-isomorphism of $\mathscr{B}_Y$ onto $\mathscr{B}_X$. Since τ must send atoms to atoms, it follows that for each $y \in Y$ there exists a unique $x = f(y)$ such that $\tau(\{y\}) = \{x\}$. It is immediately seen from the equivalences $y \in A \leftrightarrow \{y\} \subseteq A \leftrightarrow \{x\} \subseteq \tau(A) \leftrightarrow x \in \tau(A)$ that f is a Borel isomorphism between Y and X such that $f[A] = \tau(A)$ for all $A \in \mathscr{B}_Y$. Let i be the identity map $x \to x$ of X into $\tilde{X}$. Clearly $i \circ f$ is a one-one measurable map of Y into $\tilde{X}$. By Theorem 3.9, Chapter I, the range of this map is a Borel set in $\tilde{X}$. But the range of this map is precisely X. This completes the proof.

To formulate the next theorem we need a notation. Let $(X, \mathscr{B})$ be a Borel space and $Y \subseteq X$. We write $\mathscr{B}_Y$ for the σ-algebra of all subsets of Y of the form $A \cap Y$ with $A \in \mathscr{B}$.

Theorem 2.3

Let $(X_n, \mathscr{B}_n)$, $n = 1, 2, \ldots$ be standard Borel spaces and $(\tilde{X}, \tilde{\mathscr{B}})$ their cartesian product. Then $(\tilde{X}, \tilde{\mathscr{B}})$ is standard. If $(X, \mathscr{B})$ is standard and $Y \in \mathscr{B}$, then $(Y, \mathscr{B}_Y)$ is standard.

PROOF. If each $(X_n, \mathscr{B}_n)$ is standard there is no loss of generality if we assume that X_n is a complete separable metric space and that $\mathscr{B}_n$ is the class of Borel subsets of X_n. Let $\tilde{X}$ be the cartesian product of the X_n. X is, under a suitable equivalent metric, a complete separable metric space. By Theorem 1.10, Chapter I, $\tilde{\mathscr{B}}$ is the class of Borel subsets of $\tilde{X}$, and hence $(\tilde{X}, \tilde{\mathscr{B}})$ is standard.

For the second part we may once again assume that X is a complete separable metric space, and $\mathscr{B}$ is the class of Borel subsets of X. Then Y is a Borel subset of X, and hence by Theorem 2.2, $(Y, \mathscr{B}_Y)$ is standard.

Theorem 2.4

Let $(X, \mathscr{B})$ be standard, $(Y, \mathscr{C})$ countably generated and φ a one-one map of X into Y which is measurable. Then $Y' = \varphi(X) \in \mathscr{C}$ and φ is a Borel isomorphism between the Borel spaces $(X, \mathscr{B})$ and $(Y', \mathscr{C}_{Y'})$.

PROOF. There is no loss of generality if we assume the Borel spaces to be separable. Further, we may assume that X is a complete separable metric space and Y a separable metric space with $\mathscr{B} = \mathscr{B}_X$, $\mathscr{C} = \mathscr{B}_Y$. Let $\bar{Y}$ be a completion of Y. Then by Theorem 3.9, Chapter I, $Y' = \varphi(X)$ is a Borel set in $\bar{Y}$, and hence in Y. Thus $Y' \in \mathscr{C}$. The rest is just a restatement of Corollary 3.3 to Theorem 3.9, Chapter I.

In order to study the extension problem mentioned in Section I, we need, for technical reasons, the notion of inverse limits of Borel spaces. We shall restrict ourselves to separable Borel spaces. Let $(Y_1, \mathscr{C}_1)$, $(Y_2, \mathscr{C}_2), \ldots$ be separable Borel spaces and for each n let π_n be a measurable map of Y_{n+1} *onto* Y_n. The Borel space $(Y, \mathscr{C})$ is defined as the *inverse limit* of the Borel spaces $(Y_n, \mathscr{C}_n)$, $n = 1, 2, \ldots$, relative to the maps $\{\pi_n\}$, $n = 1, 2, \ldots$, if the following conditions are fulfilled:

(i) Y is the set of all sequences $(y_1, y_2, \ldots)$ such that $y_n \in Y_n$ for all n and $y_n = \pi_n(y_{n+1})$ for $n = 1, 2, \ldots$.

(ii) $\mathscr{C}$ is the smallest σ-algebra of subsets of Y relative to which the maps $\tilde{\pi}_n: (y_1, y_2, \ldots) \to y_n$ of Y onto Y_n are measurable for each $n = 1, 2, \ldots$. Obviously $(Y, \mathscr{C})$ is well-defined. $\tilde{\pi}_n$ is called the *canonical map* of Y onto Y_n.

Theorem 2.5

Let $(Y_n, \mathscr{C}_n)$ be a sequence of separable Borel spaces for $n = 1, 2, \ldots$, and for each $n = 1, 2, \ldots$ let π_n be a measurable map of Y_{n+1} onto Y_n. Then their inverse limit $(Y, \mathscr{C})$ relative to the maps π_n is a separable Borel space. If each $(Y_n, \mathscr{C}_n)$ is standard, then so is $(Y, \mathscr{C})$.

PROOF. Let $\tilde{\mathscr{C}}_n = \{\tilde{\pi}_n^{-1}(A): A \in \mathscr{C}_n\}$. Then $\mathscr{C}$ is generated by $\bigcup_n \tilde{\mathscr{C}}_n$ and so $(Y, \mathscr{C})$ is countably generated. If $y = (y_1, y_2, \ldots) \in Y$, then $\{y\} = \bigcap_n \tilde{\pi}_n^{-1}(\{y_n\})$ so that $\{y\} \in \mathscr{C}$. Hence $(Y, \mathscr{C})$ is separable. Finally, let $(\tilde{Y}, \tilde{\mathscr{C}})$ be the cartesian product of the $(Y_n, \mathscr{C}_n)$ $(n = 1, 2, \ldots)$. Clearly, $Y \subseteq \tilde{Y}$. We claim that $\mathscr{C} = \{A \cap Y: A \in \tilde{\mathscr{C}}\}$. It is enough to show that the totality of subsets of Y of the form $B(n, E) \cap Y$ generates $\mathscr{C}$ where $B(n, E) = \{(y_1, y_2, \ldots): y_m \in Y_m$ for all $m = 1, 2, \ldots,$ and $y_n \in E \in \mathscr{C}_n\}$. But $B(n, E) \cap Y = \tilde{\pi}_n^{-1}(E)$, and hence our claim is valid. To show that $(Y, \mathscr{C})$ is standard if all the $(Y_n, \mathscr{C}_n)$ are so, it is enough to prove that $(\tilde{Y}, \tilde{\mathscr{C}})$ is standard and $Y \in \tilde{\mathscr{C}}$. By Theorem 2.3 $(\tilde{Y}, \tilde{\mathscr{C}})$ is standard. Further, if $D_n = \{(y_1, y_2, \ldots): y_n = \pi_n(y_{n+1})\}$, then by Theorem 3.3, Chapter I, $D_n \in \tilde{\mathscr{C}}$ for $n = 1, 2, \ldots$. Since $Y = \bigcap_n D_n$, $Y \in \tilde{\mathscr{C}}$. This completes the proof.

Theorem 2.6

Let $(Y_n, \mathscr{C}_n)$ be the Borel space associated with a separable metric space for each $n = 1, 2, \ldots$, and let π_n be a continuous map of Y_{n+1} onto Y_n for each n. Let $(Y, \mathscr{C})$ be the inverse limit of the $(Y_n, \mathscr{C}_n)$ and let $\tilde{\pi}_n$ be the canonical map of Y onto Y_n for each n. Then the smallest topology relative to which all the $\tilde{\pi}_n$ are continuous converts Y into a separable metric space and then $\mathscr{C}$ is the class of Borel subsets of this metric space. Moreover, if each Y_n is compact, so is Y.

PROOF. Let $(\tilde{Y}, \tilde{\mathscr{C}})$ be the cartesian product of the $(Y_n, \mathscr{C}_n)$ and for each n and $(y_1, y_2, \ldots) \in \tilde{Y}$, let $p_n(y_1, y_2, \ldots) = y_n$. The product topology for $\tilde{Y}$ is the smallest topology relative to which all the p_n are continuous and $\tilde{Y}$ is a separable metric space in this topology. By Theorem 1.10, Chapter I, $\tilde{\mathscr{C}}$ is the class of Borel subsets of $\tilde{Y}$. For any n, the set $A_n = \{(y_1, y_2, \ldots) : y_n = \pi_n(y_{n+1})\}$ is a closed subset of $\tilde{Y}$ and hence $Y = \bigcap_{n=1}^{\infty} A_n$ is a closed subset of $\tilde{Y}$. The relative topology for Y is the smallest one with respect to which the maps $p_n|Y$ (p_n restricted to Y) are all continuous. But $p_n|Y = \tilde{\pi}_n$. This completes the proof of the first part of the theorem. The argument of Theorem 2.5 shows that $\mathscr{C} = \{A \cap Y, A \in \tilde{\mathscr{C}}\}$, and hence $\mathscr{C}$ is the class of Borel subsets of Y. Finally, if each Y_n is compact so is $\tilde{Y}$, and hence Y, being a closed subset of $\tilde{Y}$, is also compact.

3. THE CONSISTENCY THEOREM IN THE CASE OF INVERSE LIMITS OF BOREL SPACES

The main result of this section is that a consistent sequence of measures on a sequence of standard Borel spaces is always extendable to their inverse limit. The key idea in the proposition is to reduce its proof to the situation of a sequence of compact metric spaces and continuous mappings. We recall that M denotes the space of all sequences of 0's and 1's.

Lemma 3.1

Let $(Y_1, \mathscr{C}_1)$ and $(Y_2, \mathscr{C}_2)$ be separable Borel spaces and f a measurable map of Y_2 into Y_1. Given any isomorphism τ_1 of Y_1 onto a subset $A_1 \subseteq M$, there exists an isomorphism τ_2 of Y_2 onto a subset $A_2 \subseteq M$ and a continuous map φ of M onto M such that the following diagram is commutative:

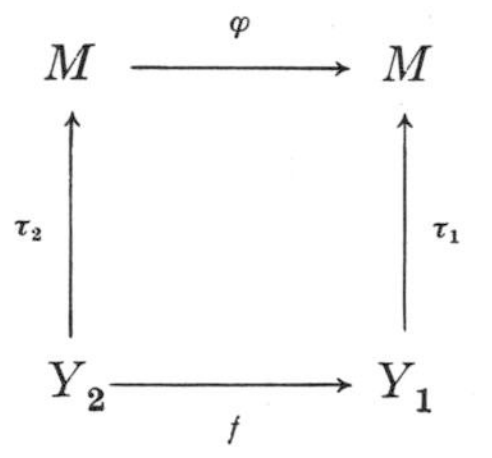

i.e., $\varphi \circ \tau_2 = \tau_1 \circ f$.

PROOF. Let $M_j = \{(a_1, a_2, \ldots): a_j = 1\}$. Since $\{M_1, M_2, \ldots\}$ generates the class of Borel subsets of M $\{M_1 \cap A_1, M_2 \cap A_1, \ldots\}$ generates the class of Borel subsets of A_1. If we write $E_j = \tau_1^{-1}(M_j \cap A_1)$ then $\{E_1, E_2, \ldots\}$ generates $\mathscr{C}_1$. We define $F_1, F_2, \ldots$ by the requirements (a) $F_{2j} = f^{-1}(E_j)$, (b) $\{F_1, F_2, \ldots\}$ generates $\mathscr{C}_2$. Clearly, this can be done. Finally, write, for $y \in Y_2$, $\tau_2(y) = (\chi_{F_1}(y), \chi_{F_2}(y), \ldots)$ and for any $(a_1, a_2, \ldots) \in M$, $\varphi(a_1, a_2, \ldots) = (a_2, a_4, \ldots)$.

τ_2 is an isomorphism of Y_2 into M because of (b). Let τ_2 be onto $A_2 \subseteq M$. If $y' \in Y_1$, then $y' \in E_j$ if and only if $\tau_1(y') \in M_j$, and hence $\tau_1(y') = (\chi_{E_1}(y'), \chi_{E_2}(y'), \ldots)$. Since $\chi_E(f(y)) = \chi_{f^{-1}(E)}(y)$ for any $y \in Y_2$ it is clear that $\tau_1(f(y)) = (\chi_{F_2}(y), \chi_{F_4}(y), \ldots)$. Thus $(\varphi \circ \tau_2)(y) = (\tau_1 \circ f)(y)$ for all $y \in Y_2$.

Lemma 3.2

Let $(Y_n, \mathscr{C}_n)$ be a separable Borel space for each $n = 1, 2, \ldots$ and let π_n be a measurable map of Y_{n+1} onto Y_n for each n. Then for each n there is a compact metric space Z_n, an isomorphism θ_n of Y_n into Z_n, and a continuous map φ_n of Z_{n+1} onto Z_n such that the following diagram is commutative:

$$\begin{array}{ccccccc} Z_1 & \overset{\varphi_1}{\leftarrow} & Z_2 & \overset{\varphi_2}{\leftarrow} & Z_3 & \overset{\varphi_3}{\leftarrow} & \cdots \\ \uparrow \theta_1 & & \uparrow \theta_2 & & \uparrow \theta_3 & & \\ Y_1 & \underset{\pi_1}{\leftarrow} & Y_2 & \underset{\pi_2}{\leftarrow} & Y_3 & \underset{\pi_3}{\leftarrow} & \cdots, \end{array}$$

i.e., $\theta_n \circ \pi_n = \varphi_n \circ \theta_{n+1}$ for $n = 1, 2, \ldots$.

PROOF. Let $Z_1 = M$ and θ_1 be any isomorphism of Y_1 into Z_1. That such an isomorphism exists follows from the proof of Theorem 2.2. Then by the previous lemma there is a continuous map φ_1 of $Z_2 = M$ onto Z_1 and an isomorphism θ_2 of Y_2 into Z_2 such that $\theta_1 \circ \pi_1 = \varphi_1 \circ \theta_2$. Applying it once again, there is a continuous map φ_2 of $Z_3 = M$ onto Z_2 and an isomorphism θ_3 of Y_3 into Z_3 such that $\theta_2 \circ \pi_2 = \varphi_2 \circ \theta_3$, and so on. This completes the proof.

Theorem 3.1

Let $Z_1, Z_2, \ldots$ be compact metric spaces, and for each n let φ_n be a continuous map of Z_{n+1} onto Z_n. Let $\mathscr{D}_n$ be the class of Borel subsets of Z_n $(Z, \mathscr{D})$ the inverse limit of the $(Z_n, \mathscr{D}_n)$, $n = 1, 2, \ldots$ and $\tilde{\varphi}_n$ the canonical *map of Z onto Z_n. If $\{\mu_n\}$ is a sequence of measures such that* (i) *μ_n is defined on $\mathscr{D}_n$ for all n;* (ii) *$\mu_n(A) = \mu_{n+1}(\varphi_n^{-1}(A))$ for all $A \in \mathscr{D}_n$ and all $n = 1, 2, \ldots$, then there exists a unique measure μ on $\mathscr{D}$ such that $\mu_n(A) = \mu(\tilde{\varphi}_n^{-1}(A))$ for all $A \in \mathscr{D}_n$ and all $n = 1, 2, \ldots$.*

PROOF. Let $\tilde{\mathscr{D}}_n = \{\tilde{\varphi}_n^{-1}(A) : A \in \mathscr{D}_n\}$ and $\mathscr{F} = \bigcup_n \tilde{\mathscr{D}}_n$. $\mathscr{F}$ is a Boolean algebra of subsets of Z and $\mathscr{F}$ generates $\mathscr{D}$. If we set $\mu(\tilde{\varphi}_n^{-1}(A)) = \mu_n(A)$ for $A \in \mathscr{D}_n$ then conditions (i) and (ii) imply that μ is well defined on $\mathscr{F}$. Since $\mathscr{F}$ generates $\mathscr{D}$ and since μ is finitely additive over $\mathscr{F}$, it remains only to prove that μ is countably additive over $\mathscr{F}$. If this were done, μ could be extended to a unique measure on $\mathscr{D}$ which would be the required one.

We shall now show that μ is countably additive on $\mathscr{F}$. It is enough to prove that if $A_1 \supseteq A_2 \supseteq \ldots$, $\bigcap A_n = \phi$, and $A_n \in \mathscr{F}$ for all n, then $\mu(A_n) \to 0$. We show, equivalently, that if $A_1 \supseteq A_2 \supseteq \ldots \mu(A_n) \geqslant \delta > 0$, and $A_n \in \mathscr{F}$ for all n, then $\bigcap_n A_n \neq \phi$. Let then A_n be such a sequence of sets. There exists an integer k_n such that $A_n \in \tilde{\mathscr{D}}_{k_n}$. We may thus write $A_n = \tilde{\varphi}_{k_n}^{-1}(B_n)$ where $B_n \in \mathscr{D}_{k_n}$. Since by Theorem 1.2, Chapter II, μ_n is regular, we can find a compact set $K_n^0 \subseteq B_n$ such that $\mu_{k_n}(B_n - K_n^0) \leqslant \delta/4^n$. Write $\tilde{K}_n = \tilde{\varphi}_{k_n}^{-1}(K_n^0)$. Since by Theorem 2.6, Z is compact and $\tilde{\varphi}_{k_n}$ is obviously continuous, $\tilde{K}_n$ is compact. Moreover, $\tilde{K}_n \subseteq A_n$ and $\mu(A_n - \tilde{K}_n) \leqslant \delta/4^n$.

Define now $K_n = \bigcap_{j=1}^n \tilde{K}_j$ $(n = 1, 2, \ldots)$. Then each K_n is compact $K_n \subseteq A_n$, $K_1 \supseteq K_2 \supseteq \ldots$. Moreover, $\mu(A_n - K_n) = \mu(\bigcap_1^n A_j - \bigcap_1^n \tilde{K}_j) \leqslant \sum_{j=1}^n \mu(A_j - \tilde{K}_j) \leqslant \sum_{m=1}^\infty \delta/4^m = \delta/3$. Consequently, $\mu(K_n) \geqslant 2\delta/3 > 0$. Hence each K_n is nonempty, and hence $\bigcap_n K_n \neq \phi$. This implies that $\bigcap_n A_n \neq \phi$.

Theorem 3.2

Let $(Y_n, \mathscr{C}_n)$ be a separable standard Borel space for $n = 1, 2, \ldots$ and π_n a measurable map of Y_{n+1} onto Y_n. Let $(Y, \mathscr{C})$ be the inverse limit of the Borel spaces $(Y_n, \mathscr{C}_n)$ relative to the maps π_n, $n = 1, 2, \ldots$. If $\mu_1, \mu_2, \ldots$ is a sequence of measures such that (i) *μ_n is defined on $\mathscr{C}_n$; and* (ii) *$\mu_n(A) = \mu_{n+1}(\pi_n^{-1}(A))$ for all $A \in \mathscr{C}_n$; then there exists a unique measure μ on $\mathscr{C}$ such that $\mu(\tilde{\pi}_n^{-1}(A)) = \mu_n(A)$ for all $A \in \mathscr{C}_n$ and each $n = 1, 2, \ldots$, where $\tilde{\pi}_n$ is the canonical map of Y onto Y_n.*

PROOF. By Lemma 3.2 and Theorem 2.2 we can find compact metric spaces $Z_1, Z_2, \ldots$, continuous maps $\varphi_1, \varphi_2, \ldots$ with φ_n mapping Z_{n+1} onto Z_n and isomorphisms $\theta_1, \theta_2, \ldots$ such that θ_n is an isomorphism of Y_n onto a Borel subset $\bar{Y}_n$ of Z_n, all in such a fashion that the following diagram is commutative:

$$\begin{array}{ccccccc} Z_1 & \xleftarrow{\varphi_1} & Z_2 & \xleftarrow{\varphi_2} & Z_3 & \xleftarrow{\varphi_3} & \cdots \\ \uparrow \theta_1 & & \uparrow \theta_2 & & \uparrow \theta_3 & & \\ Y_1 & \xleftarrow[\pi_1]{} & Y_2 & \xleftarrow[\pi_2]{} & Y_3 & \xleftarrow[\pi_3]{} & \cdots. \end{array}$$

Let $\tilde{\mathscr{C}}_n = \{\tilde{\pi}_n^{-1}(A), A \in \mathscr{C}_n\}$, $\mathscr{F} = \bigcup_n \tilde{\mathscr{C}}_n$ and for $\tilde{A} \in \mathscr{F}$, $\mu(\tilde{A}) = \mu_n(B)$ if $\tilde{A} = \tilde{\pi}_n^{-1}(B)$ with $B \in \mathscr{C}_n$. Then μ is a well-defined finitely additive nonnegative set function on $\mathscr{F}$ with $\mu(Y) = 1$. We have only to show that μ is countably additive on $\mathscr{F}$. Let $\tilde{A}_1, \tilde{A}_2, \ldots, \in \mathscr{F}$ be sets such that $\tilde{A}_1 \supseteq \tilde{A}_2 \supseteq \ldots$ and $\bigcap_n \tilde{A}_n = \phi$. We shall now prove that $\mu(\tilde{A}_n) \to 0$. This will complete the proof. Let $\tilde{A}_n = \tilde{\pi}_{k_n}^{-1}(B_n)$ for some integer k_n and $B_n \in \mathscr{C}_{k_n}$, $\mu(\tilde{A}_n) = \mu_{k_n}(B_n)$.

For $n = 1, 2, \ldots$ define the measure μ_n' on Z_n by setting $\mu_n'(A) = \mu_n(\theta_n^{-1}(A))$ for all Borel sets $A \subseteq Z_n$. By the commutativity of the diagram we may conclude that $\mu_n'(A) = \mu'_{n+1}(\varphi_n^{-1}(A))$ for all Borel sets $A \subseteq Z_n$, $n = 1, 2, \ldots$. Since $\bar{Y}_n$ is the range of θ_n it is clear that $\mu_n'(\bar{Y}_n) = 1$. Consequently, if E is any set in $\mathscr{C}_n$, $\mu_n(E) = \mu_n'(\theta_n(E))$. By Theorem 3.1 there exists a measure μ' on the inverse limit $(Z, \mathscr{B}_Z)$ of the sequence $(Z_n, \mathscr{B}_{Z_n})$ relative to the maps φ_n, such that for any $A \in \mathscr{B}_{Z_n}$, and any n, $\mu_n'(A) = \mu'[\tilde{\varphi}_n^{-1}(A)]$, where $\tilde{\varphi}_n$ is the canonical map of Z onto Z_n. Let $E_n = \tilde{\varphi}_{k_n}^{-1}(\theta_{k_n}(B_n))$, where $\tilde{A}_n = \tilde{\pi}_{k_n}^{-1}(B_n)$, $B_n \in \mathscr{C}_{k_n}$. From the commutativity of the diagram and the nature of the sequence A_n it follows that $E_1 \supseteq E_2 \supseteq \ldots$ and $\bigcap_n E_n = \phi$. Hence $\mu'(E_n) \to 0$ as $n \to \infty$. By the definition of μ on $\mathscr{F}$, we have $\mu(\tilde{A}_n) = \mu_{k_n}(B_n) = \mu'_{k_n}(\theta_{k_n}(B_n)) = \mu'[\tilde{\varphi}_{k_n}^{-1}(\theta_{k_n}(B_n))] = \mu'(E_n)$. Hence $\mu(\tilde{A}_n) \to 0$ as $n \to \infty$. This completes the proof.

4. THE EXTENSION THEOREM

We now resume our discussion in Section 1. We recall that if $(Z, \mathscr{D})$ is a countably generated Borel space and $(Z^0, \mathscr{D}^0)$ the associated canonical separable Borel space, then the canonical map of Z onto Z^0 sends $z \in Z$ into the unique atom of Z containing z.

Lemma 4.1

Let Z be a space and $\mathscr{D}_1, \mathscr{D}_2$ be two countably generated σ-algebras of subsets of Z. If $\mathscr{D}_2 \subseteq \mathscr{D}_1$ and if $(Z_j^0, \mathscr{D}_j^0)$, $j = 1, 2$ are the associated canonical separable Borel spaces, then (i) *for any nonempty atom e_1 of $\mathscr{D}_1$ there exists a unique atom e_2 of $\mathscr{D}_2$ such that $e_1 \subseteq e_2$* (ii) *the map $e_1 \to e_2$ is a measurable map of Z_1^0 onto Z_2^0.*

PROOF. Let π_j be the canonical map of Z_j onto Z_j^0. We have $\mathscr{D}_j^0 = \{\pi_j(A), A \in \mathscr{D}_j\}$, $j = 1, 2$. Suppose now $e_1 \in Z_1^0$. Since $\mathscr{E}_2^0 = \{\pi_1(A): A \in \mathscr{D}_2\}$ is countably generated, there is a unique atom E_2 of $\mathscr{E}_2^0$ such that $e_1 \in E_2$. Let $e_2 \in \mathscr{D}_2$ be such that $\pi_1(e_2) = E_2$. Then e_2 is obviously an atom of $\mathscr{D}_2$ and $e_1 \subseteq e_2$. e_2 is clearly unique.

Denote now by τ the map $e_1 \to e_2$. Suppose $F_2^0 = \pi_2(F_2)$, $F_2 \in \mathscr{D}_2$. Then $\tau^{-1}(F_2^0) = \{e_1: e_1$ is an atom of $\mathscr{D}_1$, $e_1 \subseteq e_2$ for some $e_2 \in F_2^0\} = \pi_1(F_2) \in \mathscr{D}_1^0$. This shows that τ is measurable.

We shall call τ *the canonical map of Z_1 onto Z_2 induced by the inclusion $\mathscr{D}_2 \subseteq \mathscr{D}_1$.*

Theorem 4.1

Let $(X, \mathscr{B})$ be a Borel space and $\mathscr{B}_n \subseteq \mathscr{B}$ a σ-algebra such that (i) *$\mathscr{B}_1 \subseteq \mathscr{B}_2 \subseteq \ldots$ and $\bigcup_n \mathscr{B}_n$ generates $\mathscr{B}$, and* (ii) *$(X, \mathscr{B}_n)$ is a standard Borel space for each $n = 1, 2, \ldots$. Then, in order that every consistent sequence of measures on $\mathscr{B}_1, \mathscr{B}_2, \ldots$ be extendable to a measure on $\mathscr{B}$ it is necessary and sufficient that $\bigcap_n A_n \neq \phi$ for each sequence $A_1, A_2, \ldots$ of subsets of X such that A_n is an atom of $\mathscr{B}_n$ for all n and $A_1 \supseteq A_2 \supseteq \ldots$. If this is the case then $(X, \mathscr{B})$ is also standard.*

PROOF. We first establish the necessity. Suppose $A_1, A_2, \ldots$ are subsets of X such that (a) A_n is an atom of $\mathscr{B}_n$ and (b) $A_1 \supseteq A_2 \supseteq \ldots$ and $\bigcap_n A_n = \phi$. We define measures $\mu_1, \mu_2, \ldots$, as follows: μ_n is defined on $\mathscr{B}_n$ and $\mu_n(A) = 1$ or 0, according as $A \supseteq A_n$ or $A \cap A_n = \phi$. μ_n is well defined because A_n being an atom of $\mathscr{B}_n$, for any $A \in \mathscr{B}_n$, either $A \supseteq A_n$ or $A \cap A_n = \phi$. The inclusion $A_m \supseteq A_n$ whenever $m \leqslant n$ implies that $\mu_m(A) = \mu_n(A)$ if $A \in \mathscr{B}_m$. The measures $\mu_1, \mu_2, \ldots$ are thus consistent. If $\mu(A) = \mu_n(A)$ for all $A \in \mathscr{B}_n$, then μ is well defined on $\bigcup_n \mathscr{B}_n$. μ

is however not countably additive on $\bigcup_n \mathscr{B}_n$, because $\mu(A_n) = 1$ for all n, while $A_1 \supseteq A_2 \supseteq \ldots$ with $\bigcap_n A_n = \phi$. This proves that the condition is necessary.

To prove the sufficiency let us assume the condition. Let $\mu_1, \mu_2, \ldots$ be a consistent sequence of measures and μ the set function defined on $\bigcup_n \mathscr{B}_n$. We must prove that if $E_1, E_2, \ldots \in \bigcup_n \mathscr{B}_n$ with $E_1 \supseteq E_2 \supseteq \ldots$ and $\bigcap_n E_n = \phi$, then $\mu(E_n) \to 0$.

Let $(Y_n, \mathscr{C}_n)$ be the canonical separable Borel space associated with $(X, \mathscr{B}_n)$ for $n = 1, 2, \ldots$ and π_n be the canonical measurable map of Y_{n+1} onto Y_n induced by the inclusion $\mathscr{B}_n \subseteq \mathscr{B}_{n+1}$. Let τ_n be the canonical map which sends a point $x \in X$ to the unique atom of $\mathscr{B}_n$ containing x. Let μ_n' be the measure on $\mathscr{C}_n$ defined by $\mu_n'(A) = \mu_n(\tau_n^{-1}(A))$. Clearly $\mu_n'(A) = \mu'_{n+1}(\pi_n^{-1}(A))$.

Suppose now $E_1 \supseteq E_2 \supseteq \ldots, E_n \in \bigcup_m \mathscr{B}_m$ and $\bigcap_n E_n = \phi$. We can assume without loss of generality that $E_1 \in \mathscr{B}_1$, $E_2 \in \mathscr{B}_2, \ldots$. Let $F_n = \tau_n(E_n)$. Since $E_1 \supseteq E_2 \supseteq \ldots$ it follows that $F_2 \subseteq \pi_1^{-1}(F_1)$, $F_3 \subseteq \pi_2^{-1}(F_2), \ldots$. In other words, if we write $(Y, \mathscr{C})$ for the inverse limit of the Borel spaces $(Y_n, \mathscr{C}_n)$ and $\tilde{\pi}_n$ the canonical map of Y onto Y_n, then $\tilde{\pi}_1^{-1}(F_1) \supseteq \tilde{\pi}_2^{-1}(F_2) \supseteq \ldots$. We now claim that $\bigcap_n \tilde{\pi}_n^{-1}(F_n) = \phi$.

If it is not so, then there are elements $y_1, y_2, \ldots$ such that (a) $y_n = \pi_n(y_{n+1})$ for all $n \geqslant 1$, (b) $y_n \in F_n$ for all n. Since $y_n \in F_n$, $\tau_n^{-1}(\{y_n\}) = A_n$ is an atom of $\mathscr{B}_n$. Moreover, the equations $\pi_n(y_{n+1}) = y_n$ for all n imply that $A_1 \supseteq A_2 \supseteq \ldots$. By our assumption, $\bigcap_n A_n \neq \phi$ and hence, as $A_n \subseteq E_n$ for all n, $\bigcap_n E_n \neq \phi$, which is a contradiction. Thus we have $\bigcap_n \tilde{\pi}_n^{-1}(F_n) = \phi$. Since the measures μ_n' are consistent, by Theorem 3.2, it follows that $\mu_n'(F_n) \to 0$ as $n \to \infty$. Since $\mu_n'(F_n) = \mu_n(E_n)$ we have $\mu_n(E_n) \to 0$, i.e., $\mu(E_n) \to 0$ or, in other words, μ is countably additive.

To prove the last part we may assume that $(X, \mathscr{B})$ is separable, i.e., $\{x\} \in \mathscr{B}$ for all $x \in X$. To begin with we shall prove that if $A_1 \supseteq A_2 \supseteq \ldots$ are nonempty sets with A_n an atom of $\mathscr{B}_n$ then $\bigcap_n A_n$ consists precisely of one point. In fact, let $x \neq x'$ and let x, x' belong to $\bigcap_n A_n$. The class $\mathscr{A}_0$ of all subsets E of X such that either $\bigcap_n A_n \subseteq E$ or $(\bigcap_n A_n) \cap E = \phi$ is a σ-algebra. If $E \in \mathscr{B}_m$ then E either includes A_m or is disjoint with A_m so that either $\bigcap_n A_n \subseteq E$ or $(\bigcap_n A_n) \cap E = \phi$. Thus $\mathscr{B}_m \subseteq \mathscr{A}_0$ for $m = 1, 2, \ldots$, and so $\mathscr{B} \subseteq \mathscr{A}_0$. Consequently, $\{x\} \in \mathscr{A}_0$. This is impossible since $x' \in \bigcap_n A_n$ and $x' \neq x$. Thus $\bigcap_n A_n$ consists of exactly one point.

We now define, for $(y_1, y_2, \ldots) \in Y$, $\tau(y_1, y_2, \ldots) = x$ where x is the unique point common to $\tau_1^{-1}(\{y_1\})$, $\tau_2^{-1}(\{y_2\}), \ldots$. (Note that since $\pi_n(y_{n+1}) = y_n$ for all n, $\tau_n^{-1}(\{y_n\}) \supseteq \tau_{n+1}^{-1}(\{y_{n+1}\})$ for all n.) τ is clearly a one-one map of Y onto X. Moreover, for $A \in \mathscr{B}_n$, $\tau^{-1}(A) = \tau_n(A)$ so that τ is measurable. Since by Theorem 2.5 $(Y, \mathscr{C})$ is a standard Borel space, it follows from Corollary 3.3 to Theorem 3.9 of Chapter I, that $(X, \mathscr{B})$ is standard. This completes the proof.

Another useful theorem can be obtained from the above result. Let $(X, \mathscr{B})$ be a Borel space, Δ a directed set under the ordering $<$, and for each $\alpha \in \Delta$ let $\mathscr{B}_\alpha \subseteq \mathscr{B}$ be a σ-algebra. A family $\{\mu_\alpha : \alpha \in \Delta\}$ of measures is said to be consistent if (a) μ_α is defined on $\mathscr{B}_\alpha$, (b) $\mathscr{B}_\alpha \subseteq \mathscr{B}_{\alpha'}$ if $\alpha < \alpha'$ and (c) $\mu_\alpha(A) = \mu_{\alpha'}(A)$ for all $A \in \mathscr{B}_\alpha$ if $\alpha < \alpha'$.

Theorem 4.2

Let $(X, \mathscr{B})$ be a Borel space, Δ a directed set under an ordering $<$ and for each $\alpha \in \Delta$, $\mathscr{B}_\alpha \subseteq \mathscr{B}$ a σ-algebra such that (i) *$\mathscr{B}_\alpha \subseteq \mathscr{B}_{\alpha'}$ if $\alpha < \alpha'$;* (ii) *$(X, \mathscr{B}_\alpha)$ is a standard Borel space for all α;* (iii) *$\bigcup_\alpha \mathscr{B}_\alpha$ generates $\mathscr{B}$; and* (iv) *for any sequence $A_1, A_2, \ldots$, of sets such that $A_1 \supseteq A_2 \supseteq, \ldots, A_n$ is an atom of $\mathscr{B}_{\alpha_n}$ and $\alpha_1 < \alpha_2 < \alpha_3, \ldots$, one has $\bigcap_n A_n \neq \phi$. Then given any consistent family $\{\mu_\alpha : \alpha \in \Delta\}$ of measures there exists a unique measure μ on $\mathscr{B}$ such that $\mu(A) = \mu_\alpha(A)$ for all $A \in \mathscr{B}$ and each $\alpha \in \Delta$.*

Proof. Let $\mathscr{F} = \bigcup_\alpha \mathscr{B}_\alpha$. Since Δ is directed, it is easily seen that $\mathscr{F}$ is a Boolean algebra. If $\{\mu_\alpha : \alpha \in \Delta\}$ is a consistent family of measures, then the definition $\mu(A) = \mu_\alpha(A)$ for all $A \in \mathscr{B}_\alpha$ and for all $\alpha \in \Delta$ yields a well defined finitely additive nonnegative set function on $\mathscr{F}$.

Let $A_1, A_2, \ldots \in \mathscr{F}$ be sets such that $A_1 \supseteq A_2 \supseteq \ldots$ and $\bigcap A_n = \phi$. We may assume that $A_n \in \mathscr{B}_{\alpha_n}$ and $\alpha_1 < \alpha_2 < \ldots$. $\mu(A_n) = \mu_{\alpha_n}(A_n)$. The Borel spaces $(X, \mathscr{B}_{\alpha_n})$, $n = 1, 2, \ldots$ satisfy the conditions of Theorem 4.1. Hence $\mu(A_n) \to 0$ as $n \to \infty$. This completes the proof.

5. THE KOLMOGOROV CONSISTENCY THEOREM

Let I be any index set and for each $\alpha \in I$, let $(X_\alpha, \mathscr{B}_\alpha)$ be a Borel space. For any $I' \subseteq I$ we write $(X^{I'}, \mathscr{B}^{I'}) = \prod_{\alpha \in I'} (X_\alpha, \mathscr{B}_\alpha)$. For any $x \in X^{I_1}$ and $I_2 \subseteq I_1 \subseteq I$, we denote by $\pi_{I_1 I_2}(x)$ the restriction of x to I_2.

Note that x is a function defined on I_1 such that $x(\alpha) \in X_\alpha$ for all $\alpha \in I_1$. Hence the restriction of x to I_2 is well defined. The map $\pi_{I_1 I_2}: X^{I_1} \to X^{I_2}$ is measurable. A family $\{\mu_F: F \subseteq I, F \text{ arbitrary but finite}\}$ of measures is said to be *consistent* if (a) μ_F is defined on $\mathscr{B}^F$, (b) whenever $F_2 \subseteq F_1 \subseteq I$ and F_1 and F_2 are finite, $\mu_{F_2}(A) = \mu_{F_1}(\pi_{F_1 F_2}^{-1}(A))$ for all $A \in \mathscr{B}^{F_2}$.

Theorem 5.1

Let $(X_\alpha, \mathscr{B}_\alpha)$, $\alpha \in I$ be standard separable Borel spaces. If $\{\mu_F: F \subseteq I, F$ finite$\}$ is a consistent family of measures, then there exists a unique measure μ on $\mathscr{B}^I$ such that $\mu_F(A) = \mu(\pi_{IF}^{-1}(A))$ for all $A \in \mathscr{B}^F$ and all finite $F \subseteq I$.

PROOF. Let $\mathscr{B}_F = \{\pi_{IF}^{-1}(A): A \in \mathscr{B}^F\}$. Directing the finite subsets of I by $\subseteq$ we verify that conditions (i)–(iv) of Theorem 4.2 are satisfied. Conditions (i)–(iii) are obvious. To prove (iv), let $F_1 \subseteq F_2 \subseteq \ldots (\subseteq I)$ be an increasing sequence of finite sets, A_n an atom of $\mathscr{B}_{F_n}$, and let $A_1 \supseteq A_2 \supseteq \ldots$. It is clear that there exists a $y_n \in X^{F_n}$ such that $A_n = \{x: x \in X^I, \pi_{IF_n}(x) = y_n\}$. Since $A_1 \supseteq A_2 \supseteq \ldots$, $\pi_{F_{n+1}F_n}(y_{n+1}) = y_n$ for all n. If x_0 is any function on I such that $x_0|F_n = y_n$, for all n, then $x_0 \in A_n$ for all n so that $\bigcap_n A_n \neq \phi$. Such an x_0 exists because of the "consistency" of the y_n. Now the theorem is an immediate consequence of Theorem 4.2.

6. STATEMENT OF THE SECOND PROBLEM

Given a probability space $(X, \mathscr{B}, P)$ and a σ-algebra $\mathscr{B}_1 \subseteq \mathscr{B}$, *the conditional probability of a set $A \in \mathscr{B}$ given $\mathscr{B}_1$* is any function f with the following properties: (i) f is $\mathscr{B}_1$-measurable; (ii) for any set $A_1 \in \mathscr{B}_1$, $\int_{A_1} f\, dP = P(A \cap A_1)$, where f depends on A and is denoted by $P(A|\mathscr{B}_1)$. The existence of $P(A|\mathscr{B}_1)$ is a consequence of the Radon-Nikodym theorem. Indeed the set function $P(A \cap A_1)$, $A_1 \in \mathscr{B}_1$ is a nonnegative countably additive set function which is absolutely continuous with respect to $P(A_1)$. Hence the existence of the function f with the required properties follows.

In many problems of probability theory it is necessary to construct a function $(A, x) \to P(A, x)$ such that for each $A \in \mathscr{B}$, the function $x \to P(A, x)$ is $\mathscr{B}_1$-measurable, and is the conditional probability of A given $\mathscr{B}_1$, while for fixed $x \in X$, $A \to P(A, x)$ is a measure on $\mathscr{B}$. The next section is devoted to a solution of this problem in the case when $(X, \mathscr{B})$ is a standard Borel space.

7. EXISTENCE OF CONDITIONAL PROBABILITY

Theorem 7.1

Let $(X, \mathscr{B})$ be a separable standard Borel space, $\mathscr{B}_0$ a σ-algebra $\subseteq \mathscr{B}$ and P a probability measure on $\mathscr{B}$. Then there exists a function $f: \mathscr{B} \times X \to [0, 1]$ such that (i) *for each $A \in \mathscr{B}$, $f(A, \cdot)$ is a $\mathscr{B}_0$-measurable function and $\int_{A_0} f(A, x)\, dP(x) = P(A \cap A_0)$ for all $A_0 \in \mathscr{B}_0$ and* (ii) *for each $x \in X$, $f(\cdot, x)$ is a measure on $\mathscr{B}$.*

PROOF. If X is countable then the theorem is an immediate consequence of the Radon-Nikodym theorem. If X is uncountable, then there exists a sequence $\{\mathscr{B}_n\}$ of finite σ-algebras such that (a) $\mathscr{B}_1 \subseteq \mathscr{B}_2 \subseteq \ldots$ and $\bigcup_n \mathscr{B}_n$ generates $\mathscr{B}$, (b) any consistent sequence of measures on $\mathscr{B}_1, \mathscr{B}_2, \ldots$ is extendable to a unique measure on $\mathscr{B}$. Indeed, it follows from Theorems 2.8 and 2.12, Chapter I that $(X, \mathscr{B})$ is isomorphic to $(M, \mathscr{B}_M)$, where M is the space of all sequences of 0's and 1's. Hence, it is enough to prove the existence of $\{\mathscr{B}_n\}$ in the case of $(M, \mathscr{B}_M)$. We write $\mathscr{B}_n$ for the σ-algebra generated by the sets $M_j = \{(a_1, a_2, \ldots): a_j = 1\}$, $1 \leqslant j \leqslant n$. That the $\mathscr{B}_n$'s have the required property is an immediate consequence of Theorem 4.1.

We shall now choose and fix a sequence of finite σ-algebras $\{\mathscr{B}_n\}$ satisfying (a) and (b). $\mathscr{B}_n$ has a finite number of atoms and we shall denote them by $A_{n1}, A_{n2}, \ldots, A_{nk_n}$. Any set in $\mathscr{B}_n$ is a union of some of these. Choose some versions of the conditional probabilities $P(A_{nj}|\mathscr{B}_0)$, say f_{nj}. Let N_n be the set such that $x \in X - N_n$ is equivalent to $f_{nj}(x) \geqslant 0$ for all j and $\sum_j f_{nj}(x) = 1$. Define now $f_n(\cdot, \cdot)$ on $\mathscr{B}_n \times X$ by setting $f_n(A, x) = \sum_{j: A_{nj} \subseteq A} f_{nj}(x)$, whenever $x \in X - N_n$, while for $x \in N_n$, define $f_n(A, x) = \tau_0(A)$, where τ_0 is any *fixed* probability measure on $\mathscr{B}$. f_n is well defined. For each $A \in \mathscr{B}_n$ it is $\mathscr{B}_0$-measurable, for each $x \in X$ it is a measure on $\mathscr{B}_n$, and for any $A \in \mathscr{B}_n$, $f_n(A_j) = P(A|\mathscr{B}_0)$.

Consider now f_n and f_{n+1}. Since $\mathscr{B}_n \subseteq \mathscr{B}_{n+1}$ and conditional probabilities are essentially uniquely determined by the Radon-Nikodym theorem, $P\{x: f_n(A, x) \neq f_{n+1}(A, x)\} = 0$ for each $A \in \mathscr{B}_n$ and hence, as $\mathscr{B}_n$ is finite, $P\{x: f_n(A, x) \neq f_{n+1}(A, x)$ for at least one $A \in \mathscr{B}_n\} = 0$.

We can thus find a set $N_0 \in \mathscr{B}_0$ such that $P(N_0) = 0$ and for any $x \in X - N_0$, $f_1(\cdot, x), f_2(\cdot, x), \ldots$ is a consistent sequence of measures on $\mathscr{B}_1, \mathscr{B}_2, \ldots$. For each $x \in X - N_0$, we can thus find a measure μ_x such that $\mu_x(A) = f_n(A, x)$ for all $A \in \mathscr{B}_n$ and each $n = 1, 2, \ldots$.

Now we define f on $\mathscr{B} \times X$ by $f(A, x) = \mu_x(A)$ if $A \in \mathscr{B}$ and $x \in X - N_0$, $= \tau_0(A)$ if $A \in \mathscr{B}$ and $x \in N_0$. The class of all $A \in \mathscr{B}$ for which $x \to f(A, x)$ is $\mathscr{B}_0$-measurable is a monotone class containing $\bigcup_n \mathscr{B}_n$ and hence contains $\mathscr{B}$. Thus for each $A \in \mathscr{B}$, $f(A, \cdot)$ is $\mathscr{B}_0$-measurable. By construction, $f(\cdot, x)$ is a measure on $\mathscr{B}$ for each $x \in X$. Finally, for any $A \in \bigcup_n \mathscr{B}_n$, $\int_{A_0} f(A, \cdot)\, dP(x) = P(A \cap A_0)$. The class of $A \in \mathscr{B}$ for which this equation holds for all $A_0 \in \mathscr{B}_0$ is a monotone class containing $\bigcup_n \mathscr{B}_n$, and hence coincides with $\mathscr{B}$. This proves that $f(A, \cdot) = P(A|\mathscr{B}_0)$. The proof is complete.

8. REGULAR CONDITIONAL PROBABILITY

In some problems the theorem of the previous section is not adequate and an even more delicate choice of the conditional probabilities is required. To motivate this more refined version let us start with a probability space $(X, \mathscr{B}, P)$, a *finite* set Y, and a map $\pi: X \to Y$ such that for each $y \in Y$, $\{x : \pi(x) = y\} = X_y$ is in $\mathscr{B}$ and $P(X_y) > 0$. Intuitively, the "conditional probability of any set $A \in \mathscr{B}$ given that $\pi(x) = y$" is given by $P(A \cap X_y)/P(X_y)$. Mathematically, all we need to do is to define, for each $y \in Y$, the measure P_y on $\mathscr{B}$ by $P_y(B) = P(B \cap X_y)/P(X_y)$. Then for any set $A \in \mathscr{B}$, $P(A|\pi(x) = y) = P_y(A)$. An advantage of this form of construction is that P_y, even though defined as a measure on $\mathscr{B}$, is actually concentrated in the set X_y, i.e., $P_y(X - X_y) = 0$. It is the "conditional probability of x given that $\pi(x) = y$."

It is now our aim to formalize the above construction to prove a result which is a far-reaching generalization of the theorem in the case of the finite set Y. Let $(X, \mathscr{B})$ and $(Y, \mathscr{C})$ be two Borel spaces, P a measure on $\mathscr{B}$, and π a measurable map of X onto Y. Let Q be the measure on $\mathscr{C}$ defined by $Q(C) = P(\pi^{-1}(C))$ for all $C \in \mathscr{C}$. A *regular conditional probability distribution given* π is a mapping $y \to P_y$ such that (i) for each $y \in Y$, P_y is a probability measure on $\mathscr{B}$; (ii) there exists a set $N \in \mathscr{C}$ such that $Q(N) = 0$ and for each $y \in Y -$

N, $P_y(X - X_y) = 0$, where $X_y = \{x : \pi(x) = y\}$; (iii) for any set $A \in \mathscr{B}$, the map $y \to P_y(A)$ is $\mathscr{C}$-measurable and $P(A) = \int_Y P_y(A)\, dQ(y)$. If $y \to P_y$ is a regular conditional probability distribution notice that for any $A \in \mathscr{B}$, $x \to P_{\pi(x)}(A)$ is the conditional probability of A given the σ-algebra $\pi^{-1}(\mathscr{C})$. In fact, for any $C \in \mathscr{C}$,

$$\int_{\pi^{-1}(C)} P_{\pi(x)}(A)\, dP(x) = \int_C P_y(A)\, dQ(y)$$

$$= \int_C P_y(A \cap X_y)\, dQ(y) = \int P_y(A \cap \pi^{-1}(C))\, dQ(y)$$

$$= P(A \cap \pi^{-1}(C)).$$

Further, for each $A \in \mathscr{B}$, $P_{\pi(x)}(A)$ is $\pi^{-1}(\mathscr{C})$-measurable. Hence $P_{\pi(x)}(A) = P(A | \pi^{-1}(\mathscr{C}))$.

Theorem 8.1

Let $(X, \mathscr{B})$ and $(Y, \mathscr{C})$ be separable standard Borel spaces and π a measurable map of X onto Y. Let P be a measure on $\mathscr{B}$. Then there exists a regular conditional probability distribution $y \to P_y$. If $y \to P_y'$ is another such, then $\{y\colon P_y \neq P_y'\}$ is a set in $\mathscr{C}$ whose Q-measure is zero, where $Q(C) = P(\pi^{-1}(C))$ for all $C \in \mathscr{C}$.

PROOF. In view of Lemma 3.1, there are compact metric spaces $\tilde{X}$ and $\tilde{Y}$ homeomorphic to M [$\equiv$ the space of all sequences $(a_1, a_2, \ldots)$ with $a_j = 0$ or 1 for each j] and a continuous map $\tilde{\pi}$ of $\tilde{X}$ onto $\tilde{Y}$ such that (a) $X \subseteq \tilde{X}$, $Y \subseteq \tilde{Y}$; (b) $\mathscr{B}$ and $\mathscr{C}$ are the respective classes of Borel sets in the metric spaces X and Y; (c) $\tilde{\pi}|X = \pi$. Let $\tilde{\mathscr{B}}$ and $\tilde{\mathscr{C}}$ be the σ-algebras of Borel subsets of $\tilde{X}$ and $\tilde{Y}$, respectively. For any $\tilde{A} \in \tilde{\mathscr{B}}$ we set $\tilde{P}(\tilde{A}) = P(\tilde{A} \cap X)$ and for any $\tilde{B} \in \tilde{\mathscr{C}}$ we set $\tilde{Q}(\tilde{B}) = Q(\tilde{B} \cap Y)$. Clearly $\tilde{P}$ and $\tilde{Q}$ are measures on $\tilde{X}$ and $\tilde{Y}$, respectively. Moreover, $\tilde{Q}(\tilde{B}) = \tilde{P}(\tilde{\pi}^{-1}(\tilde{B}))$ for all $\tilde{B} \in \tilde{\mathscr{C}}$.

Let τ be any homeomorphism of $\tilde{Y}$ with M and let $\tilde{B}_{nj} = \tau^{-1}(M_{nj})$, $1 \leqslant j \leqslant 2^n$ where $M_{nj} = \{(a_1, a_2, \ldots) : a_1 = i_1, \ldots, a_n = i_n\}$, $(i_1, i_2, \ldots, i_n)$ being the jth n-tuple of 0's and 1's in some order. Let $\tilde{A}_{nj} = \tilde{\pi}^{-1}(B_{nj})$. The $\tilde{A}_{nj}$ and $\tilde{B}_{nj}$ are open and closed sets. For fixed n, the $\tilde{A}_{nj}$ are disjoint and $\bigcup_j \tilde{A}_{nj} = \tilde{X}$. Let $\tilde{\mathscr{S}}_n$ be the σ-algebra generated by $\{\tilde{A}_{nj} : 1 \leqslant$

$j \leqslant 2^n\}$. Clearly, $\tilde{\mathscr{S}}_1 \subseteq \tilde{\mathscr{S}}_2 \subseteq \ldots$, and $\bigcup_n \tilde{\mathscr{S}}_n$ generates $\tilde{\pi}^{-1}(\mathscr{C})$. Let $\tilde{\mathscr{S}} = \tilde{\pi}^{-1}(\mathscr{C})$. For each n, we may redesignate the $\tilde{A}_{nj}$ so that the $\tilde{A}_{nj}$ with $1 \leqslant j \leqslant k_n (\leqslant 2^n)$ are precisely the $\tilde{A}_{nj}$ with positive $\tilde{P}$-measure.

Given any continuous function $\tilde{g}$ on $\tilde{X}$ one can easily construct a version of the conditional expectation $E(\tilde{g}|\tilde{\mathscr{S}}_n)$. In fact, let

$$\Lambda_n(\tilde{g}, \tilde{x}) = \begin{cases} \dfrac{1}{\tilde{P}(\tilde{A}_{nj})} \displaystyle\int_{\tilde{A}_{nj}} \tilde{g}\, d\tilde{P} & \text{if } \tilde{x} \in \tilde{A}_{nj}, \quad j \leqslant k_n, \\ 0 & \text{if } \tilde{x} \in \tilde{A}_{nj}, \quad j > k_n. \end{cases}$$

Λ_n is well defined for all $\tilde{g} \in C(\tilde{X})$ and $\tilde{x} \in \tilde{X}$. Clearly, for any $\tilde{g} \in C(\tilde{X})$, the function $\tilde{x} \to \Lambda_n(\tilde{g}, \tilde{x})$ is a version of $E(\tilde{g}|\tilde{\mathscr{S}}_n)$. Let $\tilde{X}_n = \bigcup_{j \leqslant k_n} \tilde{A}_{nj}$. Obviously, $\tilde{P}(\tilde{X}_n) = 1$.

The $\Lambda_n(\cdot, \cdot)$ have the following properties: (i) For each $\tilde{x} \in \tilde{X}_n$, $\tilde{g} \to \Lambda_n(\tilde{g}, \tilde{x})$ is a positive linear functional on $C(\tilde{X})$ with $\Lambda_n(1, \tilde{x}) = 1$, (ii) $|\Lambda_n(\tilde{g}, \tilde{x}) - \Lambda_n(\tilde{h}, \tilde{x})| \leqslant \max_{t \in \tilde{X}} |\tilde{g}(t) - \tilde{h}(t)| = \|\tilde{g} - \tilde{h}\|$.

Consider now a fixed $\tilde{g} \in C(\tilde{X})$. By the martingale convergence theorem ([5], Chapter VII), the sequence $\{\Lambda_n(\tilde{g}, \tilde{x})\}$, $n = 1, 2, \ldots$, of functions has a limit almost everywhere and the limit is a version of $E(\tilde{g}|\tilde{\mathscr{S}})$. Let $N_{\tilde{g}}$ be the set of points at which $\lim_{n\to\infty} \Lambda_n(\tilde{g}, \tilde{x})$ does not exist. We define

$$\Lambda(\tilde{g}, \tilde{x}) = \begin{cases} \lim\limits_{n\to\infty} \Lambda_n(\tilde{g}, \tilde{x}) & \text{if } \tilde{x} \in \tilde{X} - N_{\tilde{g}} \\ 0 & \text{if } \tilde{x} \in N_{\tilde{g}}. \end{cases}$$

Clearly, $\tilde{x} \to \Lambda(\tilde{g}, \tilde{x})$ is $\tilde{\mathscr{S}}$-measurable, $\tilde{P}(N_{\tilde{g}}) = 0$ and $\Lambda(\tilde{g}, \tilde{x}) = E(\tilde{g}|\tilde{\mathscr{S}})$.

Since $\tilde{X}$ is a compact metric space, $C(\tilde{X})$ is a separable metric space under the uniform norm. Let $\tilde{g}_1, \tilde{g}_2, \ldots$ be a dense sequence in $C(\tilde{X})$. If $N_0 = \bigcup_m N_{\tilde{g}_m}$ then $\tilde{P}(N_0) = 0$. We claim that $\lim_{n\to\infty} \Lambda_n(\tilde{g}, \tilde{x})$ exists for all $\tilde{x} \in \tilde{X} - N_0$. In fact, this limit exists whenever $\tilde{g} = \tilde{g}_m$ for some m. Since $|\Lambda_n(\tilde{g}, \tilde{x}) - \Lambda_n(\tilde{g}', \tilde{x})| \leqslant \|\tilde{g} - \tilde{g}'\|$ it is easily seen that the class of all $\tilde{g}$ for which $\lim_{n\to\infty} \Lambda_n(\tilde{g}, \tilde{x})$ exists for any $\tilde{x} \in \tilde{X} - N_0$ is a closed subset of $C(\tilde{X})$, and hence coincides with $C(\tilde{X})$.

We finally set $\tilde{X}_0 = (\tilde{X} - N_0) \cap \bigcap_n \tilde{X}_n$. Since $\tilde{P}(N_0) = 0$ and each $\tilde{P}(\tilde{X}_n) = 1$, $\tilde{P}(\tilde{X}_0) = 1$. For any $\tilde{x} \in \tilde{X}_0$, $\Lambda_n(\tilde{g}, \tilde{x})$ is a positive linear functional in $\tilde{g}$ with $\Lambda_n(1, \tilde{x}) = 1$ so that the same is true for $\Lambda(\tilde{g}, \tilde{x})$.

Consequently, by Theorem 5.8, Chapter II there exists a measure $\mu_{\tilde{x}}$ on $\tilde{X}$ such that $\Lambda(\tilde{g}, \tilde{x}) = \int_{\tilde{X}} \tilde{g}\, d\mu_{\tilde{x}}$ for all $\tilde{g} \in C(\tilde{X})$. Since, for each $\tilde{g}$, $\Lambda(\tilde{g}, \cdot)$ is $\tilde{\mathscr{S}}$-measurable, $\Lambda(\tilde{g}, \tilde{x}_1) = \Lambda(\tilde{g}, \tilde{x}_2)$, whenever $\tilde{\pi}(\tilde{x}_1) = \tilde{\pi}(\tilde{x}_2)$. We can thus write $\mu_{\tilde{x}} = \tilde{P}_{\tilde{y}}$ where $\tilde{y} = \tilde{\pi}(\tilde{x})$. Since $\tilde{X}_0 \in \tilde{\mathscr{S}}$, there is a set $\tilde{Y}_0 \in \tilde{\mathscr{C}}$ such that $\tilde{\pi}^{-1}(\tilde{Y}_0) = \tilde{X}_0$. Set $\tilde{P}_{\tilde{y}} = \mu_0$ for all $\tilde{y} \in \tilde{Y} - \tilde{Y}_0$, μ_0 being some fixed probability measure on $\tilde{X}$. Note that $\tilde{Q}(\tilde{Y} - \tilde{Y}_0) = 0$.

We have thus succeeded in associating for each $\tilde{y} \in \tilde{Y}$ a measure $\tilde{P}_{\tilde{y}}$ on $\tilde{X}$. Since for $\tilde{y} \in \tilde{Y}_0$, $\int \tilde{g}\, d\tilde{P}_{\tilde{y}} = \Lambda(\tilde{g}, \tilde{x})$, where $\tilde{\pi}(\tilde{x}) = \tilde{y}$, it follows that for each $\tilde{g} \in C(\tilde{X})$, $\varphi_{\tilde{g}} : \tilde{y} \to \int \tilde{g}\, d\tilde{P}_{\tilde{y}}$ is $\tilde{\mathscr{C}}$-measurable in $\tilde{y}$ and $\varphi_{\tilde{g}}(\tilde{\pi}(\tilde{x}))$ is a version of $E(\tilde{g}|\tilde{\mathscr{S}})$. Since the bounded $\tilde{\mathscr{B}}$-measurable functions constitute the smallest class containing $C(\tilde{X})$ and closed under bounded sequential pointwise convergence, it follows that for each bounded measurable $\tilde{f}$ on $\tilde{X}$, $\tilde{y} \to \varphi_{\tilde{f}}(\tilde{y}) = \int \tilde{f}\, d\tilde{P}_{\tilde{y}}$ is measurable and $\varphi_{\tilde{f}}(\tilde{\pi}(\tilde{x}))$ is a version of $E(\tilde{f}|\tilde{\mathscr{S}})$. In particular, if $\tilde{A} \in \tilde{\mathscr{B}}$, the function $\tilde{y} \to \tilde{P}_{\tilde{y}}(\tilde{A})$ is $\tilde{\mathscr{C}}$-measurable and $\int_{\tilde{Y}} \tilde{P}_{\tilde{y}}(A)\, d\tilde{Q}(\tilde{y}) = \tilde{P}(\tilde{A})$. To complete the argument we claim that for any $\tilde{y} \in \tilde{Y}_0$, setting $\tilde{X}_{\tilde{y}} = \{\tilde{x}\colon \tilde{\pi}(\tilde{x}) = \tilde{y}\}$, $\tilde{P}_{\tilde{y}}(\tilde{X}_{\tilde{y}}) = 1$. In fact, for each n, there is a unique $l_n \leqslant k_n$ such that $\tilde{y} \in \tilde{B}_{nl_n}$. Clearly, $\{\tilde{y}\} = \bigcap_n \tilde{B}_{nl_n}$ and so $\tilde{X}_{\tilde{y}} = \bigcap_n \tilde{A}_{nl_n}$. If m is a fixed integer, then $\chi_{\tilde{A}_{ml_m}} \in C(\tilde{X})$ and, for some $\tilde{x} \in \tilde{X}_{\tilde{y}}$,

$$
\begin{aligned}
\tilde{P}_{\tilde{y}}(\tilde{A}_{ml_m}) &= \int \chi_{\tilde{A}_{ml_m}}\, d\tilde{P}_{\tilde{y}} \\
&= \lim_{k \to \infty} \Lambda_k(\chi_{\tilde{A}_{ml_m}}, \tilde{x}) \\
&= 1
\end{aligned}
$$

because $\tilde{x} \in \tilde{A}_{ml_m}$ for all m implies that $\Lambda_k(\chi_{\tilde{A}_{ml_m}}, \tilde{x}) = 1$, for $k \geqslant m$.

In other words, $\tilde{P}_{\tilde{y}}(\tilde{A}_{ml_m}) = 1$ for all m and so $\tilde{P}_{\tilde{y}}(\tilde{X}_{\tilde{y}}) = 1$.

We now resume our threads concerning X and Y. Since $(X, \mathscr{B})$ and $(Y, \mathscr{C})$ are standard, X and Y are Borel subsets of $\tilde{X}$ and $\tilde{Y}$, respectively. Further, $Y = \pi(X) = \tilde{\pi}(X)$.

Now $\tilde{P}(X) = 1 = \int \tilde{P}_{\tilde{y}}(X)\, d\tilde{Q}(\tilde{y})$, and hence $\tilde{P}_{\tilde{y}}(X) = 1$ a.e. $\tilde{Q}$ in $\tilde{Y}$. Hence we can find a Borel set $Y_1 \in \mathscr{C}$, $Y_1 \subseteq Y$ such that $\tilde{Q}(Y_1) = 1$ and $\tilde{P}_y(X) = 1$ for all $y \in Y_1$. $\tilde{P}_y$, for $y \in Y_1$, thus gives rise to a measure P_y on X such that for all $A \in \mathscr{B}$, $\tilde{P}_y(A) = P_y(A)$. Moreover, since

$\tilde{X}_y \cap X = X_y$ and $\tilde{P}_y(\tilde{X}_y) = \tilde{P}_y(X) = 1$ for all $y \in Y_1$, $P_y(X_y) = 1$. $y \to P_y$ is thus well defined over Y_1. Define $P_y = \mu_0$ for all $y \in Y - Y_1$, μ_0 being some measure on X. It is clear that $y \to P_y$ is a regular conditional probability distribution given π.

Finally, we come to uniqueness. Let $\mathscr{F} \subseteq \mathscr{B}$ be a denumerable Boolean algebra generating $\mathscr{B}$. If $y \to P_y$ and $y \to P_y'$ are two regular conditional probability distributions, for any fixed $A \in \mathscr{F}$, $P_y(A) = P_y'(A)$ for Q almost all y (since conditional probabilities are determined essentially uniquely), and hence $Q\{y: P_y(A) = P_y'(A) \text{ for all } A \in \mathscr{F}\} = 1$. If two measures are equal on $\mathscr{F}$, they are equal on $\mathscr{B}$ and so $Q\{y: P_y = P_y'\} = 1$. This completes the proof of the theorem.

VI

PROBABILITY MEASURES IN A HILBERT SPACE

1. INTRODUCTION

In Chapter IV, generalizations of classical limit theorems of probability theory were obtained in the case of locally compact groups. We shall now discuss the special case of an infinite-dimensional Hilbert space, and show that the classical limit theorems for infinitesimal summands hold good. In particular, the Lindeberg–Lévy criterion for central limit theorem is obtained.

We shall also prove the individual and mean ergodic theorems for random variables with values in a Banach space. Even though simple proofs can be given in the case of a Hilbert space, we adopt a more complicated procedure in order to establish them in a more general situation.

2. CHARACTERISTIC FUNCTIONS AND COMPACTNESS CRITERIA

Let X be a real separable Hilbert space and let (x, y), $x \in X$, $y \in X$ denote the inner product between x and y. Let $||x||$ denote the norm of x. With vector addition and the norm topology X becomes a complete separable metric abelian group. As before we shall denote by $\mathcal{M}(X)$ the space of all probability measures or distributions on X. Convergence in $\mathcal{M}(X)$ always implies weak convergence. We shall adopt the notations of Section 5, Chapter III.

Definition 2.1

For every $\mu \in \mathcal{M}(X)$, its *characteristic function* $\hat{\mu}(y)$, $y \in X$, is defined by the formula

$$\hat{\mu}(y) = \int e^{i(x, y)}\, d\mu(x).$$

The basic properties of characteristic function are given by the following theorem.

Theorem 2.1

(1) *$\hat{\mu}(y)$ is uniformly continuous in the norm topology.*
(2) *if $\hat{\mu}_1(y) = \hat{\mu}_2(y)$ for all $y \in X$, then $\mu_1 = \mu_2$.*
(3) *$(\mu * \lambda)\hat{}\,(y) = \hat{\mu}(y)\hat{\lambda}(y)$ for all $y \in X$ and $\mu, \lambda \in \mathcal{M}(X)$.*
(4) *$\hat{\bar{\mu}}(y) = \overline{\hat{\mu}(y)}$.*

Proof. We shall first prove (1). For $y_1, y_2 \in X$, we have

$$\begin{aligned} |\hat{\mu}(y_1) - \hat{\mu}(y_2)| &\leqslant \int |e^{i(x, y_1)} - e^{i(x, y_2)}|\, d\mu(x) \\ &= \int |1 - e^{i(x, y_1 - y_2)}|\, d\mu(x) \\ &= 4 \int \sin^2 \tfrac{1}{2}(x, y_1 - y_2)\, d\mu(x). \end{aligned}$$

Let $\varepsilon > 0$ be fixed but arbitrary. Then we can choose a positive constant K such that $\mu(x\colon \|x\| > K) < \varepsilon$. From the above inequality, we obtain

$$\begin{aligned} |\hat{\mu}(y_1) - \hat{\mu}(y_2)| &\leqslant 4\varepsilon + 4 \int_{\|x\| \leqslant K} \sin^2 \tfrac{1}{2}(x, y_1 - y_2)\, d\mu(x) \\ &\leqslant 4\varepsilon + K^2 \|y_1 - y_2\|^2. \end{aligned}$$

If $||y_1 - y_2|| < \sqrt{\varepsilon}/K$, we have

$$|\hat{\mu}(y_1) - \hat{\mu}(y_2)| \leqslant 5\varepsilon.$$

This shows that $\hat{\mu}(y)$ is uniformly continuous.

In order to prove (2) we choose some system of coordinates, i.e., a complete orthonormal sequence $\{e_i\}$ of vectors in X. We shall denote by x_i the ith coordinate of the vector x, $x_i = (x, e_i)$. Then the space X is isomorphic with the space l_2 of all real sequences $(x_1, x_2, \ldots)$ such that $\sum x_i^2 < \infty$. Let $\varphi_n^{(j)}(y_1, \ldots, y_n) = \hat{\mu}_j(y_1e_1 + \ldots + y_ne_n)$, $j = 1, 2$. If $\hat{\mu}_1(y) = \hat{\mu}_2(y)$ for all $y \in X$, then, in particular, $\hat{\mu}_1(y_1e_1 + \ldots + y_ne_n) = \hat{\mu}_2(y_1e_1 + \ldots + y_ne_n)$ for all real $y_1, y_2, \ldots, y_n$, and n. μ_1 and μ_2 induce measures $\tilde{\mu}_1$ and $\tilde{\mu}_2$ in l_2, through the canonical isomorphism corresponding to the basis $\{e_i\}$. Then the functions $\varphi_n^{(1)}(y_1, \ldots, y_n)$ and $\varphi_n^{(2)}(y_1, \ldots, y_n)$ are the characteristic functions of the finite dimensional distributions of $\tilde{\mu}_1$ and $\tilde{\mu}_2$, respectively, induced by the projection

$$(x_1, x_2, \ldots) \to (x_1, x_2, \ldots, x_n).$$

Thus by Theorem 5.1, Chapter V, $\tilde{\mu}_1 = \tilde{\mu}_2$. This implies $\mu_1 = \mu_2$.

Properties (3) and (4) are obvious from the bilinearity of the inner product.

Lemma 2.1

If a sequence $\{\mu_n\}$, $\mu_n \in \mathcal{M}(X)$, $n = 1, 2, \ldots$ is conditionally compact and $\hat{\mu}_n(y) \to \varphi(y)$ as $n \to \infty$ for each $y \in X$, then there exists a $\mu \in \mathcal{M}(X)$ such that $\hat{\mu}(y) = \varphi(y)$ and $\mu_n \Rightarrow \mu$.

PROOF. Suppose the sequence $\{\mu_n\}$ is not convergent. Then we can find two subsequences Z_1 and Z_2 converging to the limits μ^1 and μ^2, $\mu^1 \neq \mu^2$, respectively. The definition of weak convergence implies that, for every $y \in X$,

$$\lim_{n, \mu_n \in Z_i} \hat{\mu}_n(y) = \hat{\mu}^i(y), \qquad i = 1, 2.$$

By the conditions of the lemma,

$$\hat{\mu}^1(y) = \hat{\mu}^2(y) = \varphi(y).$$

By Theorem 2.1, $\mu^1 = \mu^2$ which is a contradiction. This proves the lemma.

We shall choose and fix a complete orthonormal basis $\{e_i\}$ in X. Let $x_i = (x, e_i)$ and $r_N{}^2(x) = \sum_{i=N}^{\infty} (x, e_i)^2$, for all $x \in X$.

A simple sufficient condition for compactness is contained in the following theorem.

Theorem 2.2

A set $\mathscr{K} \subseteq \mathscr{M}(X)$ *is conditionally compact if*

$$\lim_{N\to\infty} \sup_{\mu \in \mathscr{K}} \int r_N{}^2(x)\, d\mu(x) = 0.$$

PROOF. We shall denote by $\psi(N)$ the quantity under the limit sign in the condition of the theorem. We shall select a sequence $N_k \uparrow \infty$ of integers and a sequence $\Lambda_k \to \infty$ of positive numbers such that the sum $\sum_{k=1}^{\infty} \Lambda_k \psi(N_k)$ does not exceed ε. For the compact set (cf. Lemma 3.1, Chapter II)

$$K = \bigcap_{k=1}^{\infty} E_k, \qquad E_k = \{x : r_{N_k}^2(x) \leqslant \Lambda_k{}^{-1}\}$$

and for all $\mu \in \mathscr{K}$, we have, by Chebyshev's inequality,

$$\mu(K') \leqslant \sum_{k=1}^{\infty} \mu(E_k') \leqslant \sum_{k=1}^{\infty} \Lambda_k\, \psi(N_k) \leqslant \varepsilon.$$

An application of Theorem 6.7, Chapter II completes the proof.

Definition 2.2

Let $\mu \in \mathscr{M}(X)$ be such that $\int ||x||^2\, d\mu < \infty$. Then *the covariance operator* S *of* μ is the Hermitian operator determined uniquely by the quadratic form

$$(Sy, y) = \int (x, y)^2\, d\mu(x).$$

Definition 2.3

A positive semidefinite Hermitian operator A is called an *S-operator* if it has finite trace, i.e., for some orthonormal basis $\{e_i\}$, $\sum_1^{\infty} (Se_i, e_i) < \infty$. In such a case the same inequality holds for every orthonormal basis. Let $\mathscr{S}$ denote the family of all S-operators. The class of sets $\{[x: (Sx, x) < 1], S \in \mathscr{S}\}$ defines a system of neighborhoods at the origin for a certain topology, which is called the *S-topology*. A net $\{x_\alpha\}$ converges to 0 in S-topology if and only if $(Sx_\alpha, x_\alpha) \to 0$ for every $S \in \mathscr{S}$.

That the S-topology is well defined is a consequence of the fact that $\mathscr{S}$ is closed under addition and multiplication by positive scalars and the inclusion relation

$$\left\{x: \left(\frac{S_1 + S_2 + \ldots + S_n}{\min\limits_{1 \leqslant i \leqslant n} c_i} x, x\right) < 1\right\}$$

$$\subseteq \{x: (S_1 x, x) < c_1, \ldots, (S_n x, x) < c_n\}$$

for all positive $c_1, \ldots, c_n$ and S-operators $S_1, \ldots, S_n$.

Definition 2.4

A family $\{S_\alpha\}$ of S-operators is said to be *compact* if the following conditions are fulfilled:

(i) $\sup_\alpha \operatorname{trace}(S_\alpha) < \infty$;

(ii) $\lim_{N \to \infty} \sup_\alpha \sum_{i=N}^{\infty} (S_\alpha e_i, e_i) = 0$ for some complete orthonormal sequence $e_1, e_2, \ldots$.

When S is the covariance operator of a measure $\mu \in \mathscr{M}(X)$ for which

$$\int ||x||^2 \, d\mu < \infty,$$

we have

$$\sum_{j=N}^{\infty} (Se_j, e_j) = \int r_N^2(x) \, d\mu(x),$$

where r_N is defined as in Theorem 2.2. In particular S is an S-operator, since $\sum_{j=1}^{\infty} (Se_j, e_j) < \infty$.

Theorem 2.3

A set $\mathscr{K} \subseteq \mathscr{M}(X)$ is conditionally compact if and only if, for every $\varepsilon > 0$, the following two conditions are satisfied:

(i) *for every* $\mu \in \mathscr{K}$ *there exists an S-operator* $S_{\mu,\varepsilon}$ *such that*

$$1 - R\hat{\mu}(y) \leqslant (S_{\mu,\varepsilon}y, y) + \varepsilon, \qquad \mu \in \mathscr{K}, \qquad y \in X,$$

(ii) *the set of S-operators* $\{S_{\mu,\varepsilon}, \mu \in \mathscr{K}\}$ *is compact.*

PROOF. First we shall prove necessity. Here R denotes real part. Let $\mathscr{K}$ be conditionally compact. By Theorem 6.7, Chapter II, we can find a compact set $K \subseteq X$ such that

$$\sup_{\mu \in \mathscr{K}} \mu(K') < \varepsilon/2.$$

Let $\psi_\varepsilon(N) = \frac{1}{2} \sup_{x \in K} r_N^2(x)$, $M_\varepsilon = \psi_\varepsilon(1)$. Then we have

$$\begin{aligned} 1 - R\hat{\mu}(y) &= \int [1 - \cos(x, y)]\, d\mu \\ &\leqslant \int_K [1 - \cos(x, y)]\, d\mu + \varepsilon \\ &\leqslant \tfrac{1}{2} \int_K (x, y)^2\, d\mu(x) + \varepsilon. \end{aligned}$$

Let $S_{\mu,\varepsilon}$ be the operator defined by

$$(S_{\mu,\varepsilon}y, y) = \tfrac{1}{2} \int_K (x, y)^2\, d\mu(x).$$

Since K is compact, $\|x\|$ being a continuous function is bounded on K, and hence $S_{\mu,\varepsilon}$ is an S-operator. Further,

$$\sup_{\mu \in \mathscr{K}} \sum_{i=N}^{\infty} (S_{\mu,\varepsilon}e_i, e_i) \leqslant \psi_\varepsilon(N),$$

and since K is compact, $\lim_{N \to \infty} \psi_\varepsilon(N) = 0$. Since

$$\operatorname{trace}(S_{\mu,\varepsilon}) = \sum_{1}^{\infty} (S_{\mu,\varepsilon}e_i, e_i) \leqslant \psi_\varepsilon(1)$$

for all $\mu \in \mathscr{K}$, it follows that $\{S_{\mu,\varepsilon}, \mu \in \mathscr{K}\}$ is a compact set of S-operators. This completes the proof of necessity.

We shall divide the proof of sufficiency into two lemmas.

Lemma 2.2

In order that $\mathscr{K} \subseteq \mathscr{M}(X)$ be conditionally compact the following two conditions are sufficient:

(a) *for every N,*

$$\lim_{A\to\infty} \inf_{\mu\in\mathscr{K}} \mu\{x\colon \max_{1\leqslant i<N} |x_i| \leqslant A\} = 1$$

b)
$$\lim_{N\to\infty} \sup_{\mu\in\mathscr{K}} J_N(\mu) = 0,$$

where

$$J_N(\mu) = \int [1 - \exp(-\tfrac{1}{2}r_N^2(x))]\, d\mu,$$

$x_i = (x, e_i)$ *and* $\{e_i\}$ *is a fixed orthonormal sequence.*

PROOF. Let $\varepsilon > 0$, $\delta \leqslant 1$ be given. For $0 \leqslant \delta \leqslant 1$, $1 - e^{-\delta} \geqslant \delta/2$, we have

$$J_N(\mu) \geqslant \int_{\{x:\frac{1}{2}r_N^2(x)\geqslant\delta^2/4\}} [1 - \exp(-\tfrac{1}{2}r_N^2(x))]\, d\mu$$

$$\geqslant \tfrac{1}{2}\cdot\delta^2/4\cdot\mu\{x\colon \tfrac{1}{2}r_N^2(x) \geqslant \delta^2/4\}. \tag{2.1}$$

By condition (b) there exists an $N_0(\varepsilon, \delta)$ such that for $N > N_0(\varepsilon, \delta)$,

$$J_N(\mu) \leqslant \varepsilon\cdot\delta^2/16, \qquad \mu\in\mathscr{K}. \tag{2.2}$$

Inequalities (2.1) and (2.2) imply

$$\mu\{x\colon r_N^2(x) < \delta^2/2\} \geqslant 1 - \varepsilon/2 \tag{2.3}$$

for all $\mu\in\mathscr{K}$. By condition (a) we can choose A_0 such that

$$\inf_{\mu\in\mathscr{K}} \mu\{x\colon \max_{1\leqslant i<N_0} |x_i| \leqslant A_0\} \geqslant 1 - \varepsilon/2. \tag{2.4}$$

Let $x^1, x^2, \ldots, x^s \in X$ be so chosen that

$$x_i^j = 0, \qquad j = 1, 2, \ldots, s, \qquad i \geqslant N_0$$

and such that for all x with $\max_{1 \leqslant i < N_0} |x_i| \leqslant A_0$,

$$\min_{1 \leqslant j \leqslant s} \sum_{j=1}^{N_0 - 1} (x_i - x_i^j)^2 \leqslant \delta^2/2. \tag{2.5}$$

Inequalities (2.3)–(2.5) imply that

$$\mu \left\{ \bigcup_{j=1}^{s} S(x^j, \delta) \right\} \geqslant 1 - \varepsilon$$

for all $\mu \in \mathscr{K}$, where $S(x, \delta)$ denotes the sphere of radius δ around x. By the Remark after Theorem 6.7, Chapter II, this completes the proof of the lemma.

Lemma 2.3

In order that $\mathscr{K} \subseteq \mathscr{M}(X)$ be conditionally compact the following two conditions are sufficient:

(a) *for every N, the family of functions*

$$\psi(y_1, y_2, \ldots, y_N; \mu) = \hat{\mu}(y_1 e_1 + \ldots + y_N e_N), \qquad \mu \in \mathscr{K}$$

is equicontinuous at the origin,

(b) $$\lim_{N \to \infty} \sup_{\mu \in \mathscr{K}} \lim_{p \to \infty} J_{N,p}(1 - R\hat{\mu}(y_N e_N + \ldots + y_{N+p-1} e_{N+p-1}))$$
$$= 0,$$

where

$$J_{N,p}(\ldots) = (2\pi)^{-p/2} \underbrace{\int \ldots \int}_{p \text{ times}} (\ldots) \exp\left(-\tfrac{1}{2} r_{N,p}^2(y)\right) dy_N \ldots dy_{N+p-1}$$

and

$$r_{N,p}^2(y) = \sum_{i=N}^{N+p-1} y_i^2. \tag{2.6}$$

PROOF. By integrating each side with respect to μ and inverting the order of integration on the right side we deduce from the equation

$$1 - \exp\{-\tfrac{1}{2} r_{N,p}^2(x)\} = J_{N,p}\left(1 - \exp i \sum_{j=N}^{N+p-1} x_j y_j\right)$$

that the integral

$$\int [1 - \exp(-\tfrac{1}{2} r_{N,p}^2(x))]\, d\mu$$

is equal to the expression under the $\lim_{p\to\infty}$ sign in condition (b) of the lemma. Hence the limit, $\lim_p J_{N,p}$, equals $J_N(\mu)$. Therefore, the conditions (b) of Lemmas 2.2 and 2.3 coincide. From condition (a) of the lemma it follows that for each fixed N, the family of continuous functions $\{\psi(y_1, \ldots, y_N; \mu),\ \mu \in \mathscr{K}\}$ is compact in the topology of uniform convergence in compacta of the N-dimensional Euclidean space. Hence by the Lévy-Cramér continuity theorem (cf. Theorem 3.3, Chapter IV), the family of N-dimensional distributions $\{\mu\pi_N^{-1},\ \mu \in \mathscr{K}\}$, where π_N is the projection $x = (x_1e_1 + \ldots + x_ne_n + \ldots) \to (x_1e_1 + \ldots + x_Ne_N)$, is conditionally compact. This implies condition (a) of Lemma 2.2 by Theorem 6.7, Chapter II. This completes the proof of Lemma 2.3.

We shall now establish that the conditions of Lemma 2.3 follow from the conditions of Theorem 2.3, and thereby complete its proof. In fact,

$$\begin{aligned} J_{N,p}(1 - R\hat{\mu}(y)) &\leqslant J_{N,p}((S_{\mu,\varepsilon/2}y, y) + \varepsilon/2) \\ &\leqslant J_{N,p}((S_{\mu,\varepsilon/2}y, y)) + \varepsilon/2, \end{aligned} \tag{2.7}$$

where

$$y = y_Ne_N + \ldots + y_{N+p-1}e_{N+p-1}.$$

But

$$J_{N,p}((S_{\mu,\varepsilon/2}y, y)) = \sum_{i=N}^{N+p-1} (S_{\mu,\varepsilon/2}e_i, e_i),$$

and hence for sufficiently large N,

$$\sum_{i=N}^{N+p-1} (S_{\mu,\varepsilon/2}e_i, e_i) < \varepsilon/2, \qquad \mu \in \mathscr{K}$$

Thus

$$\lim_p \sup_{\mu\in\mathscr{K}} J_{N,p}(1 - R\hat{\mu}(y)) \leqslant \varepsilon.$$

The equicontinuity of the functions $\psi(y_1, \ldots, y_N; \mu)$ follows immediately from conditions (i) and (ii) of Theorem 2.3. This completes the proof.

From the proof of the necessity of the conditions (i) and (ii) of Theorem 2.3, we have the following corollary.

Corollary 2.1

In order that a sequence $\{\mu_n\}$, $\mu_n \in \mathcal{M}(X)$ be conditionally compact, it is necessary that

$$\lim_{N \to \infty} \sup_n \mu_n [r_N^2(x) > \varepsilon] = 0.$$

Using Lemma 2.3, it is possible to prove a generalization of Theorem 3.2, Chapter IV.

Theorem 2.4

In order that a function $\varphi(y)$, $y \in X$, be the characteristic function of a probability measure μ the following two conditions are necessary and sufficient:

(i) $\varphi(0) = 1$, *$\varphi(y)$ is positive definite in y;*
(ii) *$\varphi(y)$ is continuous in the S-topology.*

We shall first prove sufficiency. To this end we shall choose and fix an orthonormal basis of vectors $\{e_i\}$. Since the S-topology is weaker than the norm topology it follows that $\varphi(y)$ is continuous in the norm topology. Let

$$\psi_n(y_1, y_2, \ldots, y_n) = \varphi(y_1 e_1 + \ldots + y_n e_n).$$

Then $\psi_n(y_1, y_2, \ldots, y_n)$ is a continuous positive definite function in n-real variables. Hence by Theorem 3.2, Chapter IV, there exists a probability measure $\tilde{\mu}_n$ on the n-dimensional real vector space such that

$$\psi_n(y_1, y_2, \ldots, y_n) = \int \exp\,[i(x_1 y_1 + \ldots + x_n y_n)]\, d\tilde{\mu}_n(x_1, \ldots, x_n).$$

Let us now define a probability measure in X. Let X_n be the subspace spanned by the vectors $e_1, e_2, \ldots, e_n$. Then $\tilde{\mu}_n$ can be considered as a measure in X_n and this enables us to define a measure μ_n in X as follows:

$$\mu_n(A) = \tilde{\mu}_n(A \cap X_n).$$

Then we have

$$\hat{\mu}_n(y) = \int \exp\,[i(x, y)]\, d\mu_n = \int_{X_n} \exp\,[i(x_1 y_1 + \ldots + x_n y_n)]\, d\tilde{\mu}_n$$

$$= \varphi(y_1 e_1 + \ldots + y_n e_n).$$

Thus

$$\lim_{n \to \infty} \hat{\mu}_n(y) = \varphi(y), \qquad y \in X.$$

An application of Lemma 2.1 shows that the proof of sufficiency will be complete if the sequence of measures μ_n is compact. By Lemma 2.3 it is enough to prove that

$$J = \lim_{N \to \infty} \sup_{n \geqslant N} (2\pi)^{-(n-N+1)/2} \underbrace{\int \ldots \int}_{n-N+1 \text{ times}} [1 - R\varphi(y_N e_N + \ldots + y_n e_n)]$$

$$\times \exp\left(-\tfrac{1}{2} \sum_{i=N}^{n} y_i^2\right) dy_N \ldots dy_n = 0.$$

Let $\varepsilon > 0$ be arbitrary. By hypothesis there exists an S-operator S_ε such that

$$1 - R\varphi(y) < \varepsilon$$

for all y such that $(S_\varepsilon y, y) < 2$. Since $1 - R\varphi(y) \leqslant 2$ for all $y \in X$, it follows that

$$1 - R\varphi(y) < (S_\varepsilon y, y) + \varepsilon$$

for all y. Hence, from the definition of J, we have

$$J \leqslant \lim_{N \to \infty} \sup_{n \geqslant N} \left\{\varepsilon + \sum_{k=N}^{n} (S_\varepsilon e_k, e_k)\right\} = \varepsilon.$$

Letting $\varepsilon \to 0$, we get $J = 0$.

In order to prove necessity, we choose a compact set $K \subseteq X$ such that $\mu(K') < \varepsilon/2$. Then

$$1 - R\hat{\mu}(y) = \int [1 - \cos (x, y)]\, d\mu(x)$$

$$\leqslant \frac{1}{2} \int_K (x, y)^2\, d\mu(x) + \varepsilon/2.$$

Let A be the S-operator determined by the quadratic form

$$(Ay, y) = \int_K (x, y)^2\, d\mu(x).$$

If $(\varepsilon^{-1}Ay, y) < 1$, then $1 - R\hat{\mu}(y) < \varepsilon$. The continuity of $\hat{\mu}(y)$ in S-topology follows from the inequality

$$|1 - \hat{\mu}(y)|^2 \leqslant 2(1 - R\hat{\mu}(y)).$$

Since $\varphi(y) = \hat{\mu}(y)$, this completes the proof.

Lemma 2.3 is useful in constructing examples to show that positive definiteness and norm continuity of $\varphi(y)$ need not imply, that it is the characteristic function of a measure. In order to construct examples we need the following theorem.

Theorem 2.5

The necessary and sufficient conditions for a function $\varphi(y)$, $y \in X$ to be the characteristic function of a probability measure μ for which $\int ||x||^2\, d\mu < \infty$ are the following:

(1) *$\varphi(0) = 1$, $\varphi(y)$ is positive definite,*
(2) *$\varphi(y)$ is continuous in norm,*
(3) *$\sum_{n=1}^{\infty} \int_{-\infty}^{+\infty} x^2\, dF_n(x) < \infty$, where F_n is the measure on the real line with characteristic function $\varphi_n(t) = \varphi(te_n)$.*

PROOF. As in the proof of Theorem 2.4, we shall define measures μ_n in X by the equation

$$\hat{\mu}_n(y) = \varphi(y_1e_1 + \ldots + y_ne_n),$$

where $y = \sum_{i=1}^{\infty} y_ie_i$, and $\{e_i\}$ is a fixed orthonormal basis. It is clear that the equicontinuity of $\{\hat{\mu}_n\}$ in the norm topology follows from the norm-continuity of φ. In order to establish that the sequence μ_n is compact, it is enough to show that

$$J = \lim_{N \to \infty} \sup_{n \geqslant N} (2\pi)^{-(n-N+1)/2} \underbrace{\int \cdots \int}_{n-N+1 \text{ times}} [1 - R\varphi(y_N e_N + \ldots + y_n e_n)]$$

$$\times \exp\left(-\tfrac{1}{2} \sum_{i=N}^{n} y_i^2\right) dy_N \ldots dy_n = 0.$$

But

$$1 - R\varphi(y_N e_N + \ldots + y_n e_n)$$

$$= \int [1 - \cos(y_N x_N + \ldots + y_n x_n)]\, dF^{N \ldots n}(x_N \ldots x_n)$$

$$\leqslant \tfrac{1}{2} \int (y_N x_N + \ldots + y_n x_n)^2\, dF^{N \ldots n}(x_N \ldots x_N)$$

$$= \tfrac{1}{2} \sum_{k, l = N}^{n} y_k y_l a_{kl},$$

where $F^{N \ldots n}$ is the probability measure in $n - N + 1$ dimensional space with the characteristic function $\varphi(t_N e_N + \ldots + t_n e_n)$ and $a_{kl} = \int_{-\infty}^{+\infty} \int_{-\infty}^{+\infty} xy\, dF^{kl}(x, y)$. Thus

$$J \leqslant \lim_{N \to \infty} \sup_{n \geqslant N} (2\pi)^{-(n-N+1)/2} \underbrace{\int \cdots \int}_{n-N+1 \text{ times}} \left(\tfrac{1}{2} \sum_{k, l = N}^{n} y_k y_l a_{kl}\right)$$

$$\times \exp\left(-\tfrac{1}{2} \sum_{i=N}^{n} y_i^2\right) dy_N \ldots dy_n$$

$$= \lim_{N \to \infty} \sup_{n \geqslant N} \left(\tfrac{1}{2} \sum_{l=N}^{n} a_{ll}\right) = 0,$$

since $\sum_{l=1}^{\infty} a_{ll} < \infty$ by condition (3) of the theorem. By Lemma 2.1, $\varphi(y)$ is the characteristic function of a probability measure μ in X. Further, $a_{ll} = \int x_l^2(x)\, d\mu(x)$. By Fatou's lemma, $\int ||x||^2\, d\mu < \infty$.

In order to prove necessity we have only to observe that

$$\infty > \int ||x||^2\, d\mu = \int \left(\lim_{n \to \infty} \sum_{1}^{n} x_k^2(x)\right) d\mu$$

$$= \lim_{n\to\infty} \sum_1^n \int x_k^2(x)\, d\mu$$

$$= \sum_1^\infty \int x_k^2(x)\, d\mu$$

conditions (1) and (2) follow from Theorem 3.2, Chapter III and Theorem 2.1.

EXAMPLE. Let S be a positive semidefinite Hermitian operator. Then the function $\varphi(y) = \exp\,[-\frac{1}{2}(Sy, y)]$ is the characteristic function of a probability measure on X if and only if S is an S-operator. If P is the measure corresponding to φ, then $\int ||x||^2\, dP < \infty$. Further, S is the covariance operator of P.

PROOF. Suppose S is an S-operator. Then $\varphi(0) = 1$, $\varphi(y)$ is positive definite in y and continuous in the S-topology. Hence by Theorem 2.4 there exists a measure $P \in \mathscr{M}(X)$ such that

$$\int e^{i(x,y)}\, dP(x) = \varphi(y).$$

Let F_n be the measure on the real line with characteristic function $\hat{F}_n(t) = \varphi(te_n)$, where $\{e_n\}$ is a fixed orthonormal basis. Then

$$\int_{-\infty}^{+\infty} x^2\, dF_n(x) = (Se_n, e_n).$$

Since S is an S-operator, $\sum_n (Se_n, e_n) < \infty$. Hence by Theorem 2.5, $\int ||x||^2\, dP < \infty$. That S is the covariance operator follows from

$$\int e^{i(x,ty)}\, dP = \exp\,[-\tfrac{1}{2}(Sy, y)]t^2.$$

To prove the converse, suppose that there exists a measure P such that

$$\int e^{i(x,y)}\, dP(x) = \exp\,[-\tfrac{1}{2}(Sy, y)].$$

Then by Theorem 2.4, (Sy, y) is continuous in the S-topology. Hence for any $\varepsilon > 0$, there exists an S-operator S_ε such that $(S_\varepsilon y, y) < 1$

implies that $(Sy, y) < \varepsilon$. Let now $y_0 \in X$ and $(S_\varepsilon y_0, y_0) = c^2$, $c > 0$.* Let $d > c$ be arbitrary. Then $(S_\varepsilon y_0/d, y_0/d) = c^2/d^2 < 1$. Hence, $(Sy_0/d, y_0/d)) < \varepsilon$, i.e., $(Sy_0, y_0) < \varepsilon d^2$. Letting $d \to c$, we have $(Sy_0, y_0) \leqslant \varepsilon(S_\varepsilon y_0, y_0)$. Since y_0 is arbitrary, we obtain

$$(Sy, y) \leqslant (\varepsilon S_\varepsilon y, y) \qquad \text{for all} \quad y \in X.$$

In particular for the orthonormal basis $\{e_n\}$,

$$\sum_n (Se_n, e_n) \leqslant \varepsilon \sum_n (S_\varepsilon e_n, e_n) < \infty.$$

Hence S is an S-operator. This completes the proof.

3. AN ESTIMATE OF THE VARIANCE

In order to carry out the proofs of limit theorems in a Hilbert space it is necessary to get some generalization of the celebrated Kolmogorov's inequality (cf. [12]). We shall do this in terms of concentration functions introduced by Lévy [24].

Definition 3.1

For any $\mu \in \mathscr{M}(X)$, the *concentration function* $Q_\mu(t)$ is defined for $0 < t < \infty$, as

$$Q_\mu(t) = \sup_{x \in X} \mu(S_t + x),$$

where S_t denotes the sphere $[x: ||x|| \leqslant t]$ and $S_t + x$ its translate by the element x.

Theorem 3.1

(1) $Q_\mu(t)$ *is a nondecreasing function of* t *and* $\lim_{t\to\infty} Q_\mu(t) = 1$.
(2) *If* $\mu_1 * \mu_2 = \mu$, *then for every* t, $Q_\mu(t) \leqslant \min\,[Q_{\mu_1}(t), Q_{\mu_2}(t)]$.
(3) *If* μ_n *is shift compact then* $\lim_{t\to\infty} \inf_n Q_{\mu_n}(t) = 1$.

---

* By adding a suitable S-operator to S_ε if necessary, we may assume that the quadratic form $(S_\varepsilon y, y)$ is nonvanishing, except at the origin.

PROOF. Condition (1) follows immediately from the fact that $\lim_{t\to\infty} \mu(S_t) = 1$; (2) follows from the equation

$$\mu(S_t + x_0) = \int \mu_1(S_t + x_0 - x)\, d\mu_2(x)$$
$$= \int \mu_2(S_t + x_0 - x)\, d\mu_1(x), \qquad x_0 \in X;$$

Condition (3) follows from the definition of shift compactness (cf. Section 2, Chapter III) and Theorem 6.7, Chapter II.

Let $X_1, X_2, \ldots, X_n$, be n-independent symmetric random variables in the Hilbert space X, i.e., if μ_i is the distribution of X_i, then $\mu_i = \bar{\mu}_i$, $i = 1, 2, \ldots, n$. We shall now get an estimate for the "variance" $E\|X_1 + \ldots + X_n\|^2$. This estimate is a generalization of the result of Lévy ([24], p. 138).

Theorem 3.2

Let $X_1, X_2, \ldots, X_n$ be n-mutually independent symmetric random variables in X and let $S_j = X_1 + \ldots + X_j$, $j = 1, 2, \ldots, n$. Further, let $Q(t)$ denote the concentration function of the distribution μ of the sum $S_n = X_1 + \ldots + X_n$. If T is defined as

$$T = \sup_{1 \leqslant j \leqslant n} \|S_j\|,$$

then, for all $t > 0$,

$$P\{T > 4t\} \leqslant 2[1 - Q(t)],$$

where P denotes probability.

PROOF. Let the events E_k be defined as follows:

$$E_k = [\|S_1\| \leqslant 4t, \ldots, \|S_{k-1}\| \leqslant 4t, \|S_k\| > 4t].$$

Then

$$\{T > 4t\} = \bigcup_{i=1}^{n} E_i, \qquad E_i \cap E_j = \phi, \qquad i \neq j.$$

By $P_r\{\ \}$ we shall denote the probability of the event within the brackets under the condition that E_r has occurred. We then have

$$P_r\{||S_n|| \leqslant 2t\} \leqslant P_r\{||S_n - S_r|| > 2t\} = P\{||S_n - S_r|| > 2t\}. \quad (3.1)$$

This is because E_r and $||S_n|| \leqslant 2t$ imply that $||S_n - S_r|| > 2t$ and $S_n - S_r$ is distributed independently of E_r. Let us suppose that $Q(t) > \frac{1}{2}$. Let μ_{rn} be the distribution of $S_n - S_r$. We shall denote the concentration function of μ_{rn} by $Q_{rn}(t)$. Since μ_{rn} is a factor of μ, we have by Theorem 3.1, $Q_{rn}(t) > \frac{1}{2}$. Hence for any sufficiently small $\varepsilon > 0$, there exists a point $x \in X$ such that

$$\mu_{rn}(S_t + x) > Q_{rn}(t) - \varepsilon > \tfrac{1}{2}. \quad (3.2)$$

Since μ_{rn} is a symmetric measure,

$$\mu_{rn}(S_t - x) = \mu_{rn}(-S_t + x) = \mu_{rn}(S_t + x) > \tfrac{1}{2}.$$

Since μ_{rn} is a probability measure,

$$(S_t - x) \cap (S_t + x) \neq \phi.$$

In other words, there exists a point $y \in S_t$ such that

$$||x + y|| \leqslant t, \; ||x - y|| \leqslant t.$$

Since $||x + y||^2 + ||x - y||^2 = 2(||x||^2 + ||y||^2)$, it follows that $||x|| \leqslant t$, and hence

$$S_t + x \subseteq S_{2t}.$$

Now (3.2) implies

$$\mu_{rn}(S_{2t}) \geqslant \mu_{rn}(S_t + x) > Q_{rn}(t) - \varepsilon.$$

Letting $\varepsilon \to 0$, we get

$$\mu_{rn}(S_{2t}) \geqslant Q_{rn}(t),$$

which implies

$$\begin{aligned} P\{||S_n - S_r|| > 2t\} &\leqslant 1 - Q_{rn}(t) \\ &\leqslant 1 - Q(t). \end{aligned} \quad (3.3)$$

This together with (3.1) gives

$$\begin{aligned} P\{T > 4t, ||S_n|| \leqslant 2t\} &= \sum_{r=1}^{n} P_r\{||S_n|| \leqslant 2t\} P(E_r) \\ &\leqslant \sum_{r=1}^{n} P(E_r)\,(1 - Q(t)) = P\{T > 4t\}(1 - Q(t)). \end{aligned} \quad (3.4)$$

Further,

$$P\{T \leqslant 4t, ||S_n|| \leqslant 2t\} \leqslant P\{T \leqslant 4t\} = 1 - P\{T > 4t\}. \tag{3.5}$$

Adding (3.4) and (3.5), we get

$$P\{||S_n|| \leqslant 2t\} \leqslant 1 - Q(t) P\{T > 4t\}.$$

Putting $r = 0$ in (3.3), we get

$$P\{||S_n|| \leqslant 2t\} \geqslant Q(t).$$

The above two inequalities imply

$$P\{T > 4t\} \leqslant \frac{1 - Q(t)}{Q(t)} \leqslant 2[1 - Q(t)],$$

since $Q(t) > \frac{1}{2}$. If $Q(t) \leqslant \frac{1}{2}$, the theorem is trivially true. This completes the proof.

In order to formulate the next theorem, we need the notion of expectation. Let F be a totally finite measure on X such that $\int ||x|| \, dF < \infty$. Then $\int (x, y) \, dF$ is well defined for each $y \in Y$ and

$$\left| \int (x, y) \, dF \right| \leqslant ||y|| \int ||x|| \, dF.$$

Thus $\int (x, y) \, dF$ is a linear functional with norm $\leqslant \int ||x|| \, dF$. Hence there exists an element x_0 such that

$$(x_0, y) = \int (x, y) \, dF \qquad \text{for all} \quad y \in X.$$

Definition 3.2

The element x_0 above is called the *mean* or *expectation* of the measure F, and symbolically

$$x_0 = Ex = \int x \, dF.$$

Theorem 3.3

Let $X_1, X_2, \ldots, X_n$ be n-independent random variables in X, uniformly bounded by a constant c in norm. Let each X_i have zero expectation for $i = 1, 2, \ldots, n$. In addition, let

$$P\{\sup_{1 \leqslant j \leqslant n} ||S_j|| \leqslant d\} \geqslant \varepsilon > 0,$$

where ε is a positive number and $S_j = X_1 + \ldots + X_j$. Then

$$E\|S_n\|^2 \leqslant \frac{d^2 + (c+d)^2}{\varepsilon}.$$

PROOF. Let the events E_k be defined as follows:

$$E_k = \{ \sup_{1 \leqslant j \leqslant k} \|S_j\| \leqslant d \}.$$

Then $E_1 \supseteq E_2 \supseteq \ldots \supseteq E_n$ and $P(E_n) \geqslant \varepsilon > 0$, where P denotes probability. Let

$$F_k = E_{k-1} - E_k, \qquad \alpha_k = \int_{E_k} \|S_k\|^2 \, dP.$$

We shall take E_0 to be X and $\alpha_0 = 0$. Then

$$\begin{aligned}
\alpha_k - \alpha_{k-1} &= \int_{E_k} \|S_k\|^2 \, dP - \int_{E_{k-1}} \|S_{k-1}\|^2 \, dP \\
&= \int_{E_{k-1}} \|S_k\|^2 \, dP - \int_{F_k} \|S_k\|^2 \, dP - \int_{E_{k-1}} \|S_{k-1}\|^2 \, dP \\
&= \int_{E_{k-1}} \|S_{k-1}\|^2 \, dP - 2 \int_{E_{k-1}} (S_{k-1}, X_k) \, dP + \int_{E_{k-1}} \|X_k\|^2 \, dP \\
&\quad - \int_{F_k} \|S_k\|^2 \, dP - \int_{E_{k-1}} \|S_{k-1}\|^2 \, dP.
\end{aligned}$$

Since X_k is independent of the random variable S_{k-1}, and the event E_{k-1}, the second term on the right-hand side of the above equation vanishes. Since $F_k \subseteq E_{k-1}$, $\|S_k\| \leqslant \|S_{k-1}\| + \|X_k\| \leqslant c + d$ over F_k, the fourth term is $\geqslant -(c+d)^2 P(F_k)$. Since X_k and E_{k-1} are independent, the third term is equal to $P(E_{k-1}) E\|X_k\|^2$. Thus

$$\alpha_k - \alpha_{k-1} \geqslant P(E_{k-1}) E\|X_k\|^2 - (c+d)^2 P(F_k).$$

Since $P(E_k) \geqslant P(E_n)$ for all k, and $F_1, F_2, \ldots, F_n$ are disjoint, we get, by adding both sides of the above inequality for $k = 1, 2, \ldots, n$,

$$\alpha_n \geqslant P(E_n) E\|S_n\|^2 - (c+d)^2.$$

Since $||S_n|| \leqslant d$ on E_n,

$$\alpha_n = \int_{E_n} ||S_n||^2 \, dP \leqslant d^2.$$

The above two inequalities together imply

$$E||S_n||^2 \leqslant \frac{d^2 + (c+d)^2}{P(E_n)} \leqslant \frac{d^2 + (c+d)^2}{\varepsilon}.$$

This completes the proof.

Theorem 3.4

Let $X_1, X_2, \ldots, X_n$ be symmetric independent random variables in X such that $||X_i|| \leqslant c$ for $i = 1, 2, \ldots, n$. Let $Q(t)$ denote the concentration function of $S_n = X_1 + \ldots + X_n$. Then

$$E||S_n||^2 \leqslant \frac{16t^2 + (c+4t)^2}{2Q(t) - 1}$$

for any t such that $Q(t) > \frac{1}{2}$.

PROOF. This follows immediately from Theorems 3.2 and 3.3 and the fact that a bounded symmetric random variable has zero expectation.

4. INFINITELY DIVISIBLE DISTRIBUTIONS

In this section we will obtain a representation for the characteristic function of an infinitely divisible distribution. The definition of an infinitely divisible distribution is the same as Definition 4.1, Chapter IV, but since the Hilbert space is a divisible group, it is equivalent to the classical definition which requires that μ be expressible as λ_n^n for each n.

We shall first note that a Hilbert space has no nontrivial compact subgroups, and hence there are no nontrivial idempotent distributions (cf. Theorem 3.1, Chapter III).

Theorem 4.1

The infinitely divisible distributions constitute a closed subsemigroup in $\mathcal{M}(X)$.

Theorem 4.2

If μ is an infinitely divisible distribution then its characteristic function $\hat{\mu}(y)$ is nonvanishing at all $y \in X$.

For every finite measure F the infinitely divisible distribution $e(F)$ is defined as in Definition 4.2, Chapter IV. We then have the following theorem.

Theorem 4.3

Let $\mu_n = e(F_n)$. In order that μ_n may be shift compact it is necessary that

(i) *for every neighborhood N of the identity F_n restricted to N' is weakly conditionally compact,*

(ii) $\sup_n \int [1 - \cos (x, y)]\, dF_n < \infty$, *for each $y \in X$.*

Theorem 4.4

Let $\mu_n \in \mathcal{M}(X)$, $\mu \in \mathcal{M}(X)$ and $\mu_n \Rightarrow \mu$ as $n \to \infty$. Then $\hat{\mu}_n(y) \to \hat{\mu}(y)$ uniformly over every bounded sphere.

The proofs of Theorems 4.1–4.4 are exactly similar to the proofs of Theorems 4.1–4.3 and 3.3, respectively, of Chapter IV. In the proof of Theorem 4.2 it is even simpler since there are no idempotent distributions. In the proof of Theorem 4.4 we have to appeal to the first paragraph of the proof of Theorem 3.3, Chapter IV.

Theorem 4.5

Let $\mu_n \in \mathcal{M}(X)$ be shift compact and $\hat{\mu}_n(y) \to \hat{\mu}(y)$ uniformly over bounded spheres. Then $\mu_n \Rightarrow \mu$.

PROOF. Since μ_n is shift compact we can choose x_n in X such that $\mu_n * x_n$ is compact. We shall now prove that the sequence x_n is conditionally compact. If this were not so we could choose a subsequence, which we shall denote by x_n again, having no further convergent subsequences. Since $\mu_n * x_n$ is conditionally compact, it has a subsequence $\mu_{n_j} * x_{n_j}$ converging weakly. Thus $\hat{\mu}_{n_j}(y) \exp [i(x_{n_j}, y)]$, as well as $\hat{\mu}_{n_j}(y)$ converge uniformly over bounded spheres. Since from the compactness of $|\mu_n|^2$ one can conclude the existence of a sphere S such that $\inf_n |\hat{\mu}_n(y)|^2 \geqslant \varepsilon > 0$ for all y in S, it follows that $[\exp i(x_{n_j}, y)]$ converges uniformly over S, and hence x_{n_j} converges in norm. This proves the theorem.

We shall now obtain a variation of Theorem 4.3 which will enable us to get the representation for infinitely divisible distributions. We need two lemmas.

Lemma 4.1

Let $f(y)$ be a nonnegative function on X such that $f(2y) \leqslant 4f(y)$ for all $y \in X$. If $f(y) \leqslant \varepsilon$ whenever $(Sy, y) \leqslant \delta$ where ε and δ are positive constants and S is an S-operator then

$$f(y) \leqslant (S_1 y, y) + \varepsilon$$

for all $y \in X$, where $S_1 = 4\varepsilon\delta^{-1}S$.

PROOF. Let $S_0 = \varepsilon\delta^{-1}S$. Then $f(y) \leqslant \varepsilon$ whenever $(S_0 y, y) \leqslant \varepsilon$. Suppose now $(S_0 y, y) \leqslant 4^n\varepsilon$, where n is a positive integer. If $y_n = 2^{-n}y$, we have

$$(S_0 y_n, y_n) = 4^{-n}(S_0 y, y) \leqslant \varepsilon.$$

Since $f(2y) \leqslant 4f(y)$,

$$f(y) \leqslant f(2^n y_n) \leqslant 4^n f(y_n) \leqslant 4^n \varepsilon.$$

Thus

$$f(y) \leqslant 4^n\varepsilon \qquad \text{if} \quad (S_0 y, y) \leqslant 4^n\varepsilon \tag{4.1}$$

for all nonnegative integral n.

Let now $y \in X$ and $(S_0 y, y) = t$. Let $t > \varepsilon$. Then there exists a nonnegative integer n such that

$$4^n\varepsilon < t \leqslant 4^{n+1}\varepsilon.$$

Since $(S_0 y, y) \leqslant 4^{n+1}\varepsilon$, we have by (4.1)

$$f(y) \leqslant 4^{n+1}\varepsilon \leqslant 4t = 4(S_0 y, y). \tag{4.2}$$

If $t < \varepsilon$, we have from the definition of S_0,

$$f(y) \leqslant \varepsilon. \tag{4.3}$$

Equations (4.2) and (4.3) give

$$\begin{aligned} f(y) &\leqslant \max\,[\varepsilon, (4S_0y, y)] \\ &\leqslant (S_1y, y) + \varepsilon. \end{aligned}$$

Lemma 4.2

If $a_1, a_2, \ldots, a_m$ are any real numbers such that $|a_j| \leqslant 1$ for $1 \leqslant j \leqslant m$, then

$$1 - a_1a_2 \ldots a_m \leqslant \sum_{j=1}^{m} (1 - a_j).$$

PROOF. Suppose all the $a_1, a_2, \ldots$ are positive. If $n = 1$ then the inequality is trivial. Suppose the inequality has been proved for $m = k$. Then

$$\begin{aligned} 1 - a_1a_2 \ldots a_ka_{k+1} &= (1 - a_1a_2 \ldots a_k) + (a_1a_2 \ldots a_k)(1 - a_{k+1}) \\ &\leqslant \sum_{i=1}^{k} (1 - a_i) + (1 - a_{k+1}) \\ &= \sum_{i=1}^{k+1} (1 - a_i). \end{aligned}$$

Thus the inequality follows by induction.

Suppose now at least one a_j is negative. Let it be a_r. Then

$$\begin{aligned} 1 - a_1a_2 \ldots a_m \leqslant 1 + |a_1a_2 \ldots a_m| &\leqslant 1 + |a_r| \\ &= 1 - a_r \leqslant \sum_{i=1}^{m} (1 - a_i). \end{aligned}$$

Theorem 4.6

Let F_n be a sequence of finite measures such that $e(F_n)$ is shift compact. Then

$$\sup_n \int_{||x|| \leqslant 1} ||x||^2 \, dF_n < \infty.$$

PROOF. Without loss of generality we may and do assume that each F_n vanishes outside the unit sphere. Otherwise by Theorem 5.1, Chapter

III, we can consider the restriction of F_n to the unit sphere instead of F_n. Let $M_n = F_n + \bar{F}_n$. Then $e(M_n) = |e(F_n)|^2 = \lambda_n$ is compact. We shall now show that $\int ||x||^2 \, dM_n$ is uniformly bounded. To this end we assume that the total mass of M_n is an integer for every n. If this were not so we could write $M_n = M_n^{(1)} + M_n^{(2)}$ where $M_n^{(1)}$ is symmetric with an integral total mass and $M_n^{(2)}$ has total mass less than unity. Consequently,

$$\int_{||x|| \leqslant 1} ||x||^2 \, dM_n^{(2)} \leqslant 1.$$

Since our aim is to prove that

$$\sup_n \int_{||x|| \leqslant 1} ||x||^2 \, dM_n < \infty,$$

it suffices to show that

$$\sup_n \int_{||x|| \leqslant 1} ||x||^2 \, dM_n^{(1)} < \infty.$$

Now since the total mass of M_n is an integer k_n we can write

$$M_n = k_n F_n,$$

where F_n is a symmetric probability measure and has zero expectation. Let μ_n denote the convolution of F_n taken k_n times. Then

$$\mu_n = F_n^{k_n}.$$

We then have

$$\int ||x||^2 \, d\mu_n = k_n \int ||x||^2 \, dF_n = \int ||x||^2 \, dM_n.$$

Hence it suffices to show that

$$\sup_n \int ||x||^2 \, d\mu_n < \infty.$$

If $Q_n(t)$ denotes the concentration function of μ_n, we have from Theorem **3.4**,

$$\int \|x\|^2 \, d\mu_n \leqslant \frac{16t^2 + (4t+1)^2}{2Q_n(t) - 1},$$

whenever $Q_n(t) > \frac{1}{2}$. Therefore, it is enough to prove the existence of a t_0 such that

$$\inf_n Q_n(t_0) \geqslant \tfrac{3}{4}.$$

By Theorem **3.1**, the above inequality will follow if we show that μ_n is conditionally compact.

Since $\hat{F}_n(y)$ is a real characteristic function and

$$\hat{\mu}_n(y) = [\hat{F}_n(y)]^{k_n}$$

it follows from Lemma **4.2** that

$$\begin{aligned} 1 - \hat{\mu}_n(y) &\leqslant k_n(1 - \hat{F}_n(y)) \\ &= \int [1 - \cos(x, y)] \, dM_n. \end{aligned} \tag{4.4}$$

Let now

$$f_n(y) = \int [1 - \cos(x, y)] \, dM_n.$$

Then, putting $\lambda_n = e(M_n)$, we have

$$\hat{\lambda}_n(y) = e(M_n)\hat{\ } (y) = \exp[-f_n(y)].$$

Hence for any $\varepsilon > 0$, there exists a δ depending only on ε such that

$$f_n(y) \leqslant \varepsilon \quad \text{if} \quad 1 - \hat{\lambda}_n(y) \leqslant \delta. \tag{4.5}$$

Since λ_n is conditionally compact, it follows from Theorem **2.3** that for any $\delta > 0$ there exists a compact sequence $\{S_n\}$ of S-operators depending only on δ such that

$$1 - \hat{\lambda}_n(y) \leqslant (S_n y, y) + \delta/2.$$

This together with (4.5) implies that

$$f_n(y) \leqslant \varepsilon \qquad \text{whenever} \quad (S_n y, y) \leqslant \delta/2.$$

Since $(1 - \cos 2\alpha) \leqslant 4(1 - \cos \alpha)$, we have $f_n(2y) \leqslant 4f_n(y)$. Hence by Lemma 4.1,

$$f_n(y) \leqslant (S_n' y, y) + \varepsilon,$$

where $S_n' = 8\varepsilon\delta^{-1}S_n$. Since $\{S_n\}$ is compact so is $\{S_n'\}$. Hence (4.4) and Theorem 2.3 imply that μ_n is conditionally compact. This completes the proof of the theorem.

Let $K(x, y)$ denote the function

$$K(x, y) = e^{i(x, y)} - 1 - i(x, y)/(1 + ||x||^2). \tag{4.6}$$

Theorem 4.7

Let $\mu_n = e(F_n)$ where F_n is an increasing sequence of measures for every n. Let $\mu_n * x_n \Rightarrow \mu$ for some suitably chosen elements x_n in X. Then F_n increases to a measure F which may be σ-finite but has finite mass outside every neighborhood of the origin and for which

$$\int_{||x|| \leqslant 1} ||x||^2 \, dF < \infty.$$

Further,

$$\hat{\mu}(y) = \exp\left[i(x_0, y) + \int K(x, y)\, dF(x)\right],$$

where x_0 is a fixed element of X.

PROOF. Let λ_n be the shift of μ_n by the element

$$z_n = -\int \frac{x}{1 + ||x||^2} dF_n$$

(cf. Definition 3.2). Then

$$\hat{\lambda}_n(y) = \exp\left\{\int K(x, y)\, dF_n(x)\right\}.$$

We shall now prove that $\hat{\lambda}_n(y)$ converges uniformly over bounded spheres. We have

$$\int K(x, y)\, dF_n = \int_{||x|| \leqslant 1} K(x, y)\, dF_n + \int_{||x|| > 1} K(x, y)\, dF_n. \tag{4.7}$$

Let F be the limit of F_n. By Theorems 4.3 and 4.6, it follows that F is finite outside every neighborhood of the origin and

$$\int_{||x|| \leqslant 1} ||x||^2\, dF < \infty.$$

Since

$$|K(x, y)| \leqslant 2 + (||x||\, ||y||/1 + ||x||^2) \leqslant 2 + ||y||,$$

it follows that

$$\lim_{n \to \infty} \sup_{y \in S} \left| \int_{||x|| > 1} K(x, y)\, dF_n - \int_{||x|| > 1} K(x, y)\, dF \right| = 0 \tag{4.8}$$

for every bounded sphere S. On the other hand, if $||x|| \leqslant 1$,

$$\begin{aligned} |K(x, y)| &\leqslant |e^{i(x, y)} - 1 - i(x, y)| + (|(x, y)|\, ||x||^2/1 + ||x||^2) \\ &\leqslant c(x, y)^2 + |(x, y)|\, ||x||^2 \\ &\leqslant c\, ||x||^2\, ||y||^2 + ||y||\, ||x||^2, \end{aligned}$$

where c is an absolute constant. Since $\int_{||x|| \leqslant 1} ||x||^2\, dF$ is finite, it follows that

$$\lim_{n \to \infty} \sup_{y \in S} \left| \int_{||x|| \leqslant 1} K(x, y)\, dF_n - \int_{||x|| \leqslant 1} K(x, y)\, dF \right| = 0. \tag{4.9}$$

Equations (4.7)–(4.9) imply

$$\lim_{n \to \infty} \sup_{y \in S} |\hat{\lambda}_n(y) - \hat{\lambda}(y)| = 0,$$

where

$$\hat{\lambda}(y) = \exp\left[\int K(x, y)\, dF\right].$$

Since λ_n is shift compact it follows from Theorem 4.5 that $\lambda_n \Rightarrow \lambda$ and is a shift of λ. This completes the proof.

Theorem 4.8

Let $\varphi(y)$ be a function of the form

$$\varphi(y) = \exp\left[\int K(x, y)\, dF(x)\right],$$

where F is a σ-finite measure which has finite mass outside every neighborhood of the origin and for which

$$\int_{||x|| \leqslant 1} ||x||^2 \, dF < \infty.$$

Then $\varphi(y)$ is the characteristic function of an infinitely divisible distribution μ.

PROOF. Let N_n denote the sphere of radius $1/n$ around the origin and F_n the restriction of F to N_n'. Then F_n increases to F. Let

$$\hat{\mu}_n(y) = \exp\left[\int K(x, y)\, dF_n\right].$$

From the proof of Theorem 4.7, it follows that

$$\lim_{n \to \infty} \sup_{y \in S} |\hat{\mu}_n(y) - \varphi(y)| = 0$$

for every bounded sphere S. In view of Theorems 4.1 and 4.5, it is enough to show that μ_n is shift compact or that $\lambda_n = |\mu_n|^2$ is compact. Let $M_n = F_n + \bar{F}_n$. Then

$$\lambda_n = |\mu_n|^2 = |e(F_n)|^2 = e(M_n).$$

Since F_n increases to F, it follows that M_n increases to $M = F + \bar{F}$. Without loss of generality we may assume that F, and hence M vanishes outside the sphere $||x|| \leqslant 1$. Then

$$1 - \hat{\lambda}_n(y) = 1 - \exp\left[\int [\cos (x, y) - 1]\, dM_n\right]$$

$$= 1 - \exp\left[-\int (1 - \cos (x, y))\, dM_n\right]$$

$$\leqslant \int [1 - \cos (x, y)] \, dM_n$$

$$\leqslant \int (1 - \cos (x, y)) \, dM$$

$$\leqslant \tfrac{1}{2} \int_{||x|| \leqslant 1} (x, y)^2 \, dM$$

$$= \tfrac{1}{2} (S_0 y, y).$$

Since

$$\int_{||x|| \leqslant 1} ||x||^2 \, dM = 2 \int_{||x|| \leqslant 1} ||x||^2 \, dF < \infty$$

it follows that S_0 is an S-operator. Since S_0 is a fixed S-operator independent of n, it follows from Theorem 2.3 that λ_n is conditionally compact. The theorem is proved.

Gaussian distributions in a Hilbert space are defined exactly as in Definition 6.1, Chapter IV.

Theorem 4.9

A distribution μ on X is Gaussian if and only if $\hat{\mu}(y)$ is of the form

$$\hat{\mu}(y) = \exp \{i(x_0, y) - \tfrac{1}{2}(Sy, y)\}$$

where x_0 is a fixed element and S is an S-operator.

PROOF. Let $\{y_1, y_2, \ldots\}$ be a countable dense set in X and let τ be the map defined by

$$\tau(x) = (e^{i(x, y_1)}, e^{i(x, y_2)}, \ldots).$$

τ maps X into K^∞, the countable product of circle groups. Let $H = \tau(X)$. Since τ is continuous and one–one, by Theorem 3.9, Chapter I, H is a Borel subgroup of X and τ^{-1} is measurable. If μ is Gaussian on X, we shall prove that $\mu\tau^{-1}$ is Gaussian in K^∞. Suppose $\mu\tau^{-1}$ is not Gaussian. Then

$$\mu\tau^{-1} = e(F) * \nu,$$

where F is a finite measure on K^∞ and ν is infinitely divisible in K^∞. We have

$$1 = \mu\tau^{-1}(H) = \int e(F)(H - x)\, d\nu(x).$$

Hence

$$e(F)(H - x) = 1, \qquad \text{a.e.} \quad (\nu).$$

Since the identity of K^∞ has positive mass with respect to $e(F)$, and H is a subgroup, $H - x = H$ a.e. (ν). Thus $e(F)(H) = 1$, and hence F is concentrated in H. Similarly, it follows from

$$1 = \mu\tau^{-1}(H) = \int \nu(H - x)\, d[e(F)]\,(x)$$

that

$$\nu(H - x) = 1 \qquad \text{a.e.} \quad e(F).$$

Since the identity of K^∞ has positive mass according to $e(F)$, $\nu(H) = 1$. Since τ^{-1} is measurable,

$$\mu = e(F\tau) * (\nu\tau),$$

and hence μ is not Gaussian. This is a contradiction. Thus $\mu\tau^{-1}$ is Gaussian, and by Theorem 6.1, Chapter IV,

$$(\mu\tau^{-1})\hat{}\ (\theta) = \theta(z_0) \exp[-\varphi(\theta)],$$

for every character θ on K^∞. z_0 is a fixed point in K^∞, $\theta(z)$ is the value of the character θ at the point $z \in K^\infty$, and φ satisfies the equation

$$\varphi(\theta_1 + \theta_2) + \varphi(\theta_1 - \theta_2) = 2[\varphi(\theta_1) + \varphi(\theta_2)] \tag{4.10}$$

for any two characters θ_1 and θ_2. Let $z = (z_1, z_2, \ldots)$, where z_n is the nth coordinate of z. To any character θ, there correspond integers $n_1, n_2, \ldots, n_k$ such that

$$\theta(z) = z_1^{n_1} z_2^{n_2} \ldots z_k^{n_k}, \qquad z \in K^\infty.$$

Hence

$$\begin{aligned}(\mu\tau^{-1})\hat{}\ (\theta) &= \int \exp[i(x, n_1 y_1 + \ldots + n_k y_k)]\, d\mu(x) \\ &= \hat{\mu}(n_1 y_1 + \ldots + n_k y_k).\end{aligned} \tag{4.11}$$

Let

$$h(y) = -\log |\hat{\mu}(y)|.$$

Then from (4.10) and (4.11) we have

$$h(y+y') + h(y-y') = 2[h(y) + h(y')],$$

$$h(y) \geqslant 0.$$

Hence $h(y)$ is the quadratic form of a positive semidefinite Hermitian operator, i.e., $h(y) = \frac{1}{2}(Sy, y)$, where S is a positive semidefinite Hermitian operator. From the example after Theorem 2.5, it follows that S must be an S-operator. If we now consider the distribution λ on X defined by the equation

$$\hat{\lambda}(y) = \exp[-\tfrac{1}{2}(Sy, y)],$$

we have

$$(\hat{\lambda\tau^{-1}})(\theta) = \exp[-\varphi(\theta)].$$

Hence $\lambda\tau^{-1}$ is a shift of $\mu\tau^{-1}$. Since both $\lambda\tau^{-1}$ and $\mu\tau^{-1}$ have unit mass for the subgroup H of K^∞, the element z_0 by which $\lambda\tau^{-1}$ is shifted to obtain $\mu\tau^{-1}$ belongs to H, and hence $z_0 = \tau(x_0)$ for some $x_0 \in X$. Consequently,

$$\mu = \lambda * x_0$$

or

$$\hat{\mu}(y) = \exp[i(x_0, y) - \tfrac{1}{2}(Sy, y)].$$

Conversely, if $\hat{\mu}(y)$ is of the above form, the distribution $\mu\tau^{-1}$ in K^∞ is Gaussian, and hence μ is Gaussian.

Theorem 4.10

A function $\varphi(y)$ is the characteristic function of an infinitely divisible distribution μ on X if and only if it is of the form

$$\varphi(y) = \exp\left[i(x_0, y) - \tfrac{1}{2}(Sy, y) + \int K(x, y)\, dM(x)\right], \qquad (4.12)$$

where x_0 is a fixed element of X, S is an S-operator and M is a σ-finite measure with finite mass outside every neighborhood of the origin and

$$\int_{\|x\| \leqslant 1} \|x\|^2 \, dM(x) < \infty.$$

Here $K(x, y)$ *is the function* $[e^{i(x, y)} - 1 - (i(x, y)/1 + \|x\|^2)]$.

The representation (4.12) *is unique.*

Proof. Let $\varphi(y) = \hat{\mu}(y)$ where μ is infinitely divisible. Then exactly as in the proof of Theorem 7.1, Chapter IV, we can construct a sequence of distributions λ_n such that (i) $\lambda_n = e(M_n)$, (ii) M_n increases to M, (iii) $\lambda_n * x_n \Rightarrow \lambda$, (iv) $\mu = \lambda * \mu_0$ where μ_0 is Gaussian.

Then by Theorems 4.7 and 4.9, it follows that $\varphi(y)$ is of the form (4.12). Sufficiency follows from Theorems 4.8 and 4.9. Uniqueness is proved in exactly the same manner as Theorem 8.1, Chapter IV, but keeping in mind that the space X playing the role of the character group is connected.

5. COMPACTNESS CRITERIA

We shall now find necessary and sufficient conditions in order that a sequence μ_n of infinitely divisible distributions may be conditionally compact.

If μ is any infinitely divisible distribution, by $\mu = [x, S, M]$ we mean that the three quantities occurring in the representation of Theorem 4.10 are, respectively, x, S, and M. Let T denote the associated S-operator given by

$$(Ty, y) = (Sy, y) + \int_{\|x\| \leqslant 1} (x, y)^2 \, dM(x). \tag{5.1}$$

The operator T is an S-operator, since

$$\int \|x\|^2 \, dM(x) < \infty.$$

Lemma 5.1

In order that a sequence μ_n *of Gaussian distributions with covariance operators* S_n *be shift compact it is necessary and sufficient that the sequence* S_n *should be compact* (*see Definition* 2.4).

PROOF. Sufficiency is immediate from Theorem 2.2. In order to prove necessity we shall assume that μ_n is shift compact and hence $|\mu_n|^2$ is conditionally compact. But $|\mu_n|^2$ is Gaussian with mean zero and covariance operator $2S_n$. In fact,

$$|\hat{\mu}_n(y)|^2 = \exp\,[-(S_n y, y)].$$

By Theorem 2.3, for any $\varepsilon > 0$ there exists a compact sequence U_n of S-operators such that

$$1 - \exp\,[-(S_n y, y)] \leqslant (U_n y, y) + \varepsilon \qquad \text{for all} \quad n.$$

Without loss of generality we may assume that all the U_n are positive definite. This implies that there exists a $\delta > 0$ such that for any n and y, $(U_n y, y) \leqslant \delta$ implies that $(S_n y, y) \leqslant 1$. Let $y_0 \in X$ be arbitrary and $(U_n y_0, y_0) = c_n^2$, $c_n > 0$. Then $(U_n \delta^{1/2} c_n^{-1} y_0, \delta^{1/2} c_n^{-1} y_0) = \delta$. Hence $(S_n \delta^{1/2} c_n^{-1} y_0, \delta^{1/2} c_n^{-1} y_0) \leqslant 1$, i.e., $(S_n y_0, y_0) \leqslant \delta^{-1}(U_n y_0, y_0)$. Thus

$$(S_n y, y) \leqslant (\delta^{-1} U_n y, y) \qquad \text{for all} \quad y \in X.$$

Since δ does not depend on n and the sequence U_n is compact, the sequence S_n is compact. This completes the proof.

Lemma 5.2

Let μ be a symmetric infinitely divisible distribution with $\mu = [0, 0, M]$. Further, let M be concentrated in the unit sphere. Then

$$\int ||x||^4 \, d\mu \leqslant \int ||x||^4 \, dM + 3\left[\int ||x||^2 \, dM\right]^2 < \infty.$$

PROOF. It is enough to prove the lemma when M is finite since the other case can be obtained by approximating M by an increasing sequence of finite measures M_n. Let $M(X) = t$ and let F be the measure $t^{-1} M$. Then

$$\mu = e^{-t} \sum_{r=0}^{\infty} t^r F^r / r!,$$

$$\begin{aligned}\int ||x||^4 \, dF^r &= E||X_1 + \ldots + X_r||^4 \\ &= rE||X_1||^4 + r(r-1)(E||X_1||^2)^2 + 2r(r-1)\, E(X_1, X_2)^2 \\ &\leqslant rE||X_1||^4 + 3r(r-1)(E||X_1||^2)^2,\end{aligned}$$

where E denotes expectation with respect to F and $X_1, X_2, \ldots, X_r$ are independent random variables in X with the same distribution F. Terms with zero expectation have been omitted.

$$\int ||x||^4 \, d\mu \leqslant e^{-t} \sum r \frac{t^r E||X_1||^4}{r!} + 3e^{-t} \sum r(r-1) t^r \frac{(E||X_1||^2)^2}{r!}$$

$$= tE||X_1||^4 + 3t^2(E||X_1||^2)^2$$

$$= t\int ||x||^4 \, dF + 3t^2\left(\int ||x||^2 \, dF)\right)^2$$

$$= \int ||x||^4 \, dM + 3\left(\int ||x||^2 \, dM\right)^2.$$

Lemma 5.3

Let μ_n be symmetric infinitely divisible distributions such that

$$\mu_n = [0, 0, M_n]$$

with M_n vanishing outside the sphere $[x\colon ||x|| \leqslant 1]$ for all n. If μ_n is conditionally compact then

$$\sup_n \int ||x||^4 \, d\mu_n < \infty.$$

Proof. Since M_n is concentrated in the unit sphere

$$\int ||x||^4 \, dM_n \leqslant \int ||x||^2 \, dM_n.$$

By Theorem 4.6 and the fact that each M_n can be approximated by finite measures, we have

$$\sup_n \int ||x||^2 \, dM_n < \infty.$$

Hence an application of Lemma 5.2 completes the proof.

Lemma 5.4

If μ is infinitely divisible and $\mu = [0, 0, M]$, where M is symmetric and vanishes outside the unit sphere $[x\colon ||x|| \leqslant 1]$, then

$$\int (x, y)^2 \, d\mu(x) = \int (x, y)^2 \, dM(x).$$

PROOF. The lemma is proved in exactly the same way as Lemma 5.2.

Lemma 5.5

Let μ_n be a conditionally compact sequence of symmetric distributions such that

$$\sup_n \int \|x\|^4 \, d\mu_n < \infty.$$

If S_n is the covariance operator of μ_n, then $\{S_n\}$ is compact.

PROOF. We have

$$(S_n y, y) = \int (x, y)^2 \, d\mu_n(x) \qquad \text{for all} \quad n \quad \text{and} \quad y \in X.$$

Let $\{e_i\}$ be an orthonormal basis and $r_N^2(x) = \sum_{i=N}^{\infty} (x, e_i)^2$. Then $\|x\|^2 \geqslant r_N^2(x)$. Further, by Schwarz's inequality,

$$\begin{aligned}
\sum_N^{\infty} (S_n e_i, e_i) &= \int r_N^2(x) \, d\mu_n \\
&\leqslant \int_{\{x : r_N^2(x) \leqslant \varepsilon\}} r_N^2(x) \, d\mu_n + \int_{\{x : r_N^2(x) > \varepsilon\}} r_N^2(x) \, d\mu_n \\
&\leqslant \varepsilon + \int_{\{x : r_N^2(x) > \varepsilon\}} \|x\|^2 \, d\mu_n \\
&\leqslant \varepsilon + (\mu_n\{x : r_N^2(x) > \varepsilon\})^{1/2} \left[\int \|x\|^4 \, d\mu_n(x) \right]^{1/2},
\end{aligned}$$

where $\varepsilon > 0$ is arbitrary. Thus

$$\sup_n \sum_N^{\infty} (S_n e_i, e_i) \leqslant \varepsilon + c \sup_n (\mu_n\{x : r_N^2(x) > \varepsilon\})^{1/2},$$

where

$$c = \sup_n \left(\int ||x||^4 \, d\mu_n \right)^{1/2}.$$

The arbitrariness of ε and Corollary 2.1 to Theorem 2.3 complete the proof of the lemma.

Theorem 5.1

Let μ_n be symmetric infinitely divisible distributions with representations

$$\mu_n = [0, S_n, M_n].$$

Then, in order that $\{\mu_n\}$ be conditionally compact, the following two conditions are necessary and sufficient:

(i) *$\{M_n\}$ restricted to the complement of any neighborhood of the identity is weakly conditionally compact,*

(ii) *the associated sequence of S-operators T_n in (5.1) is compact.*

PROOF. We shall first prove sufficiency. Let us choose the neighborhood of origin to be the unit sphere. Let $M_n = M_n^{(1)} + M_n^{(2)}$ where $M_n^{(1)}$ and $M_n^{(2)}$ are, respectively, the restrictions of M_n to the unit sphere and the complement of the unit sphere. Since $M_n^{(2)}$ is weakly conditionally compact and $F_n \Rightarrow F$ implies $e(F_n) \Rightarrow e(F)$, it is enough to show that the sequence of distributions

$$\lambda_n = [0, S_n, M_n^{(1)}]$$

is conditionally compact. We have by Lemma 5.4,

$$\begin{aligned} \int (x, y)^2 \, d\lambda_n(x) &= (S_n y, y) + \int_{||x|| \leqslant 1} (x, y)^2 \, dM_n^{(1)}(x) \\ &= (S_n y, y) + \int_{||x|| \leqslant 1} (x, y)^2 \, dM_n(x) \\ &= (T_n y, y). \end{aligned}$$

Since $\{T_n\}$ is compact, sufficiency now follows from Theorem 2.2. Necessity of (i) follows from Theorem 4.3 and (ii) follows from Lemmas 5.1, 5.2, and 5.5.

Theorem 5.2

In order that a sequence μ_n of infinitely divisible distributions with representations $\mu_n = [x_n, S_n, M_n]$ be shift compact it is necessary and sufficient that

(i) *$\{M_n\}$ restricted to the complement of any neighborhood of the origin is weakly conditionally compact.*

(ii) *$\{T_n\}$ as defined in (5.1) is compact.*

PROOF. Since μ_n is shift compact if and only if $|\mu_n|^2$ is conditionally compact, we need to find necessary and sufficient conditions for the conditional compactness of

$$|\mu_n|^2 = [0, 2S_n, M_n + \bar{M}_n].$$

Further, we have

$$\int_{||x|| \leqslant 1} (x, y)^2 \, d(M_n + \bar{M}_n) = 2 \int_{||x|| \leqslant 1} (x, y)^2 \, dM_n.$$

Hence the theorem follows from Theorem 5.1.

Theorem 5.3

In order that a sequence μ_n of infinitely divisible distributions with representations $\mu_n = [x_n, S_n, M_n]$ be conditionally compact it is necessary and sufficient that in addition to the conditions of Theorem 5.2, the sequence x_n should be compact in X.

PROOF. In order to prove the theorem it suffices to show that whenever $\mu_n = [x_n, S_n, M_n]$ is shift compact, $\lambda_n = [0, S_n, M_n]$ is conditionally compact. Suppose F_n is a sequence of totally finite measures converging weakly to a totally finite measure F. Since the family of functions $\{(x, y)/(1 + ||x||^2), ||y|| \leqslant 1\}$ is uniformly bounded and equicontinuous, it follows from Theorem 6.8, Chapter II, that

$$\lim_{n \to \infty} \int \frac{x}{1 + ||x||^2} \, dF_n = \int \frac{x}{1 + ||x||^2} \, dF,$$

where the limit is taken in norm. Because of this fact we may and do assume that M_n vanishes outside the unit sphere $\{x: ||x|| \leqslant 1\}$ for all n. Let us now consider

$$f_n(y) = \int K(x, y)\, dM_n(x) - \tfrac{1}{2}(S_n y, y).$$

We have

$$|K(x, y)| \leqslant |e^{i(x,y)} - 1 - i(x, y)| + \frac{|(x, y)|\, ||x||^2}{1 + ||x||^2}$$

$$\leqslant c|(x, y)|^2 + \frac{|(x, y)|\, ||x||^2}{1 + ||x||^2},$$

where c is an absolute constant. Hence

$$|f_n(y)| \leqslant c \int_{||x|| \leqslant 1} (x, y)^2\, dM_n(x) + \int_{||x|| \leqslant 1} \frac{|(x, y)|\, ||x||^2}{1 + ||x||^2}\, dM_n(x) + \tfrac{1}{2}(S_n y, y)$$

$$\leqslant c'(T_n y, y) + \int_{||x|| \leqslant 1} |(x, y)|\, ||x||^2\, dM_n(x)$$

$$\leqslant c'(T_n y, y) + \left[\int_{||x|| \leqslant 1} (x, y)^2\, ||x||^2\, dM_n \cdot \int_{||x|| \leqslant 1} ||x||^2\, dM_n \right]^{1/2}$$

$$\leqslant c''[(T_n y, y) + (T_n y, y)^{1/2}]$$

for all y, where c' and c'' are constants independent of n and y. Thus for any $\rho > 0$, there exists a $\delta > 0$ such that $|f_n(y)| \leqslant \rho$, whenever $(T_n y, y) < \delta$. Since

$$\hat{\lambda}_n(y) = \exp f_n(y),$$

for any $\varepsilon > 0$, there exists a $\rho > 0$ such that $1 - R\hat{\lambda}_n(y) \leqslant \varepsilon$, whenever $|f_n(y)| \leqslant \rho$. Consequently, for any $\varepsilon > 0$, there exists a $\delta > 0$ such that whenever $(T_n y, y) \leqslant \delta$, it follows that $1 - R\hat{\lambda}_n(y) \leqslant \varepsilon$. Since $1 - \cos 2\alpha \leqslant 4(1 - \cos \alpha)$ for all α, it follows that $1 - R\hat{\lambda}_n(y)$ satisfies the conditions of Lemma 4.1. Now an application of Theorem 2.3 shows that λ_n is conditionally compact. This completes the proof of the theorem, since $\{T_n\}$ is compact.

REMARK. In defining the operator T we could have taken any bounded sphere around the origin instead of the unit sphere. Then also Theorems 5.2 and 5.3 hold good.

Theorem 5.4

Let μ_n be a sequence of infinitely divisible distributions $[x_n, S_n, M_n]$. If $\mu_n \Rightarrow \mu$, μ is Gaussian if and only if

$$\lim_{n \to \infty} M_n(N') = 0$$

for every neighborhood of the origin.

PROOF. Let μ be Gaussian. Since μ cannot be written as $e(F) * \lambda$, where λ is infinitely divisible, it follows that $M_n(N') \to 0$ as $n \to \infty$ for every neighborhood N of the origin. Conversely, if $M_n(N') \to 0$ for every neighborhood N of the origin, in exactly the same manner as in the proof of Theorem 6.1, Chapter IV, one can show that $\hat{\mu}(y)$ is of the form

$$\hat{\mu}(y) = \exp\,[i(x_0, y) - \tfrac{1}{2}(Sy, y)],$$

where S is an S-operator. In other words, μ is Gaussian.

As a consequence of Theorems 5.3 and 5.4, we have the following theorem.

Theorem 5.5

In order that a sequence of infinitely divisible distributions $\mu_n = [x_n, S_n, M_n]$ may converge weakly to $\mu = [x_0, S_0, M_0]$ it is necessary and sufficient that

(1) $\lim_n x_n = x_0$.
(2) $M_n \Rightarrow M_0$ *outside every closed neighborhood N of the origin.*
(3) *the associated sequence of S-operators $\{T_n\}$ is compact and*

$$\lim_{\varepsilon \to 0} \overline{\lim_{n \to \infty}} \int_{\|x\| \leqslant \varepsilon} (x, y)^2 \, dM_n + (S_n y, y) = (S_0 y, y).$$

6. ACCOMPANYING LAWS

Definition 6.1

A sequence $\{\alpha_{nj}\}$, $j = 1, 2, \ldots, k_n$, $n = 1, 2, \ldots$ of distributions is said to be *uniformly infinitesimal* if, for any neighborhood N of the origin,

$$\lim_{n\to\infty} \inf_{1\leqslant j\leqslant k_n} \alpha_{nj}(N) = 1.$$

REMARK. It is clear from Theorem 4.4 that for a uniformly infinitesimal sequence of distributions, one has

$$\lim_{n\to\infty} \sup_{1\leqslant j\leqslant k_n} \sup_{\|y\|\leqslant k} |\hat{\alpha}_{nj}(y) - 1| = 0$$

for every positive constant k.

Theorem 6.1

Let $\{\alpha_{nj}\}$ $j = 1, 2, \ldots, k_n$ be a uniformly infinitesimal sequence of symmetric distributions with nonnegative characteristic functions. Let

$$\mu_n = \prod_{j=1}^{k_n} \alpha_{nj}, \qquad \lambda_n = \prod_{j=1}^{k_n} e(\alpha_{nj}).$$

In order that $\mu_n \Rightarrow \mu$ it is necessary and sufficient that $\lambda_n \Rightarrow \mu$.

PROOF. Let μ_n be conditionally compact. Since $e^{x-1} \geqslant x$ for $0 \leqslant x \leqslant 1$, we have

$$e(\alpha_{nj})\hat{}\ (y) \geqslant \hat{\alpha}_{nj}(y), \qquad j = 1, 2, \ldots, k_n, \quad n = 1, 2, \ldots .$$

Since $\hat{\alpha}_{nj}(y)$ is nonnegative,

$$\hat{\lambda}_n(y) \geqslant \hat{\mu}_n(y)$$

or

$$1 - \hat{\lambda}_n(y) \leqslant 1 - \hat{\mu}_n(y).$$

From the conditional compactness of $\{\mu_n\}$ and Theorem 2.3, it follows that $\{\lambda_n\}$ is conditionally compact. Now let $\{\lambda_n\}$ be conditionally compact. It follows from Theorem 5.2 and the remark made after Theorem 5.3 that

(i) $F_n = \sum_{j=1}^{k_n} \alpha_{nj}$ restricted to N' is weakly conditionally compact for every neighborhood N of the origin;

(ii) the sequence S_n of S-operators defined by

$$(S_n y, y) = \int_{\|x\|\leqslant t} (x, y)^2 \, dF_n(x)$$

is compact for every t.

We now have by Lemma 4.2

$$1 - \hat{\mu}_n(y) \leqslant \sum_j (1 - \hat{\alpha}_{nj}(y)) = \int [1 - \cos(x, y)]\, dF_n(x)$$

$$= \int_{\|x\| \leqslant t} [1 - \cos(x, y)]\, dF_n(x) + \int_{\|x\| > t} [1 - \cos(x, y)]\, dF_n(x)$$

$$\leqslant \tfrac{1}{2} \int_{\|x\| \leqslant t} (x, y)^2\, dF_n(x) + 2F_n[\|x\| > t]$$

$$= \tfrac{1}{2}(S_n y, y) + 2F_n[\|x\| > t].$$

Since F_n is weakly compact outside any neighborhood of the origin, by Theorem 6.7, Chapter II, we can choose t such that for all n,

$$F_n[\|x\| > t] < \varepsilon/2.$$

Since for a fixed t, $\{S_n\}$ is compact it follows from Theorem 2.3 that μ_n is conditionally compact.

We shall complete the proof by showing that, whenever λ_n is conditionally compact, for every constant k,

$$\lim_{n \to \infty} \sup_{\|y\| \leqslant k} |\hat{\lambda}_n(y) - \hat{\mu}_n(y)| = 0. \tag{6.0}$$

It follows from the uniform infinitesimality that

$$\hat{\lambda}_n(y) \geqslant \hat{\mu}_n(y) > 0$$

for all y such that $\|y\| \leqslant k$ and sufficiently large n (which depends only on k). Thus for all sufficiently large n,

$$\sup_{\|y\| \leqslant k} |\log \hat{\lambda}_n(y) - \log \hat{\mu}_n(y)|$$

$$\leqslant \sup_{\|y\| \leqslant k} \sum |\hat{\alpha}_{nj}(y) - 1 - \log \hat{\alpha}_{nj}(y)|$$

$$\leqslant c \cdot \sup_{\|y\| \leqslant k} \sum |\hat{\alpha}_{nj}(y) - 1|^2$$

$$\leqslant c \cdot \sup_{\|y\| \leqslant k} \sup_{1 \leqslant j \leqslant k_n} |\hat{\alpha}_{nj}(y) - 1| \sup_{\|y\| \leqslant k} \sum_j |\hat{\alpha}_{nj}(y) - 1|,$$

where c is a constant independent of n. Thus, in order to prove (6.0), it is enough to show that

$$\sup_n \sup_{\|y\| \leqslant k} \sum_j |\hat{\alpha}_{nj}(y) - 1| < \infty.$$

But the expression on the left-hand side of the above inequality is equal to

$$\sup_n \sup_{\|y\| \leqslant k} \int [1 - \cos(x, y)]\, dF_n$$

$$\leqslant \sup_n \sup_{\|y\| \leqslant k} \left\{ \int_{\|x\| \leqslant 1} [1 - \cos(x, y)]\, dF_n + 2F_n(\|x\| > 1) \right\}$$

$$\leqslant \tfrac{1}{2}k^2 \sup_n \int_{\|x\| \leqslant 1} \|x\|^2\, dF_n + 2 \sup_n F_n(\|x\| > 1)$$

$$< \infty.$$

The last step follows from the conditional compactness of $\lambda_n = e(F_n)$.

Lemma 6.1

Let $\{\alpha_{nj}\}$, $j = 1, 2, \ldots, k_n$ be a uniformly infinitesimal sequence of distributions. Let x_{nj} be the element defined by

$$x_{nj} = \int_{\|x\| \leqslant 1} x\, d\alpha_{nj}.$$

Then

$$\lim_{n \to \infty} \sup_{1 \leqslant j \leqslant k_n} \|x_{nj}\| = 0.$$

PROOF. That the elements x_{nj} are well defined follows from the fact that $\int_{\|x\| \leqslant 1} (x, y)\, d\alpha_{nj}$ is a bounded linear functional of y. Let $\varepsilon > 0$ be arbitrary, and V be the sphere $\{x: \|x\| \leqslant \varepsilon\}$. Then

$$\|x_{nj}\| \leqslant \int_V \|x\|\, d\alpha_{nj} + \int_{\varepsilon < \|x\| \leqslant 1} \|x\|\, d\alpha_{nj}$$

$$\leqslant \varepsilon + \alpha_{nj}(V').$$

The arbitrariness of ε and the uniform infinitesimality of $\{\alpha_{nj}\}$ imply

$$\lim_{n\to\infty} \sup_{1\leqslant j\leqslant k_n} \|x_{nj}\| = 0.$$

Lemma 6.2

Let $\{\alpha_{nj}\}$, $j = 1, 2, \ldots, k_n$ *be uniformly infinitesimal. Let* x_{nj} *be defined as in Lemma* 6.1. *If* $\theta_{nj} = \alpha_{nj} * (-x_{nj})$, *then there exists an* n_0, *such that for all* $1 \leqslant j \leqslant k_n$ *and* $n \geqslant n_0$,

$$\left\| \int_{\|x\|\leqslant 1} x\, d\theta_{nj} \right\| \leqslant 2\theta_{nj}[\|x\| > \tfrac{1}{2}].$$

PROOF. Let n_0 be such that

$$\sup_{1\leqslant j\leqslant k_n} \|x_{nj}\| \leqslant \tfrac{1}{4} \qquad \text{for all} \quad n > n_0.$$

Then, for $n > n_0$ and $1 \leqslant j \leqslant k_n$,

$$\begin{aligned}
\left\| \int_{\|x\|\leqslant 1} x\, d\theta_{nj} \right\| &= \left\| \int_{\|x - x_{nj}\|\leqslant 1} (x - x_{nj})\, d\alpha_{nj} \right\| \\
&= \left\| \int_{\|x - x_{nj}\|\leqslant 1} x\, d\alpha_{nj} - x_{nj}\alpha_{nj}[\|x - x_{nj}\| \leqslant 1] \right\| \\
&= \left\| \int_{\|x - x_{nj}\|\leqslant 1} x\, d\alpha_{nj} - \int_{\|x\|\leqslant 1} x\, d\alpha_{nj} + x_{nj}\alpha_{nj}[\|x - x_{nj}\| > 1] \right\| \\
&\leqslant \int_{[\|x - x_{nj}\|\leqslant 1] \Delta [\|x\|\leqslant 1]} \|x\|\, d\alpha_{nj} + \tfrac{1}{4}\theta_{nj}[\|x\| > 1] \\
&\leqslant \int_{3/4\leqslant\|x\|\leqslant 5/4} \|x\|\, d\alpha_{nj} + \tfrac{1}{4}\theta_{nj}[\|x\| > 1] \\
&\leqslant 5/4\, \alpha_{nj}[\|x\| > \tfrac{3}{4}] + \tfrac{1}{4}\theta_{nj}[\|x\| > 1] \\
&\leqslant 2\theta_{nj}[\|x\| > \tfrac{1}{2}],
\end{aligned}$$

where Δ denotes symmetric difference.

Lemma 6.3

Let F_n be a sequence of σ-finite measures such that F_n restricted to N' is finite and weakly conditionally compact for every neighborhood N of the origin. Then, for any $\varepsilon > 0$, there exists a compact set K such that

$$F_n(K') \leqslant \varepsilon \qquad \textit{for all} \quad n.$$

PROOF. Let $\varepsilon > 0$ be fixed. Choose a sequence N_r of open spheres decreasing to the origin and such that $N_{r+1} \subseteq N_r$, where N_0 is taken as the whole space. Let $A_r = N_{r-1} - N_r$. By Theorem 6.7, Chapter II, we can find a compact set $K_r \subseteq A_r$ such that, for all n,

$$F_n(A_r - K_r) \leqslant \varepsilon/2^r.$$

Let

$$K = \bigcup_{r=1}^{\infty} K_r \cup \{0\}.$$

Since

$$K \cap N_r' = K_1 \cup K_2 \cup \ldots \cup K_r$$

and N_r decreases to the origin it follows that K is compact and

$$F_n(K') \leqslant \sum_{r=1}^{\infty} F_n(A_r - K_r) \leqslant \varepsilon.$$

This completes the proof.

We shall now state and prove the main result of this section.

Theorem 6.2

Let $\{\alpha_{nj}\}$, $j = 1, 2, \ldots, k_n$ be a uniformly infinitesimal sequence of distributions on X. Let

$$\mu_n = \prod_{j=1}^{k_n} \alpha_{nj},$$

$$x_{nj} = \int_{\|x\| \leqslant 1} x \, d\alpha_{nj},$$

$$\theta_{nj} = \alpha_{nj} * (-x_{nj}),$$

$$\lambda_n = \prod_{j=1}^{k_n} e(\theta_{nj}) * \left(\sum_{j=1}^{k_n} x_{nj} \right).$$

Then λ_n is shift compact if and only if μ_n is shift compact and in such a case,

$$\lim_{n\to\infty} \sup_{\|y\| \leqslant t} |\hat{\lambda}_n(y) - \hat{\mu}_n(y)| = 0$$

for every $t \geqslant 0$.

PROOF. Suppose μ_n is shift compact. Then $|\mu_n|^2$ is conditionally compact But

$$|\mu_n|^2 = \prod_{j=1}^{k_n} |\alpha_{nj}|^2 = \prod_{j=1}^{k_n} |\theta_{nj}|^2.$$

Let

$$F_n = \sum_j |\alpha_{nj}|^2 = \sum_j |\theta_{nj}|^2. \tag{6.1}$$

It follows from Theorem 6.1 that $e(F_n)$ is conditionally compact. From Theorem 5.2 and Lemma 6.3 we deduce that for any $\varepsilon > 0$, there exists a compact set K such that

$$F_n(K') \leqslant \varepsilon \qquad \text{for} \quad n = 1, 2, \ldots. \tag{6.2}$$

Let us now define the S-operators T_n by the formula

$$(T_n y, y) = \int_{\|x\| \leqslant t} (x, y)^2 dF_n(x).$$

By Theorem 5.2, the sequence T_n is compact for every t. Let

$$G_n = \sum_j \theta_{nj}. \tag{6.3}$$

In order to prove the 'if' part we have to show that $e(G_n)$ is shift compact or equivalently by Theorem 5.2,

(a) G_n is weakly conditionally compact when restricted to the complement of any neighborhood of the identity;

(b) the sequence of S-operators S_n defined by

$$(S_n y, y) = \int_{\|x\| \leqslant 1} (x, y)^2 \, dG_n$$

is compact.

Since $\{\alpha_{nj}\}$ is uniformly infinitesimal, Lemma 6.1 implies that $\{\theta_{nj}\}$ is uniformly infinitesimal. Hence for any $\varepsilon > 0$ there exists a compact set C such that

$$\theta_{nj}(C) \geqslant 1 - \varepsilon \qquad \text{for all} \quad n \quad \text{and} \quad 1 \leqslant j \leqslant k_n.$$

We have, for all n and $1 \leqslant j \leqslant k_n$,

$$\begin{aligned} |\theta_{nj}|^2(K') &= \int \theta_{nj}(K' + x) \, d\theta_{nj}(x) \\ &\geqslant \int_C \theta_{nj}(K' + x) \, d\theta_{nj}(x) \\ &\geqslant (1 - \varepsilon) \inf_{x \in C} \theta_{nj}(K' + x) \\ &= (1 - \varepsilon) \inf_{x \in C} \theta_{nj}((K + x)') \\ &\geqslant (1 - \varepsilon)\theta_{nj}([K + C]') \\ &= (1 - \varepsilon)\theta_{nj}(K_1'), \end{aligned} \tag{6.4}$$

where $K_1 = K + C$ is compact. We have used the fact that $K + x \subseteq K + C$ for $x \in C$.

In a similar manner it can be shown that if V and N are two neighborhoods of the origin such that $V + V \subseteq N$ and $\theta_{nj}(V) \geqslant 1 - \varepsilon$ for all $n \geqslant n_0$ and $1 \leqslant j \leqslant k_n$, then

$$|\theta_{nj}|^2(V') \geqslant (1 - \varepsilon)\theta_{nj}(N') \qquad \text{for} \quad n \geqslant n_0, \qquad 1 \leqslant j \leqslant k_n. \tag{6.5}$$

Equations (6.2)–(6.4) imply that for any $\varepsilon > 0$ there exists a compact set K_1 such that

$$G_n(K_1') \leqslant \varepsilon. \tag{6.6}$$

On the other hand (6.1), (6.3), (6.5), and the weak compactness of F_n, when restricted to the complement of any neighborhood of the origin, imply that for any neighborhood N of the origin

$$\sup_n G_n(N') < \infty. \tag{6.7}$$

Equations (6.6) and (6.7), and Theorem 6.7, Chapter II imply that G_n is weakly conditionally compact when restricted to the complement of any neighborhood of the origin. Thus (a) is proved. In order to prove (b) we consider

$$\begin{aligned}\int_{\|x\|\leqslant 2} (x, y)^2\, d|\theta_{nj}|^2(x) &= \iint_{\|x_1 - x_2\|\leqslant 2} (x_1 - x_2, y)^2\, d\theta_{nj}(x_1)\, d\theta_{nj}(x_2) \\ &\geqslant \iint_{\|x_1\|\leqslant 1,\, \|x_2\|\leqslant 1} (x_1 - x_2, y)^2\, d\theta_{nj}(x_1)\, d\theta_{nj}(x_2) \\ &= 2\theta_{nj}(\|x\| \leqslant 1) \int_{\|x\|\leqslant 1} (x, y)^2\, d\theta_{nj}(x) \\ &\quad - 2\left[\int_{\|x\|\leqslant 1} (x, y)\, d\theta_{nj}\right]^2.\end{aligned}$$

Since $\{\theta_{nj}\}$ is uniformly infinitesimal we can assume that $\theta_{nj}[\|x\| \leqslant 1] \geqslant \frac{1}{2}$, for all suitably large n and all $1 \leqslant j \leqslant k_n$. Hence, adding over j, we get

$$(S_n y, y) \leqslant (T_n y, y) + 2(U_n y, y),$$

where

$$(U_n y, y) = \sum_{j=1}^{k_n} \left[\int_{\|x\|\leqslant 1} (x, y)\, d\theta_{nj}(x)\right]^2,$$

and t is taken to be 2. Note that U_n is an S-operator. Since $\{T_n\}$ is compact it is enough to show that $\{U_n\}$ is compact. It is enough to prove that the trace of $U_n \to 0$ as $n \to \infty$. Let $y_{nj} = \int_{\|x\|\leqslant 1} x\, d\theta_{nj}$. Then

$$\begin{aligned}\operatorname{trace}(U_n) &= \sum_{j=1}^{k_n} \|y_{nj}\|^2 \\ &\leqslant \sup_{1\leqslant j\leqslant k_n} \|y_{nj}\| \left(\sum_{j=1}^{k_n} \|y_{nj}\|\right).\end{aligned}$$

Lemmas 6.1 and 6.2, and Eq. (6.7) imply that the right-hand side of the above inequality tends to zero as $n \to \infty$. This proves the "if" part of the theorem.

In order to prove the "only if" part, suppose that λ_n is shift compact. We have by Lemma 4.2,

$$
\begin{aligned}
1 - |\hat{\mu}_n(y)|^2 &= 1 - \prod_{j=1}^{k_n} |\hat{\theta}_{nj}(y)|^2 \\
&\leqslant \sum_{j=1}^{k_n} [1 - |\hat{\theta}_{nj}(y)|^2] \\
&\leqslant 2 \sum_j [1 - R\hat{\theta}_{nj}(y)] \\
&= 2 \int_{\|x\| \leqslant t} [1 - \cos(x, y)]\, dG_n(x) + 2G_n[\|x\| > t] \\
&\leqslant \int_{\|x\| \leqslant t} (x, y)^2\, dG_n(x) + 2G_n[\|x\| > t] \\
&= (S_n' y, y) + 2G_n[\|x\| > t]. \qquad (6.8)
\end{aligned}
$$

From the shift compactness of λ_n and Theorem 5.2, we can, for any $\varepsilon > 0$, choose a t such that

$$G_n[\|x\| > t] \leqslant \varepsilon/2 \qquad \text{for all} \quad n.$$

Further by the same theorem, the sequence of S-operators S_n' defined by

$$(S_n' y, y) = \int_{\|x\| \leqslant t} (x, y)^2\, dG_n(x)$$

is compact. Thus (6.8) and Theorem 2.3 imply that $|\mu_n|^2$ is conditionally compact and hence μ_n is shift compact.

In order to prove the last part we observe that since $\{\theta_{nj}\}$ is uniformly infinitesimal,

$$\lim_{n \to \infty} \sup_{\|y\| \leqslant t} \sup_{1 \leqslant j \leqslant k_n} |\hat{\theta}_{nj}(y) - 1| = 0$$

(see the Remark after Definition 6.1). Exactly as in the proof of Theorem 5.1, Chapter IV, it is sufficient to prove that

$$\sup_n \sup_{\|y\| \leqslant t} \sum_{j=1}^{k_n} |\hat{\theta}_{nj}(y) - 1| < \infty. \tag{6.9}$$

To this end we have

$$\begin{aligned}
|\hat{\theta}_{nj}(y) - 1| &= \left| \int [e^{i(x,y)} - 1] \, d\theta_{nj}(x) \right| \\
&= \left| \left[\int_{\|x\| \leqslant 1} [e^{i(x,y)} - 1 - i(x, y)] \, d\theta_{nj} + i \int_{\|x\| \leqslant 1} (x, y) \, d\theta_{nj} \right.\right. \\
&\quad \left.\left. + \int_{\|x\| > 1} [e^{i(x,y)} - 1] \, d\theta_{nj}(x) \right] \right| \\
&\leqslant c \int_{\|x\| \leqslant 1} (x, y)^2 \, d\theta_{nj} + \|y\| \left\| \int_{\|x\| \leqslant 1} x \, d\theta_{nj} \right\| + 2\theta_{nj}(\|x\| > 1),
\end{aligned}$$

where c is an absolute constant. Equation (6.9) follows immediately from the above inequality, the compactness of the sequence $\{S_n'\}$ of S-operators, Lemma 6.2, and Eq. (6.7). This completes the proof of the theorem.

Corollary 6.1

In order that $\mu_n * x_n \Rightarrow \mu$ where x_n is a sequence of points in X and μ_n are as in Theorem 6.2, it is necessary and sufficient that $\lambda_n * x_n \Rightarrow \mu$.

Corollary 6.2

Limit distributions of sums of independent uniformly infinitesimal random variables in X are infinitely divisible.

Corollary 6.3

Let $\mu_n * x_n \Rightarrow \mu$, where μ_n are as in Theorem 6.2. Then μ is Gaussian if and only if, for every neighborhood N of the origin

$$\lim_{n \to \infty} G_n(N') = 0,$$

where

$$G_n = \sum_{j=1}^{k_n} \theta_{nj}.$$

Theorem 6.3

Let $\{\alpha_{nj}\}$ $j = 1, 2, \ldots, k_n$ be a uniformly infinitesimal sequence of distributions. In order that there may exist a sequence x_n of points in X such that the sequence

$$\left(\prod_{j=1}^{k_n} \alpha_{nj}\right) * x_n$$

may converge to the Gaussian distribution with characteristic function $\exp\left[-\frac{1}{2}(S_0 y, y)\right]$, *the following conditions are necessary and sufficient. For every $\varepsilon > 0$,*

$$(1) \quad \lim_{n\to\infty} \sum_j \alpha_{nj}(\|x - x_{nj}\| > \varepsilon) = 0,$$

$$(2) \quad \lim_{n\to\infty} \sum_j \int_{\|x\|<\varepsilon} (x - x_{nj}, y)^2 \, d\alpha_{nj} = (S_0 y, y), \qquad y \in X,$$

$$(3) \quad \lim_{N\to\infty} \sup_n \sum_j \int_{\|x\|\leqslant 1} r_N^2(x - x_{nj}) \, d\alpha_{nj} = 0,$$

$$(4) \quad \sup_n \sum_j \int_{\|x\|\leqslant 1} \|x - x_{nj}\|^2 \, d\alpha_{nj} < \infty,$$

where

$$x_{nj} = \int_{\|x\|\leqslant 1} x \, d\alpha_{nj},$$

$$r_N^2(x) = \sum_{i=N}^{\infty} (x, e_i)^2,$$

and $\{e_i\}$ is any fixed orthonormal basis.

Proof. This is a consequence of Theorems 6.2, 5.5, and Corollary 6.3.

7. REPRESENTATION OF CONVOLUTION SEMIGROUPS

We shall now consider the representation problem for a one-parameter convolution semigroup of distributions. Such a semigroup is defined exactly as in Section 10, Chapter IV.

The following theorem is proved exactly in the same way as Theorem 10.1, Chapter IV.

Theorem 7.1

Let $\{\mu_t\}$, $t > 0$ be a one-parameter convolution semigroup of distributions such that μ_t converges weakly to the distribution degenerate at the origin as $t \to 0$. Then $\hat{\mu}_t(y)$ has the canonical representation

$$\hat{\mu}_t(y) = \exp t\left[\int\left[(x, y) - 1 - \frac{i(x, y)}{1 + ||x||^2}\right] dM(x) - \tfrac{1}{2}(S_0 y, y) + (x_0, y)\right],$$

where x_0 is an element of X, M is a σ-finite measure with finite mass outside every neighborhood of the origin, S is an S-operator and $\int_{||x|| \leqslant 1} ||x||^2\, dM(x) < \infty$, where x_0, S, and M are uniquely determined by $\{\mu_t\}$.

8. DECOMPOSITION THEOREM

The following two theorems are proved exactly in the same manner as Theorems 11.2 and 11.3, respectively, of Chapter IV.

Theorem 8.1

Let μ be a distribution in X without any indecomposable factors. Then μ is infinitely divisible.

Theorem 8.2

Any distribution μ on X can be written as $\lambda_1 * \lambda_2$ where λ_1 is the convolution of a finite or a countable number of indecomposable distributions, and λ_2 is an infinitely divisible distribution without indecomposable factors.

9. ERGODIC THEOREMS

The aim of this section is to prove a generalized version of the classical ergodic theorems due to Birkhoff in the case of a Hilbert space. In fact, our proof demands that the space in which the random variables assume their values is only a Banach space.

Let (Ω, S, P) be a probability space and X a complete separable metric space. Let $\mathscr{B}_X$ denote the Borel σ-field of X. Let $\xi_1, \xi_2, \ldots$ be a stationary sequence of X-valued random variables in Ω. Suppose $(X^\infty, \mathscr{B}^\infty)$ is the product of countable number of copies of $(X, \mathscr{B}_X)$. The measure P on Ω induces a measure μ on X^∞. Stationarity of the sequence $\xi_1, \xi_2, \ldots$ implies that μ is invariant under the shift transformation T which sends any point $\mathbf{x} = (x_1, x_2, \ldots) \in X^\infty$ to $T\mathbf{x} = (x_2, x_3, \ldots)$. $(X^\infty, \mathscr{B}^\infty, \mu)$ is a probability space with the property $\mu = \mu T^{-1}$. Let $\mathscr{F}$ denote the σ-field of invariant subsets of X^∞, i.e., $\mathscr{F} = \{A : A \in \mathscr{B}^\infty, A = T^{-1}A\}$. Since $(X^\infty, \mathscr{B}^\infty)$ is a standard space, by Theorem 7.1, Chapter V, there exists a conditional probability distribution $\lambda(A, \mathbf{x})$ with the following properties:

(i) for each fixed $A \in \mathscr{B}^\infty$, $\lambda(A, \mathbf{x})$ is an $\mathscr{F}$-measurable function in $\mathbf{x}$;

(ii) for each fixed $\mathbf{x} \in X^\infty$, $\lambda(A, \mathbf{x})$ is a probability measure in A, $A \in \mathscr{B}^\infty$;

(iii) for each $A \in \mathscr{B}^\infty$, $B \in \mathscr{F}$,

$$\int_B \lambda(A, \mathbf{x})\, d\mu(\mathbf{x}) = \mu(A \cap B).$$

Note that the last equation can be rewritten as

$$\int_B \int \chi_A(\mathbf{y}) \lambda(d\mathbf{y}, \mathbf{x})\, d\mu(\mathbf{x}) = \int_B \chi_A(\mathbf{y})\, d\mu(\mathbf{y}).$$

Let now f be a nonnegative measurable function on X^∞ with the property $\int f\, d\mu < \infty$. Since f can be approximated pointwise by an increasing sequence of bounded measurable functions and a bounded measurable function can be approximated uniformly by a sequence of simple functions, it follows from the last equation that

$$\int_B \left[\int f(\mathbf{y}) \lambda(d\mathbf{y}, \mathbf{x})\right] d\mu(\mathbf{x}) = \int_B f(\mathbf{y})\, d\mu(\mathbf{y}).$$

If f is any integrable function, then its positive and negative parts are integrable and hence the above equation holds for all f such that $\int |f(\mathbf{x})| \, d\mu(\mathbf{x}) < \infty$ and $A \in \mathscr{B}^{\infty}$, $B \in \mathscr{F}$. The function

$$E(f|\mathscr{F}) = \int f(\mathbf{y})\lambda(d\mathbf{y}, \mathbf{x})$$

is called the *conditional expectation* of f given the invariant σ-field $\mathscr{F}$.

The classical theorem of Birkhoff (cf. Doob [5], Chap. X) asserts that for every real valued function f on X^{∞} such that $\int |f(\mathbf{x})| \, d\mu(\mathbf{x}) < \infty$,

$$\lim_{n \to \infty} \frac{f(\mathbf{x}) + f(T\mathbf{x}) + \ldots + f(T^{n-1}\mathbf{x})}{n} = E\{f|\mathscr{F}\},$$

almost everywhere $[\mu]$.

We can interpret this result in the following manner. Let $\lambda_n(A, \mathbf{x})$ be the measure with mass $1/n$ at each of the points $\mathbf{x}, T\mathbf{x}, \ldots, T^{n-1}\mathbf{x}$, and $\lambda(A, \mathbf{x})$ the conditional probability distribution given $\mathscr{F}$. Then for every real valued function f on X^{∞} with the property $\int |f(x)| \, d\mu(\mathbf{x}) < \infty$, one has

$$\lim_{n \to \infty} \int f(\mathbf{y})\lambda_n(d\mathbf{y}, \mathbf{x}) = \int f(\mathbf{y})\lambda(d\mathbf{y}, \mathbf{x})$$

almost everywhere $[\mu]$.

Definition 9.1

Let X be a separable metric space and $\mathscr{B}_X$ the Borel σ-field of X. A *random measure* on X is a function $\lambda(A, x)$, with $x \in X$, $A \in \mathscr{B}_X$ with the following properties: (i) for each fixed x, λ is a probability measure on $\mathscr{B}_X$; and (ii) for each fixed $A \in \mathscr{B}_X$, λ is a real valued measurable function.

Definition 9.2

Let $(X, \mathscr{B}_X, \mu)$ be a probability space, where X and $\mathscr{B}_X$ are as in the previous definition. A sequence of random measures $\{\lambda_n, \lambda; n = 1, 2, \ldots\}$ on X is said to possess the *ergodic property* if, for every real valued function $f(x)$ on X for which $\int [\int |f(y)| \lambda(dy, x)] \, d\mu < \infty$,

$$\lim_{n \to \infty} \int f(y)\lambda_n(dy, x) = \int f(y)\lambda(dy, x)$$

almost everywhere $[\mu]$.

Theorem 9.1

Let $\{\lambda_n, \lambda; n = 1, 2, \ldots\}$ be a sequence of random measures on $(X, \mathscr{B}_X, \mu)$ possessing the ergodic property. Then

$$\mu\{x: \lambda_n(\cdot, x) \Rightarrow \lambda(\cdot, x)\} = 1.$$

PROOF. By the definition of ergodic property we have

$$\mu\left[x: \lim_{n\to\infty} \int f(y)\lambda_n(dy, x) = \int f(y)\lambda(dy, x)\right] = 1$$

for every bounded measurable function f. By Theorem 6.6, Chapter II, there exists a sequence $g_1, g_2, \ldots \in C(X)$ such that, for every sequence $\nu_n \in \mathscr{M}(X)$, $\nu_n \Rightarrow \nu$, $\nu \in \mathscr{M}(X)$ if and only if $\int g_k\, d\nu_n \to \int g_k\, d\nu$ as $n \to \infty$ for $k = 1, 2, \ldots$. This completes the proof of the theorem.

Theorem 9.2

Let $\{\lambda_n, \lambda; n = 1, 2, \ldots\}$ be a sequence of random measures on $(X, \mathscr{B}_X, \mu)$ with the ergodic property. Let $\mathscr{A}_0$ be a family of continuous functions on X satisfying the following two conditions: (i) *there exists a continuous function $g(x)$ on X such that $|f(x)| \leqslant g(x)$ for each $f \in \mathscr{A}_0$ and $x \in X$;* (ii) $\iint g(y)\lambda(dy, x)\, d\mu(x) < \infty$; *and* (iii) *$\mathscr{A}_0$ is equicontinuous at every $x \in X$. Then $\mu\{x: \eta_n(x) \to 0\} = 1$, where*

$$\eta_n(x) = \sup_{f\in\mathscr{A}_0} \left| \int f(y)\lambda_n(dy, x) - \int f(y)\lambda(dy, x) \right|. \tag{9.1}$$

PROOF. Since the sequence $\{\lambda_n, \lambda\}$ possesses the ergodic property, we have

$$\mu\left\{x: \lambda_n(\cdot, x) \Rightarrow \lambda(\cdot, x), \int g(y)\lambda_n(dy, x) \to \int g(y)\lambda(dy, x)\right\} = 1. \tag{9.2}$$

Let $E = \{x: g(x) > 0\}$. Then E is open in X. Let x_0 be a point such that $\lambda_n(\cdot, x_0) \Rightarrow \lambda(\cdot, x_0)$ and $\int g(y)\lambda_n(dy, x_0) \to \int g(y)\lambda(dy, x_0)$ as $n \to \infty$. Let

$$\nu_n = \lambda_n(\cdot, x_0), \qquad \nu = \lambda(\cdot, x_0),$$

$$\nu_n'(A) = \int_A g\, d\nu_n, \qquad \nu'(A) = \int_A g\, d\nu, \qquad A \in \mathscr{B}_X.$$

First of all we shall prove that ν_n' converges weakly to ν'. Since g is a continuous function, the sequence $\{\nu_n g^{-1}\}$ converges weakly to the distribution νg^{-1} in the real line. We can therefore find a sequence k_r of continuity points in the real line for the distribution νg^{-1} such that $k_r \uparrow \infty$ as $r \to \infty$ and

$$\lim_{n \to \infty} \nu_n\{x: g(x) \leqslant k_r\} = \nu\{x: g(x) \leqslant k_r\}$$

for every r. Since $\{x: g(x) \leqslant k_r\}$ is closed, it follows from the weak convergence of ν_n and Theorem 6.1, Chapter II that

$$\lim_{n \to \infty} \int_{\{x: g(x) \leqslant k_r\}} fg \, d\nu_n = \int_{\{x: g(x) \leqslant k_r\}} fg \, d\nu \tag{9.3}$$

for all $f \in C(X)$. Since $\int g \, d\nu_n \to \int g \, d\nu$ as $n \to \infty$, and (9.3) holds when $f = 1$, we have

$$\lim_{n \to \infty} \int_{\{x: g(x) > k_r\}} g \, d\nu_n = \int_{\{x: g(x) > k_r\}} g \, d\nu. \tag{9.4}$$

Thus by (9.3) and (9.4), we have

$$\begin{aligned}
&\overline{\lim_{n \to \infty}} \left| \int fg \, d\nu_n - \int fg \, d\nu \right| \\
&\leqslant \overline{\lim_{n \to \infty}} \left| \int_{\{x: g(x) > k_r\}} fg \, d\nu_n - \int_{\{x: g(x) > k_r\}} fg \, d\nu \right| \\
&\leqslant 2\|f\| \int_{\{x: g(x) > k_r\}} g \, d\nu,
\end{aligned}$$

where $\|f\| = \sup_x |f(x)|$. Now letting $r \to \infty$, we have

$$\lim_{n \to \infty} \int f \, d\nu_n' = \int f \, d\nu', \qquad f \in C(x).$$

In other words, $\nu_n' \Rightarrow \nu'$. E is an open set and the measures ν_n' and ν' are concentrated in E. Thus by Theorem 6.1, Chapter II, ν_n' converges weakly to ν' in the space E.

The fact that E is open also implies that the family of functions $\mathscr{A}_1 = [f/g : f \in \mathscr{A}_0]$ is uniformly bounded by unity and equicontinuous at each $x \in E$. A trivial modification of Theorem 6.8, Chapter II for nonprobability measures shows that

$$\lim_{n\to\infty} \sup_{f\in\mathscr{A}_0} \left| \int f(y)\lambda_n(dy, x_0) - \int f(y)\lambda(dy, x_0) \right| = 0.$$

Now an application of (9.2) completes the proof.

The following lemma facilitates the passage from almost everywhere convergence of Theorem 9.2 to convergence in the mean of order $1 + \alpha$, $\alpha \geqslant 0$.

Lemma 9.1

Let (X, S, μ) be a measure space. Let f_n be a sequence of nonnegative integrable functions converging almost everywhere to an integrable function f. If $\lim_{n\to\infty} \int f_n \, d\mu = \int f \, d\mu$, then

$$\lim_{n\to\infty} \int |f_n - f| \, d\mu = 0.$$

PROOF. Let $g_n = f_n - f$. Then it is easy to see that $0 \leqslant g_n^-(x)$* $\leqslant f(x)$. Further, $g_n^-(x) \to 0$ a.e. $[\mu]$. Thus by the dominated convergence theorem

$$\lim_{n\to\infty} \int g_n^- \, d\mu = 0.$$

Further,

$$\lim_{n\to\infty} \int (g_n^+ - g_n^-) \, d\mu = \lim_{n\to\infty} \int (f_n - f) \, d\mu = 0.$$

Thus

$$\lim_{n\to\infty} \int g_n^+ \, d\mu = 0.$$

---

* $g_n^-(x) = -g_n(x)$ if $g_n(x) < 0$ and $= 0$ if $g_n(x) \geqslant 0$, $g_n^+(x) = g_n(x)$ if $g_n(x) > 0$ and $= 0$ if $g_n(x) \leqslant 0$.

Hence,

$$\lim_{n\to\infty}\int |f_n - f|\, d\mu = \lim_{n\to\infty}\int (g_n^+ + g_n^-)\, d\mu = 0.$$

This completes the proof.

Theorem 9.3

Let $\{\lambda_n, \lambda; n = 1, 2, \ldots\}$ be a sequence of random measures on $(X, \mathscr{B}_X, \mu)$ with the ergodic property. Let for every $f(x)$, for which $\int |f(y)|\,\lambda(dy, x)\, d\mu(x) < \infty$, $\lim_{n\to\infty} \int f(y)\lambda_n(dy, x)\, d\mu(x) = \int f(y)\lambda(dy, x)\, d\mu(x)$. Then for every family $\mathscr{A}_0$ of real valued continuous functions satisfying (i) $|f(x)| \leqslant g(x)$ *for each $f \in \mathscr{A}_0$, $x \in X$;* (ii) *$g(x)$ is continuous and $\int g(y)^{1+\alpha}\lambda(dy, x)\, d\mu(x) < \infty$ for some $\alpha \geqslant 0$; and* (iii) *$\mathscr{A}_0$ is equicontinuous at every point $x \in X$, the following holds:*

$$\lim_{n\to\infty}\int \eta_n^{1+\alpha}(x)\, d\mu(x) = 0,$$

where η_n is defined as in (9.1).

PROOF. Let

$$h_n(x) = \int g(y)^{1+\alpha}\lambda_n(dy, x),$$

$$h(x) = \int g(y)^{1+\alpha}\lambda(dy, x).$$

Then by the conditions of the theorem,

$$\mu\{x : h_n(x) \to h(x)\} = 1,$$

$$\lim_{n\to\infty}\int h_n(x)\, d\mu(x) = \int h(x)\, d\mu(x).$$

By Lemma 9.1,

$$\lim_{n\to\infty}\int |h_n(x) - h(x)|\, d\mu(x) = 0. \tag{9.5}$$

Let $\varepsilon > 0$ be arbitrary and $E_n = \{x: \eta_n(x) > \varepsilon\}$. Then we have

$$\begin{aligned}\int \eta_n^{1+\alpha}\,d\mu &\leqslant \int\limits_{\{x:\eta_n(x)\leqslant\varepsilon\}} \eta_n^{1+\alpha}\,d\mu + \int\limits_{E_n} \eta_n^{1+\alpha}\,d\mu \\ &\leqslant \varepsilon + \int\limits_{E_n} \eta_n^{1+\alpha}\,d\mu. \qquad (9.6)\end{aligned}$$

By Holder's inequality and (9.1), we have

$$\begin{aligned}\eta_n^{1+\alpha}(x) &\leqslant \sup_{f\in\mathscr{A}_0} \left| \int f(y)\lambda_n(dy, x) - \int f(y)\lambda(dy, x) \right|^{1+\alpha} \\ &\leqslant \left[\int g(y)\lambda_n(dy, x) + \int g(y)\lambda(dy, x) \right]^{1+\alpha} \\ &\leqslant 2^{1+\alpha}[h_n(x) + h(x)] \\ &\leqslant 2^{1+\alpha}[|h_n(x) - h(x)| + 2h(x)]. \qquad (9.7)\end{aligned}$$

Since by Theorem 9.2, $\lim_{n\to\infty} \mu(E_n) = 0$, (9.5)–(9.7) imply that

$$\lim_{n\to\infty} E\eta_n^{1+\alpha} \leqslant \varepsilon.$$

Letting $\varepsilon \to 0$, we complete the proof of the theorem.

Making use of Theorems 9.2 and 9.3 we shall prove the ergodic theorems for Banach space-valued random variables. In order to formulate the ergodic theorems we need the notion of Bochner integrals (cf. Hille and Phillips [14], Chap. III, pp. 71–85).

Let X be a separable Banach space and $(\Omega, \mathscr{S}, P)$ any probability space. As before, $\mathscr{B}_X$ denotes the Borel σ-field in X. Let $\omega \to \xi(\omega)$ be any measurable map from Ω into X such that $\int_\Omega \|\xi(\omega)\|\,dP(\omega) < \infty$, where $\|\cdot\|$ is the norm of the Banach space X. Then there exists a unique element $E\xi \in X$ with the property

$$x^*(E\xi) = \int x^*(\xi(\omega))\,dP(\omega)$$

for all $x^* \in X^*$, where X^* is the adjoint of X. Symbolically, we write

$$E\xi = \int \xi(\omega)\,dP(\omega),$$

where $E\xi$ is called the Bochner integral of ξ with respect to P. Its existence is guaranteed by Theorem 3.7.4, p. 80 of Reference [14].

Suppose $\mathscr{F} \subseteq \mathscr{S}$ is a sub σ-field of $\mathscr{S}$ and there exists a conditional probability distribution $Q(A, \omega)$, which is $\mathscr{F}$-measurable for fixed $A \in \mathscr{S}$, a measure on $\mathscr{S}$ for fixed $\omega \in \Omega$ and $\int_B Q(A, \omega)\, dP(\omega) = P(A \cap B)$ for all $B \in \mathscr{F}$ and $A \in \mathscr{S}$. Since $\int ||\xi(\omega)||\, dP(\omega) < \infty$, it follows that $\int ||\xi(\omega')||Q(d\omega', \omega) < \infty$, a.e. $\omega[P]$. Hence, the Bochner integral $\int \xi(\omega')Q(d\omega', \omega)$ is well defined almost everywhere $\omega[P]$. It is easy to verify from the definition of the Bochner integral that $\int \xi(\omega')Q(d\omega', \omega)$ is an $\mathscr{F}$-measurable function. We write $E(\xi|\mathscr{F}) = \int \xi(\omega')Q(d\omega', \omega)$.

We shall now formulate the ergodic theorems. Let (Ω, S, P) be a probability space and X a separable Banach space. Let $\xi_1, \xi_2, \ldots$ be a stationary sequence of random variables defined on Ω and taking values on X. According to the discussion made before Definition 9.1, P induces a measure μ on the space $(X^\infty, \mathscr{B}^\infty)$ which is the countable product of $(X, \mathscr{B}_X)$. μ is invariant under the shift transformation T on X^∞. Let $\mathscr{F}$ denote the σ-field of T-invariant measurable subsets of X, i.e., $\mathscr{F} = \{A : A \in \mathscr{B}^\infty, T^{-1}A = A\}$. Since $(X^\infty, \mathscr{B}^\infty)$ is a standard space there exists a conditional probability distribution $\lambda(A, \mathbf{x})$ for μ when the sub σ-field is $\mathscr{F}$. Any point $\mathbf{x} \in X^\infty$ can be written as a sequence $\mathbf{x} = (x_1, x_2, \ldots)$ where each $x_i \in X$. Let $x_n(\mathbf{x}) = x_n$, $S_n(\mathbf{x}) = n^{-1}(x_1 + x_2 + \ldots + x_n)$. With these notations we have the following theorem.

Theorem 9.4

Let $\int ||x_1(\mathbf{x})||\, d\mu < \infty$. *Then*

$$\lim_{n\to\infty} ||S_n - E(x_1|\mathscr{F})|| = 0 \qquad \text{a.e.} \quad [\mu].$$

PROOF. Let $\lambda_n(A, \mathbf{x})$ be the random measure with mass $1/n$ at each of the points $\mathbf{x}, T\mathbf{x}, \ldots, T^{n-1}\mathbf{x}$, where T is the shift transformation. Let $\lambda(A, \mathbf{x})$ be the conditional probability distribution of μ given $\mathscr{F}$. Then by the individual ergodic theorem of Birkhoff, the sequence $\{\lambda_n, \lambda; n = 1, 2, \ldots\}$ possesses the ergodic property. Let $\mathscr{A}_0$ be the family of functions $\{x^*, ||x^*|| \leqslant 1\}$, which is the unit sphere in the adjoint of X. Then $|x^*(x_1)| \leqslant ||x_1||$ for all $x^* \in \mathscr{A}_0$ and

$$\int ||x_1(\mathbf{y})||\lambda(d\mathbf{y}, \mathbf{x})\, d\mu(\mathbf{x}) = \int ||x_1(\mathbf{x})||\, d\mu(\mathbf{x}) < \infty.$$

Further,

$$\int x^*(x_1(\mathbf{y}))\lambda_n(d\mathbf{y}, \mathbf{x}) = x^*(S_n),$$

$$\int x^*(x_1(\mathbf{y}))\lambda(d\mathbf{y}, \mathbf{x}) = x^*(E(x_1|\mathscr{F})),$$

$$\sup_{x^* \in \mathscr{A}_0} |x^*(S_n) - x^*(E(x_1|\mathscr{F}))| = ||S_n - E(x_1|\mathscr{F})||.$$

Since $\mathscr{A}_0$ is equicontinuous at every $x \in X$, an application of Theorem 9.2 completes the proof.

Theorem 9.5

With the same notations as in the previous theorem, let $\int ||x_1(\mathbf{x})||^{1+\alpha} d\mu < \infty$ *for some* $\alpha \geqslant 0$. *Then*

$$\lim_{n \to \infty} \int ||S_n - E(x_1|\mathscr{F})||^{1+\alpha} d\mu = 0.$$

PROOF. This follows from Theorem 9.3 and the mean ergodic theorem of order $1 + \alpha$ for real valued random variables.

VII

PROBABILITY MEASURES ON $C[0, 1]$ AND $D[0, 1]$

1. INTRODUCTION

It is well-known that probability measures in the space of continuous functions and the space of functions with only discontinuities of the first kind play an important role in the theory of stochastic processes and certain problems of nonparametric tests of hypothesis. The aim of this chapter is to describe the weakly compact subsets of the space of all probability measures on such function spaces and derive the Kolmogorov-Smirnov criteria.

Let $(\Omega, \mathscr{S}, P)$ be a probability space and T a subset of the real line. By a *stochastic process* is meant an indexed family $\{\xi_t, t \in T\}$ of real valued random variables on Ω. Generally, T is an interval on the real line. Given $\omega \in \Omega$, $\varphi_\omega : t \to \xi_t(\omega)$ is a real function on T. It is called a *realization* of the stochastic process.

Let X be the space of all real valued functions on T. For each $t \in T$, the mapping $x \to x(t)$ maps X into the real line. Let $\mathscr{B}$ be the smallest σ-algebra of subsets of X with respect to which all these maps, for all possible $t \in T$, are measurable. If $\{\xi_t : t \in T\}$ is a stochastic process, the map $\varphi : \omega \to \varphi_\omega$ is a measurable map of Ω into X (relative to the σ-algebras $\mathscr{S}$ and $\mathscr{B}$), and hence we obtain a measure μ on $\mathscr{B}$ by setting

$\mu(A) = P[\varphi^{-1}(A)]$ for all $A \in \mathscr{B}$. μ is called the *measure* or *distribution corresponding* to the stochastic process. Sometimes $(X, \mathscr{B}; \mu)$ itself is called the stochastic process.

From the above point of view it is clear that the study of stochastic processes reduces to the study of measures on the function space $(X, \mathscr{B})$. However, X being the space of all functions is not especially suited for applications. It is preferable to have the basic space on which the measures are to be dealt with as a separable metric space or a complete separable metric space so that the results of earlier chapters can be used with facility. We shall therefore restrict our attention to measures on $(X, \mathscr{B})$ which can somehow be defined in such subsets of X wherein one can introduce a suitably well-behaved topology. Two simple but important cases of such a subset are obtained when we take $T = [0, 1]$ and consider the subsets $C[0, 1]$ and $D[0, 1]$ of X. $C[0, 1]$ is the space of all continuous functions on $[0, 1]$. $D[0, 1]$ is the space of all functions defined on $[0, 1]$ and possessing right and left limits at every point.

2. PROBABILITY MEASURES ON $C[0, 1]$

We observe that $C[0, 1]$ is a separable Banach space if we define for $x \in C[0, 1]$,

$$||x|| = \sup_{0 \leqslant t \leqslant 1} |x(t)|.$$

For every $x \in C[0, 1]$ and $\delta > 0$, we define

$$\omega_x(\delta) = \sup_{|t' - t''| \leqslant \delta} |x(t') - x(t'')|.$$

Since a continuous function on $[0, 1]$ is uniformly continuous, it follows that $\omega_x(\delta) \to 0$ as $\delta \to 0$ for each x. We shall write C instead of $C[0, 1]$. Notice that both $x \to ||x||$ and $x \to \omega_x(\delta)$ are continuous over C.

Theorem 2.1

The class $\mathscr{B}_C$ of the Borel subsets of C coincides with the smallest σ-algebra of subsets of C with respect to which the maps $\pi^t: x \to x(t)$ are measurable for all $t \in [0, 1]$. If μ and ν are two measures on C, a necessary and sufficient condition that $\mu = \nu$ is that $\mu^{t_1, \ldots, t_k} = \nu^{t_1, \ldots, t_k}$ for all k and

$t_1, t_2, \ldots, t_k \in [0, 1]$, *where* $\mu^{t_1,\ldots,t_k}$ and $\nu^{t_1,\ldots,t_k}$ *are measures in the k-dimensional vector space* R^k *induced by* μ *and* ν, *respectively, through the map* $\pi^{t_1,\ldots,t_k}: x \to (x(t_1), \ldots, x(t_k))$.

PROOF. Let $\mathscr{A}$ be the smallest σ-algebra of subsets of C with respect to which the maps π^t are measurable for all t. Since each π^t is continuous on C, $\mathscr{A} \subseteq \mathscr{B}_C$. To prove that $\mathscr{B}_C \subseteq \mathscr{A}$, it is enough to show that $\mathscr{A}$ contains all open sets. Since C is separable, every open set is a union of countably many closed spheres and so it is enough to prove that $\mathscr{A}$ contains all closed spheres. If a is any real number > 0, $x_0 \in C$ and $r_1, r_2, \ldots$ is an enumeration of rationals in $[0, 1]$, we have $\{x: \|x - x_0\| \leqslant a\} = \bigcap_{n=1}^{\infty} \{x: |x(r_n) - x_0(r_n)| \leqslant a\}$. Since the intersection on the right side of this equation lies in $\mathscr{A}$, it follows that the sphere $\{x: \|x - x_0\| \leqslant a\} \in \mathscr{A}$. Thus $\mathscr{A} = \mathscr{B}_C$.

To prove the second part write $\mathscr{A}_{t_1,\ldots,t_k} = \{(\pi^{t_1,\ldots,t_k})^{-1}(A): A \subseteq R^k$, A a Borel set$\}$, $\bigcup_{k,t_1,\ldots,t_k} \mathscr{A}_{t_1,\ldots,t_k} = \mathscr{F}$. Obviously, $\mu^{t_1,\ldots,t_k} = \nu^{t_1,\ldots,t_k}$ for all k and $t_1, \ldots, t_k \in [0, 1]$ implies that $\mu(E) = \nu(E)$ for all $E \in \mathscr{F}$. $\mathscr{F}$ is a Boolean algebra generating $\mathscr{A}$ so that we have then $\mu(E) = \nu(E)$ for all $E \in \mathscr{A}$. This proves that $\mu = \nu$.

Since C is a complete separable metric space, by Theorem 3.2, Chapter II, every measure on C is tight. We shall now give a criterion for compactness of a set of probability measures on C.

Lemma 2.1

Let $A \subseteq C$. *In order that* $\bar{A}$ *be compact it is necessary and sufficient that the following two conditions be satisfied simultaneously:*

(i) $\sup_{x \in A} |x(0)| < \infty$,

(ii) $\lim_{\delta \downarrow 0} \sup_{x \in A} \omega_x(\delta) = 0$.

PROOF. This is an immediate consequence of the Ascoli theorem (see Kelley [16], pp. 233–234) and the compactness of the unit interval.

Lemma 2.2

Let Γ *be a set of probability measures on* C. *In order that* $\bar{\Gamma}$ *be compact it is necessary and sufficient that for each* $\varepsilon > 0$ *there exists a constant* $M_\varepsilon > 0$ *and a function* $\omega(\delta, \varepsilon)$ *which decreases to zero as* $\delta \downarrow 0$ *such that*

(i) $\mu(\{x: |x(0)| \leqslant M_\varepsilon\}) > 1 - \varepsilon/2$

(ii) $\mu(\{x: \omega_x(\delta) \leqslant \omega(\delta, \varepsilon)$ *for all* $\delta\}) > 1 - \varepsilon/2$ *for all* $\mu \in \Gamma$.

PROOF. Suppose that Γ is a set of measures satisfying the conditions above. For $\varepsilon > 0$, write

$$A_\varepsilon = \{x: |x(0)| \leqslant M_\varepsilon\},$$

$$B_\varepsilon = \{x: \omega_x(\delta) \leqslant \omega(\delta, \varepsilon) \text{ for all } \delta\}.$$

Then $K_\varepsilon = A_\varepsilon \cap B_\varepsilon$ is a closed set. By Lemma 2.1, K_ε is compact. Clearly $\mu(K_\varepsilon) > 1 - \varepsilon$ for all $\mu \in \Gamma$. By Theorem 6.7, Chapter II, $\bar{\Gamma}$ is compact.

Conversely, let $\bar{\Gamma}$ be compact. Then by Theorem 6.7, Chapter II, there exists a compact set K_ε such that $\mu(K_\varepsilon) > 1 - \varepsilon/2$ for all $\mu \in \Gamma$. Let

$$M_\varepsilon = \sup_{x \in K_\varepsilon} |x(0)|,$$

$$\omega(\delta, \varepsilon) = \sup_{x \in K_\varepsilon} \omega_x(\delta).$$

By Lemma 2.1, $M_\varepsilon < \infty$ and $\omega(\delta, \varepsilon) \downarrow 0$ as $\delta \downarrow 0$. Clearly

$$\mu(\{x: |x(0)| \leqslant M_\varepsilon\}) \geqslant \mu(K_\varepsilon) > 1 - \varepsilon/2,$$

$$\mu(\{x: \omega_x(\delta) \leqslant \omega(\delta, \varepsilon) \quad \text{for all} \quad \delta\}) \geqslant \mu(K_\varepsilon) > 1 - \varepsilon/2$$

for all $\mu \in \Gamma$.

Theorem 2.2

Let Γ be a set of probability measures on C. In order that $\bar{\Gamma}$ be compact it is necessary and sufficient that the following conditions be satisfied:

(i) *for each $\varepsilon > 0$ there should exist a constant M_ε such that*

$$\mu(\{x: |x(0)| \leqslant M_\varepsilon\}) > 1 - \varepsilon/2 \qquad \textit{for all} \quad \mu \in \Gamma;$$

(ii) *for each $\varepsilon > 0$ and $\delta > 0$ there should exist an $\eta = \eta(\varepsilon, \delta) > 0$ such that*

$$\mu(\{x: \omega_x(\eta) \leqslant \delta\}) > 1 - \varepsilon/2 \qquad \textit{for all} \quad \mu \in \Gamma.$$

PROOF. That (i) is necessary has been proved in the preceding lemma. As for (ii) note that there exists a function $\omega(\delta, \varepsilon) \downarrow 0$ as $\delta \downarrow 0$ such that

$$\mu(\{x: \omega_x(\delta) \leqslant \omega(\delta, \varepsilon) \quad \text{for all} \quad \delta\}) > 1 - \varepsilon/2$$

for all $\mu \in \Gamma$. We can find a $\eta = \eta(\varepsilon, \delta)$ such that $\omega(\eta, \varepsilon) \leqslant \delta$. Then obviously

$$\mu(\{x: \omega_x(\eta) \leqslant \delta\}) > 1 - \varepsilon/2 \qquad \text{for all} \quad \mu \in \Gamma.$$

To prove the sufficiency we proceed as follows. For each integer $n = 1, 2, \ldots,$ and a given $\varepsilon > 0$ there exists an $\eta_{\varepsilon, n}$ such that if

$$F_{\varepsilon, n} = \{x: \omega_x(\eta_{\varepsilon, n}) \leqslant 1/n\}$$

then

$$\mu(F_{\varepsilon, n}) > 1 - \varepsilon/2^{n+1}$$

for all $\mu \in \Gamma$. Let

$$K_\varepsilon = \{x: |x(0)| \leqslant M_\varepsilon\} \cap \bigcap_{n=1}^{\infty} F_{\varepsilon, n}.$$

Obviously,

$$\mu(K_\varepsilon) \geqslant 1 - \varepsilon$$

for all $\mu \in \Gamma$. If $x \in K_\varepsilon$, then for each n, $x \in F_{\varepsilon, n}$ so that there exists an $\eta_{\varepsilon, n}$ having the property that $\omega_x(\eta_{\varepsilon, n}) \leqslant 1/n$. In other words, $\sup_{x \in K_\varepsilon} \omega_x(\eta) \to 0$ as $\eta \to 0$. Since $\sup_{x \in K_\varepsilon} |x(0)| \leqslant M_\varepsilon < \infty$, it follows that K_ε is compact. Hence by Theorem 6.7, Chapter II, $\bar{\Gamma}$ is compact.

3. A CONDITION FOR THE REALIZATION OF A STOCHASTIC PROCESS IN C

So far we have been examining properties of measures on C. The question now naturally arises as to what are those stochastic processes whose corresponding measures are defined on C. More precisely, let $\{\xi_t, 0 \leqslant t \leqslant 1\}$ be a stochastic process and let $P^{t_1, \ldots, t_k}$ be the finite dimensional probability distributions of the stochastic process. What additional condition must be satisfied in order that there exist a measure μ on C such that $\mu^{t_1,\ldots,t_k} = P^{t_1,\ldots,t_k}$ for all k and $t_1,\ldots, t_k \in [0, 1]$? By Theorem 2.1, if there exists a μ, it is unique. The following is an interesting sufficient condition.

Theorem 3.1

Let $\{\xi_t: 0 \leqslant t \leqslant 1\}$ be a stochastic process and $P^{t_1,\ldots,t_k}$ be the probability distribution on R^k of the vector $(\xi_{t_1},\ldots \xi_{t_k})$. If there are constants α, δ, $K > 0$ such that

$$E|\xi_{t_1} - \xi_{t_2}|^\alpha = \iint_{R^2} |u - v|^\alpha \, dP^{t_1,t_2}(u, v) \leqslant K|t_1 - t_2|^{1+\delta}$$

for all $t_1, t_2 \in [0, 1]$, then there exists a unique measure μ on C such that

$$P^{t_1\ldots t_k} = \mu^{t_1\ldots t_k}$$

for all k and $t_1,\ldots, t_k \in [0, 1]$.

PROOF. Let X be the space of *all* real functions on $[0, 1]$ and $\mathscr{B}$ the smallest σ-algebra of subsets of X relative to which the maps $\pi^t: x \to x(t)$ of X into the real line are all measurable. Then by Theorem 5.1, Chapter V there exists a measure P on $\mathscr{B}$ such that

$$P^{t_1\ldots t_k}(A) = P(\{x: \pi^{t_1\ldots t_k}(x) \in A\})$$

for all $k, t_1,\ldots, t_k \in [0, 1]$ and Borel sets $A \subseteq R^k$.

For any $x \in X$ and any integer $n = 1, 2,\ldots,$ write $x_n^* = \pi_n(x)$ as the unique continuous function on $[0, 1]$ which equals x at the points $0, 1/2^n, 2/2^n,\ldots, 1$ and is linear between successive pairs of these points. $\pi_n: x \to x_n^*$ is, for fixed n, a map of X into C. It is easily seen to be measurable. It is easily verified that

$$\max_{0\leqslant t\leqslant 1} |\pi_n(x) - \pi_{n-1}(x)| \leqslant \max_{1\leqslant i\leqslant 2^n} |x(i/2^n) - x(\overline{i - 1}/2^n)|.$$

We shall now prove that $\pi_n(x)$ converges in C for almost all x in X. Since C is a complete metric space it is sufficient to prove that

$\|\pi_n(x) - \pi_m(x)\| \to 0$ as $n, m \to \infty$ for almost all $x \in X$. To this end we note that for any $a > 0$,

$$P(\{x: \|\pi_n(x) - \pi_{n-1}(x)\| > a\})$$

$$\leqslant P(\{x: \max_i |x(i/2^n) - x(\overline{i-1}/2^n)| > a\})$$

$$\leqslant \sum_{i=1}^{2^n} P(\{x: |x(i/2^n) - x(\overline{i-1}/2^n)| > a\})$$

$$\leqslant a^{-\alpha}\left[\sum_{i=1}^{2^n} E|\xi_{i/2^n} - \xi_{\overline{i-1}/2^n}|^\alpha\right] \leqslant ka^{-\alpha}2^{-n\delta}.$$

Here we have used Chebyshev's inequality and the condition of the theorem. Let θ be such that $0 < \theta < \delta/\alpha$. Then setting $a = 2^{-n\theta}$ we have

$$P(\{x: \|\pi_n(x) - \pi_{n-1}(x)\| > 2^{-n\theta}\}) \leqslant K \cdot 2^{n(\alpha\theta - \delta)}.$$

Since $\sum_1^\infty 2^{-n(\delta - \theta\alpha)} < \infty$ it follows from the Borel-Cantelli lemma that for almost all x, $\|\pi_n(x) - \pi_{n-1}(x)\| \leqslant 2^{-n\theta}$ for all sufficiently large n. Consequently, for almost all x, the series

$$\sum_n \|\pi_n(x) - \pi_{n-1}(x)\|$$

is convergent. Since for $m < n$,

$$\|\pi_m(x) - \pi_n(x)\| \leqslant \sum_{j=m+1}^{n} \|\pi_j(x) - \pi_{j-1}(x)\|$$

it follows that

$$\lim_{n, m \to \infty} \|\pi_n(x) - \pi_m(x)\| = 0$$

for almost all $x \in X$. Let $X_0 \subseteq X$ be the set of all x such that this limit is zero. For any $x \in X_0$, there exists an $x^* \in C$ such that $\|\pi_n(x) - x^*\| \to 0$ as $n \to \infty$. Define

$$\pi^*(x) = \begin{cases} x^* & \text{if} \quad x \in X_0, \\ 0 & \text{if} \quad x \in X - X_0. \end{cases}$$

π^* is a measurable map of X into C. Let μ be the measure on C defined by

$$\mu(E) = P(\{x : \pi^*(x) \in E\})$$

for all $E \in \mathscr{B}_C$.

We notice that for each fixed $t \in [0, 1]$, $x^*(t) = x(t)$ for almost all x. This is obvious if t is of the form $k/2^l$ since in this case $(\pi_n(x))(t) = x(t)$ for all sufficiently large n. If t is not of the form $k/2^l$, let $t_1, t_2, \ldots$ be numbers of the form $k/2^l$, $t_j \to t$ as $j \to \infty$. $x^*(t_j) = x(t_j)$ for almost all x. Since $E(|\xi_{t_j} - \xi_t|^\alpha) \to 0$ as $j \to \infty$, it is clear that for a subsequence $j_1, j_2, \ldots, \to \infty$, $x(t_{j_r}) \to x(t)$ as $r \to \infty$ for almost all x. Since $x^*(t_{j_r}) \to x^*(t)$ for all $x \in X$, we have $x(t) = x^*(t)$ for almost all x.

The proof is now completed by showing that $\mu^{t_1, \ldots, t_k} = P^{t_1, \ldots, t_k}$ for all k and $t_1, \ldots, t_k \in [0, 1]$. In fact, since $x^*(t) = x(t)$ for each t for almost all x, for any Borel set $A \subseteq R^k$,

$$\begin{aligned} \mu^{t_1 \ldots t_k}(A) &= \mu(\{y : y \in C, (y(t_1) \ldots y(t_k)) \in A\}) \\ &= P(\{x : (x^*(t_1), \ldots, x^*(t_k)) \in A\}) \\ &= P(\{x : (x(t_1), \ldots, x(t_k)) \in A\}) \\ &= P^{t_1 \ldots t_k}(A). \end{aligned}$$

This completes the proof.

As an easy application of the above theorem we have the following theorem.

Theorem 3.2

There exists a unique measure W on $(C, \mathscr{B}_C)$ with the following properties:

(i) $W(\{x : x(0) = 0\}) = 1$,

(ii) if $0 \leqslant t_1 < t_2 < t_3 \ldots < t_n \leqslant 1$, *the random variables* $u_1, u_2, \ldots, u_n$, *where* $u_1(x) = x(t_1)$, $u_j(x) = x(t_j) - x(t_{j-1})$ *for* $1 < j \leqslant n$, *are independent on the probability space* $(C, \mathscr{B}_C, W)$,

(iii) *if* $0 \leqslant s \leqslant t \leqslant 1$, *the random variable* u *where* $u(x) = x(t) - x(s)$ *is normal with mean* 0 *and variance* $t - s$.

PROOF. By a simple verification of the consistency requirements we conclude that there exists a stochastic process $\{\xi_t : 0 \leqslant t \leqslant 1\}$ such that

(i) $\xi_t - \xi_s$ has a normal distribution with mean 0 and variance $t - s$ where $0 \leqslant s \leqslant t \leqslant 1$ and (ii) if $0 \leqslant t_1 < t_2 < \ldots < t_n \leqslant 1$, the random variables $\xi_{t_1}, \xi_{t_2} - \xi_{t_1}, \ldots, \xi_{t_n} - \xi_{t_{n-1}}$ are independent. Since $E|\xi_t - \xi_s|^4 = 3(E|\xi_t - \xi_s|^2)^2 = 3|t - s|^2$ it follows from Theorem 3.1 that there exists a measure W on C satisfying (ii) and (iii). (i) is an easy consequence of the fact that $\xi_{1/n^2} \to 0$ with probability 1 as $n \to \infty$.

REMARK. The stochastic process $x(t)$ of the above theorem is called the *Brownian motion* and the measure W on the space C is called the *Wiener measure*.

4. CONVERGENCE TO BROWNIAN MOTION

Now we shall examine a very interesting relation between the Wiener measure on C and sums of independent random variables obeying the central limit theorem. Let

$$\xi_{n1}, \xi_{n2}, \ldots, \xi_{nk_n}$$

be a triangular sequence of real valued random variables and obeying the Lindeberg criterion. In this case, the distribution of $\xi_{n1} + \ldots + \xi_{nk_n}$ converges to the normal distribution. What is more remarkable is that the distributions of a whole series of functionals of the partial sums such as $\max_i (\xi_{n1} + \ldots + \xi_{ni})$, $\max_i |\xi_{n1} + \ldots + \xi_{ni}|$, etc., have limits as $n \to \infty$ which are independent of the distributions of the ξ_{ni}. We shall use the theory developed so far to obtain a general theorem in this direction.

Lemma 4.1

Let $\xi_1, \xi_2, \ldots, \xi_n$ be n independent real valued random variables defined on a probability space $(X, \mathscr{B}, P)$ and $\zeta_k = \sum_{i=1}^k \xi_i$, $k = 1, 2, \ldots, n$, $\zeta_0 = 0$. Then

$$P(\{\max_{1 \leqslant k \leqslant n} |\zeta_k| > 2t\}) \leqslant \alpha^{-1} P(\{|\zeta_n| > t\})$$

whenever $P(\{|\zeta_n - \zeta_k| \leqslant t\}) \geqslant \alpha$ for $k = 0, 1, 2, \ldots, n$.

PROOF. Let A_k and B_k be the events defined by $A_k = \{|\zeta_1| \leqslant 2t, \ldots, |\zeta_{k-1}| \leqslant 2t, |\zeta_k| > 2t\}$, $B_k = \{|\zeta_n - \zeta_k| \leqslant t\}$, $k = 0, 1, \ldots, n$. Then,

$$E = \{|\zeta_n| > t\} \supseteq \bigcup_{k=1}^{n} (A_k \cap B_k).$$

$A_1, A_2, \ldots, A_n$ are disjoint and for each fixed k, A_k and B_k are independent. Hence

$$\begin{aligned} P(\{|\zeta_n| > t\}) &\geqslant P\left\{\bigcup_{k=1}^{n} (A_k \cap B_k)\right\} \\ &= \sum_{k=1}^{n} P(A_k)P(B_k) \geqslant \alpha \sum_{k=1}^{n} P(A_k) \\ &= \alpha P(\{\max_{1 \leqslant k \leqslant n} |\zeta_k| > 2t\}). \end{aligned}$$

This completes the proof.

Let $\{\xi_{ni}\}$, $i = 1, 2, \ldots, k_n$ be a triangular sequence of random variables defined on a probability space $(X, \mathscr{B}, P)$ satisfying the following conditions:

(i) for each fixed n, the random variables $\{\xi_{ni}\}$ are independent.

(ii) $E\xi_{ni} = 0$, $V(\xi_{ni}) = b_{ni}$, $\sum_{i=1}^{k_n} b_{ni} = 1$, V denoting variance.

(iii) the distribution functions F_{ni} of the random variables ξ_{ni}, $i = 1, 2, \ldots, k_n$ satisfy the Lindeberg condition, i.e., for every $\varepsilon > 0$,

$$\lim_{n \to \infty} \sum_{i=1}^{k_n} \int_{|u| > \varepsilon} u^2 \, dF_{ni}(u) = 0.$$

Let $\xi_n(t)$, $t \in [0, 1]$ be the random function defined as follows:

$$\xi_n(t) = S_{nk} + \frac{t - t_{nk}}{t_{nk+1} - t_{nk}} [S_{nk+1} - S_{nk}], \qquad t \in [t_{nk}, t_{nk+1}],$$

where

$$t_{n0} = 0, \quad S_{n0} = 0, \quad t_{nk} = \sum_{i=1}^{k} b_{ni}, \quad S_{nk} = \sum_{i=1}^{k} \xi_{ni}, \quad k \geqslant 1.$$

It is clear that $\xi_n(t) = S_{nk}$ whenever $t = t_{nk}$ and $\xi_n(t)$ is the straight line joining (t_{nk}, S_{nk}) and (t_{nk+1}, S_{nk+1}) in the interval $[t_{nk}, t_{nk+1}]$. Thus $\xi_n(t)$ is continuous with probability one. Thus there corresponds a measure P_n in the space $(C, \mathscr{B}_C)$, according to which the stochastic process $\xi_n(t)$, $t \in [0, 1]$ is distributed.

Theorem 4.1

Let $\xi_n(t)$ be the process described above and P_n the distribution of $\xi_n(t)$ in the space $(C, \mathscr{B}_C)$. Then $P_n \Rightarrow W$ as $n \to \infty$ where W is the Wiener measure on $(C, \mathscr{B}_C)$.

PROOF. Let $w(t)$ denote the Brownian motion process and W its distribution in C. We shall first establish that the finite dimensional distributions of the process $\xi_n(t)$ converge weakly to the corresponding finite dimensional distributions of the process $w(t)$. Let

$$\xi_n'(t) = \sum_{t_{ni} < t} \xi_{ni}, \qquad t \in [0, 1],$$

$$\xi_n'(0) = 0.$$

Then, for any $\alpha > 0$,

$$P(\{|\xi_n'(t) - \xi_n(t)| > \alpha\}) \leqslant P(\{\sup_i |\xi_{ni}| > \alpha\})$$

$$\leqslant \sum_{i=1}^{k} P(\{|\xi_{ni}| > \alpha\}) = \sum_{i=1}^{k_n} \int_{|u|>\alpha} dF_{ni}(u)$$

$$\leqslant \alpha^{-2} \sum_{i=1}^{k_n} \int_{|u|>\alpha} u^2 \, dF_{ni}.$$

By condition (iii) the last term on the right of the above inequality tends to zero as $n \to \infty$. Thus, in order to prove the convergence of the finite dimensional distributions of $\xi_n(t)$, it is sufficient to do the same for $\xi_n'(t)$. Since $w(t)$ and $\xi_n'(t)$ are processes with independent increments and $w(0) = \xi_n'(0) = 0$, it is sufficient to prove the convergence of the distribution of $\xi_n'(t'') - \xi_n'(t')$ to the distribution of $w(t'') - w(t')$ for all $0 \leqslant t' \leqslant t'' \leqslant 1$. We note that

$$\xi_n'(t'') - \xi_n'(t') = \sum_{t' \leqslant t_{ni} \leqslant t''} \xi_{ni}$$

which is a sum of independent random variables obeying the Lindeberg condition. Hence by the central limit theorem (cf. [10], pp. 101–103), the distribution of $\xi_n'(t'') - \xi_n'(t')$ converges to the normal distribution with mean 0 and variance equal to

$$\lim_{n\to\infty} \sum_{t'\leqslant t_{ni}\leqslant t''} V(\xi_{ni}) = t'' - t'.$$

Indeed, for any $\varepsilon > 0$,

$$\left| \sum_{t'\leqslant t_{ni}\leqslant t''} V(\xi_{ni}) - (t''-t') \right| \leqslant \max_i b_{ni}$$

$$\leqslant \varepsilon^2 + \max_i \int\limits_{|u|>\varepsilon} u^2\, dF_{ni}(u) \leqslant \varepsilon^2 + \sum_{i=1}^{k_n} \int\limits_{|u|>\varepsilon} u^2\, dF_{ni}(u),$$

and the last term on the right-hand side of the above inequality tends to zero as $n \to \infty$. This completes the proof of the convergence of the finite dimensional distributions of $\xi_n(t)$.

We shall now show that the sequence of measures $\{P_n\}$ in C is conditionally compact. Let $\Gamma = \{P_n : n = 1, 2, \ldots\}$. That Γ satisfies condition (i) of Theorem 2.2 follows immediately from the fact that

$$P\{\xi_n(0) = 0\} = 1.$$

In order to prove condition (ii) of Theorem 2.2, it is equivalent to showing that, for every $\varepsilon > 0$,

$$\lim_{h\to 0} \overline{\lim_{n\to\infty}} P\{\sup_{|t'-t''|\leqslant h} |\xi_n(t') - \xi_n(t'')| > \varepsilon\} = 0. \tag{4.1}$$

Since

$$\sup_{|t'-t''|\leqslant h} |\xi_n(t') - \xi_n(t'')| \leqslant 2 \sup_k \sup_{kh<t\leqslant \overline{k+2h}} |\xi_n(t) - \xi_n(kh)|$$

$$\leqslant 4 \sup_k \sup_{kh<t\leqslant (k+1)h} |\xi_n(t) - \xi_n(kh)|,$$

we have

$$P\{\sup_{|t'-t''|\leqslant h} |\xi_n(t') - \xi_n(t'')| > \varepsilon\}$$

$$\leqslant \sum_{kh<1} P\{\sup_{kh<t\leqslant (k+1)h} |\xi_n(t) - \xi_n(kh)| > \varepsilon/4\}. \tag{4.2}$$

But

$$\sup_{kh < t \leqslant (k+1)h} |\xi_n(t) - \xi_n(kh)| \leqslant 2 \sup_{j_{nk} < r \leqslant j_{n,k+1}} \left| \sum_{j=j_{nk}}^{r} \xi_{nj} \right| \tag{4.3}$$

where $j_{n_k} = \max\{j : t_{nj} \leqslant kh\}$. By Chebyshev's inequality

$$P\left\{ \left| \sum_{j=j_{nk}}^{j_{n,k+1}} \xi_{nj} \right| > \varepsilon/8 \right\} \leqslant 64/\varepsilon^2 \sum_{j=j_{nk}}^{j_{n,k+1}} V(\xi_{nj}) \to 64h/\varepsilon^2 \tag{4.4}$$

as $n \to \infty$. Equations (4.3) and (4.4), and Lemma 4.1, imply

$$\overline{\lim_{n\to\infty}} P\{ \sup_{kh < t \leqslant (k+1)h} |\xi_n(t) - \xi_n(kh)| > \varepsilon/4\}$$

$$\leqslant \overline{\lim_{n\to\infty}} \frac{1}{(1 - 64h/\varepsilon^2)} \sup_k P\left\{ \left| \sum_{j=j_{nk}}^{j_{n,k+1}} \xi_{nj} \right| > \varepsilon/8 \right\}$$

$$= \overline{\lim_{n\to\infty}} \frac{1}{(1 - 64h/\varepsilon^2)} \sup_k P\{|\xi_n(t_{nj_{n,k+1}}) - \xi_n(t_{nj_{nk}})| > \varepsilon/8\}.$$

From the convergence of the finite dimensional distributions we have

$$\overline{\lim_{n\to\infty}} P\{|\xi_n(t_{nj_{nk+1}}) - \xi_n(t_{nj_{nk}})| > \varepsilon/8\}$$

$$= 1/\sqrt{2\pi h} \int_{|u| > \varepsilon/8} \exp(-u^2/2h)\, du$$

for every k. From (4.2) we now obtain

$$\overline{\lim_{n\to\infty}} P\{ \sup_{|t'-t''| \leqslant h} |\xi_n(t') - \xi_n(t'')| > \varepsilon\}$$

$$\leqslant \sum_{k : kh < 1} \frac{1}{(1 - 64h/\varepsilon^2)} \frac{1}{\sqrt{2\pi}} \int_{|u| > \varepsilon/8\sqrt{h}} \exp(-u^2/2)\, du$$

$$\leqslant \frac{1}{\sqrt{2\pi}} \cdot \frac{1}{1 - 64h/\varepsilon^2} \cdot \frac{1}{h} \int_{|u| > \varepsilon/8\sqrt{h}} \exp(-u^2/2)\, du$$

Since

$$\frac{1}{h}\int_{|u|>c/\sqrt{h}} \exp(-u^2/2)\,du \leqslant \frac{1}{c^2}\int_{|u|>c/\sqrt{h}} u^2\exp(-u^2/2)\,du \to 0$$

as $h \to 0$, we have proved (4.1). By Theorem 2.2, Γ is conditionally compact. Hence $P_n \Rightarrow W$ in C.

Corollary 4.1

For any real valued continuous functional φ on the space C, the distribution of $\varphi(\xi_n)$ converges weakly to the distribution of $\varphi(w)$ as $n \to \infty$.

5. DISTRIBUTIONS OF CERTAIN RANDOM VARIABLES ASSOCIATED WITH THE BROWNIAN MOTION

Let W be the Wiener measure in the space C. For any continuous function $x \in C$, let

$$f_1(x) = \max_{t\in[0,1]} x(t)$$

$$f_2(x) = \max_{t\in[0,1]} |x(t)|.$$

It is clear that f_1 and f_2 are continuous functionals on C. We shall now find the distributions of f_1 and f_2 when x is distributed according to W.

For any $a \neq 0$, let $\tau_a(x)$ be such a point in $[0, 1]$ that $x(t)/a \leqslant 1$ for $t \leqslant \tau_a$ and for any $\delta > 0$, $\sup_{\tau_a \leqslant t \leqslant \tau_a+\delta} [x(t)/a] > 1$. If however $x(t)/a \leqslant 1$ for all t, then $\tau_a(x)$ is defined to be $+\infty$. τ_a is then a well-defined functional on C and is called the time of first crossing of the level a.

Let $\tau_a'(x)$ be such a point that $x(t)/a < 1$ for all $t < \tau_a'$ and $x(\tau_a') = a$. If however $x(t)/a < 1$ for all t, then τ_a' is defined to be $+\infty$. Then τ_a' is a well-defined functional on C and is called the time of first hit of the level a.

Lemma 5.1

$$W\{x: \tau_a'(x) = \tau_a(x)\} = 1.$$

PROOF. Since $x(t)$ and $-x(t)$ have the same distribution under W we may assume without loss of generality that $a > 0$. We have

$$\{x: \tau_a'(x) < \tau_a(x)\} \subseteq \bigcup_{\substack{r,m=1 \\ r \leqslant m}}^{\infty} \{x: \max_{0 \leqslant t \leqslant r/m} x(t) = a\}.$$

Since $\tau_a'(x) \leqslant \tau_a(x)$ for all $x \in C$, it is enough to show that

$$W\{x: \max_{0 \leqslant s \leqslant t} x(s) = a\} = 0$$

for every t. Since, for any $t_1 < t$,

$$\{x: \max_{0 \leqslant s \leqslant t} x(s) = a\} \subseteq \{x: \max_{0 \leqslant s \leqslant t_1} x(s) = a\} \cup \{x: \max_{t_1 < s \leqslant t} x(s) = a\},$$

and $x(t_1)$ and $\max_{t_1 < s \leqslant t} \{x(s) - x(t_1)\}$ are independent random variables in the probability space $(C, \mathscr{B}_C, W)$ and $x(t_1)$ is distributed normally with variance t_1, we have

$$W\{x: \max_{0 \leqslant s \leqslant t} x(s) = a\} \leqslant W\{x: \max_{0 \leqslant s \leqslant t_1} x(s) = a\}$$
$$+ \frac{1}{\sqrt{2\pi t_1}} \int W\{x: \max_{t_1 < s \leqslant t} [x(s) - x(t_1)] = a - u\} \exp(-u^2/2t_1)\, du.$$

Since $W\{x: \max_{t_1 < s \leqslant t} [x(s) - x(t_1)] = z\} = 0$, except for a countable set of z, the second term on the right-hand side of the above inequality is zero. Thus

$$W\{x: \max_{0 \leqslant s \leqslant t} x(s) = a\} \leqslant W\{x: \max_{0 \leqslant s \leqslant t_1} x(s) = a\}$$

for every $t_1 < t$. Thus the function $W\{x: \max_{0 \leqslant s \leqslant t} x(s) = a\}$ is non-decreasing as $t \downarrow 0$. Since $W\{x: x(0) = 0\} = 1$, we have $W\{\max_{0 \leqslant s \leqslant t} x(s) > \varepsilon\} \to 0$ as $t \to 0$, for every $\varepsilon > 0$. Thus

$$W\{x: \max_{0 \leqslant s \leqslant t} x(s) = a\} \leqslant \lim_{t \downarrow 0} W\{x: \max_{0 \leqslant s \leqslant t} x(s) > a/2\}$$
$$= 0.$$

This completes the proof of the lemma.

Since $\tau_a = \tau_a'$ with probability one we shall denote both of them by τ_a.

The next lemma describes the invariance of W under certain types of reflection transformations in the space C.

Lemma 5.2

For any $x \in C$ and $a \neq 0$, let $T_a x$ be the function defined as follows:

$$(T_a x)(t) = x(t) \qquad \text{if} \quad t < \tau_a,$$

$$= 2a - x(t) \qquad \text{if} \quad t \geq \tau_a.$$

The Wiener measure W is invariant under the transformation T_a, i.e., $W = WT_a^{-1}$.

PROOF. Let $x_{n_k} = x(k/n) - x(\overline{k-1}/n)$, $x^{(n)}(t) = \sum_{k \leq nt} x_{n_k}$, $x_1^{(n)}(t) = \sum_{k \leq nt} (-1)^{\varepsilon_{n_k}} x_{n_k}$, where $\varepsilon_{n_k} = 0$ if $\sup_{j \leq k-1} [x_1^{(n)}(j/n)]/a \leq 1$ and $\varepsilon_{n_k} = 1$ if $\sup_{j \leq k-1} [x_1^{(n)}(j/n)]/a > 1$. Then the random variables $(-1)^{\varepsilon_{n_k}} x_{n_k}$ are independently and identically distributed. This is because x_{n_k} is independent of $\varepsilon_{n_k}, x_{n_1}, \ldots, x_{n_{k-1}}$. Since x_{n_k} and $-x_{n_k}$ are identically distributed it follows that $(-1)^{\varepsilon_{n_k}} x_{n_k}$ is distributed normally with mean zero and variance $1/n$. Hence the finite dimensional distributions of the processes $x^{(n)}(t)$ and $x_1^{(n)}(t)$ coincide. Since the functions $x^{(n)}(t)$ and $x_1^{(n)}(t)$ converge uniformly to $x(t)$ and $(T_a x)(t)$, respectively, with probability one as $n \to \infty$, it follows that $W = WT_a^{-1}$.

Theorem 5.1

For $a > 0$,

$$W\{x: \max_{0 \leq t \leq T} x(t) > a, \quad x(T) \in [c, d]\}$$

$$= \frac{1}{\sqrt{2\pi T}} \int_{\max[c, a]}^{\max[d, a]} \exp(-u^2/2T)\, du + \frac{1}{\sqrt{2\pi T}} \int_{\max[2a-d, a]}^{\max[2a-c, a]} \exp(-u^2/2T)\, du.$$

PROOF. We have, since $W\{x: x(T) = a\} = 0$,

$$\begin{aligned}
&W\{x: \max_{0 \leqslant t \leqslant T} x(t) > a, \quad x(T) \in [c, d]\} \\
&= W\{x: x(T) \in [c, d] \cap [a, \infty)\} \\
&\quad + W\{x: \max_{0 \leqslant t \leqslant T} x(t) > a, \quad x(T) \in [c, d] \cap (-\infty, a]\}. \qquad (5.1)
\end{aligned}$$

Let T_a be the transformation defined in Lemma 5.2. Since by the proof of Lemma 5.1, $W\{x: \max_{0 \leqslant t \leqslant T} x(t) = a\} = 0$, we have by Lemma 5.2,

$$\begin{aligned}
&W\{x: \max_{0 \leqslant t \leqslant T} x(t) > a, \quad x(T) \in [c, d] \cap (-\infty, a]\} \\
&= W\{x: \max_{0 \leqslant t \leqslant T} (T_a x)(t) > a, \quad (T_a x)(T) \in [c, d] \cap (-\infty, a]\} \\
&= W\{x: \max_{0 \leqslant t \leqslant T} x(t) \geqslant a, \quad x(T) \in [2a - d, 2a - c] \cap [a, \infty)\}.
\end{aligned}$$

But the event $\{x(T) \in [2a - d, 2a - c] \cap [a, \infty)\}$ implies the event $\{\max_{0 \leqslant t \leqslant T} x(t) \geqslant a\}$. Hence

$$\begin{aligned}
&W\{x: \max_{0 \leqslant t \leqslant T} x(t) > a, x(T) \in [c, d] \cap (-\infty, a]\} \\
&= \frac{1}{\sqrt{2\pi T}} \int_{\max[2a-d, a]}^{\max[2a-c, a]} e^{-u^2/2T} \, du. \qquad (5.2)
\end{aligned}$$

Further

$$\begin{aligned}
&W\{x: x(T) \in [c, d] \cap [a, \infty)\} \\
&= \int_{\max[c, a]}^{\max[d, a]} \frac{1}{\sqrt{2\pi T}} \exp(-u^2/2T) \, du. \qquad (5.3)
\end{aligned}$$

Equations (5.1)–(5.3) complete the proof of the theorem.

By taking $[c, d] = (-\infty, +\infty)$ in the above theorem we obtain

Corollary 5.1

For $a > 0$,

$$W\{x: \max_{0 \leqslant t \leqslant T} x(t) > a\} = \frac{2}{\sqrt{2\pi T}} \int_a^\infty \exp(-u^2/2T) \, du.$$

Theorem 5.2

Let $a_1 < 0 < a_2$ *and* $[c, d] \subset [a_1, a_2]$. *Then*

$$W\{x: \min_{0 \leqslant t \leqslant T} x(t) > a_1, \max_{0 \leqslant t \leqslant T} x(t) < a_2, x(T) \in [c, d]\}$$

$$= \frac{1}{\sqrt{2\pi T}} \sum_{-\infty}^{+\infty} \int_c^d \left\{ \exp\left[-\frac{1}{2T} (u + 2k(a_2 - a_1))^2 \right] \right.$$

$$\left. - \exp\left[-\frac{1}{2T} (u - 2a_2 + 2k(a_2 - a_1))^2 \right] \right\} du. \tag{5.4}$$

PROOF. Let $A_k^{(i)}$ be the event that in the interval $[0, T]$, $x(t)$ crosses the level a_i before crossing a_j $(j \neq i, i, j = 1, 2)$, crosses the interval $[a_1, a_2]$ at least k times and $x(T) \in [c, d]$. By crossing the interval $[a_1, a_2]$, k times in the period $[0, T]$ we mean that the function $\operatorname{sgn}(x(t) - a_1) + \operatorname{sgn}(x(t) - a_2)$* changes sign k times in the interval $[0, T]$. Then the expression on the left-hand side of Eq. (5.4) can be written as

$$W\{x: x(T) \in [c, d]\} - W(A_0^{(1)}) - W(A_0^{(2)}). \tag{5.5}$$

In order to calculate $W(A_0^{(i)})$ we shall find the probability

$$W(A_k^{(i)}) + W(A_{k+1}^{(j)}) = W(A_k^{(i)} \cup A_{k+1}^{(j)}) \qquad (i \neq j, \quad i = 1, 2).$$

The event $A_k^{(i)} \cup A_{k+1}^{(j)}$ is the same as saying that in the interval $[0, T]$, $x(t)$ crosses the level a_i, crosses the interval $[a_1, a_2]$ at least k times and falls in $[c, d]$ at time T. Let τ_1 be the time of first crossing of the level a_i, τ_2 the time of first crossing of the level a_j after τ_1, and τ_3 the time of first crossing of the level a_i after τ_2, etc. Let

$$\begin{aligned}
(T_1 x)(t) &= x(t) \qquad \text{if } t < \tau_1, \\
&= 2x(\tau_1) - x(t) \qquad \text{if } t \geqslant \tau_1, \\
(T_2 x)(t) &= (T_1 x)(t) \qquad \text{if } t < \tau_2, \\
&= 2(T_1 x)(\tau_2) - (T_1 x)(t) \qquad \text{if } t \geqslant \tau_2. \\
&\cdots\cdots\cdots\cdots\cdots\cdots \\
(T_n x)(t) &= (T_{n-1} x)(t) \qquad \text{if } t < \tau_n, \\
&= 2(T_{n-1} x)(\tau_n) - (T_{n-1} x)(t) \qquad \text{if } t \geqslant \tau_n.
\end{aligned}$$

---

* $\operatorname{sgn} x$ denotes the function defined by $\operatorname{sgn} x = +1$ if $x \geqslant 0$, $= -1$ if $x < 0$.

Since $T_{l-1}x$ crosses the level $a_i + (l-1)(a_i - a_j)$ for the first time at τ_l, it follows from Lemma 5.2 and induction that W is invariant under the transformations $T_1, T_2, \ldots$. If the event $A_k^{(i)} \cup A_{k+1}^{(j)}$ occurs then the function $(T_{k+1}x)(t)$ crosses successively the levels

$$a_i, a_i + (a_i - a_j), \ldots, a_i + k(a_i - a_j)$$

during the interval $[0, T)$, and at time T falls in the interval $[c_k, d_k]$, where

$$\left.\begin{aligned} c_k &= c + (k+1)(a_i - a_j) \\ d_k &= d + (k+1)(a_i - a_j) \end{aligned}\right\} \quad \text{if } k \text{ is odd,}$$

$$\left.\begin{aligned} c_k &= 2a_i - d + k(a_i - a_j) \\ d_k &= 2a_i - c + k(a_i - a_j) \end{aligned}\right\} \quad \text{if } k \text{ is even.} \tag{5.6}$$

Conversely, if $(T_{k+1}x)(T)$ satisfies the conditions mentioned above, then the event $A_k^{(i)} \cup A_{k+1}^{(j)}$ takes place. This is because $x(0) = 0$ with probability one and in order that $(T_{k+1}x)(t)$ may fall in the interval $[c_k, d_k]$ at time T, it must cross the levels $a_i + l(a_i - a_j)$, $l = 0, \ldots, k$. Hence

$$\begin{aligned} W(A_k^{(i)} \cup A_{k+1}^{(j)}) &= W\{(T_{k+1}x)(t) \in [c_k, d_k]\} \\ &= W\{x \colon x(T) \in [c_k, d_k]\}. \end{aligned} \tag{5.7}$$

Since a continuous function cannot cross the interval $[a_1, a_2]$ more than a finite number of times in the period $[0, T]$, it follows that $W(A_k^{(i)}) \to 0$ as $k \to \infty$. Hence letting $n \to \infty$ in the relation

$$\begin{aligned} W(A_0^{(1)}) + W(A_0^{(2)}) &= (-1)^{n+1}\left[\sum_{i=1}^{2} W(A_{n+1}^{(i)})\right] \\ &\quad + \sum_{k=0}^{n} (-1)^k \left\{\sum_{i=1}^{2} [W(A_k^{(i)}) + W(A_{k+1}^{(i)})]\right\}, \end{aligned}$$

we obtain

$$W(A_0^{(1)}) + W(A_0^{(2)}) = \sum_{0}^{\infty} (-1)^k \left\{\sum_{i=1}^{2} [W(A_k^{(i)}) + W(A_{k+1}^{(i)})]\right\}. \tag{5.8}$$

From Eqs. (5.6)–(5.8) we have

$$W(A_0^{(1)}) + W(A_0^{(2)}) = \frac{1}{\sqrt{2\pi T}} \sum_{k=0}^{\infty} \Bigg[\int_{2a_1 - d + 2k(a_1 - a_2)}^{2a_1 - c + 2k(a_1 - a_2)} + \int_{2a_2 - d + 2k(a_2 - a_1)}^{2a_2 - c + 2k(a_2 - a_1)}$$

$$- \int_{c + 2(k+1)(a_1 - a_2)}^{d + 2(k+1)(a_1 - a_2)} - \int_{c + 2(k+1)(a_2 - a_1)}^{d + 2(k+1)(a_2 - a_1)} \exp(-u^2/2T)\, du \Bigg]$$

Equation (5.5) and the above equation yield (5.4). This completes the proof.

Corollary 5.2

For $a_1 < 0$, $a_2 > 0$,

$$W\{x: \min_{0 \leqslant t \leqslant T} x(t) > a_1, \max_{0 \leqslant t \leqslant T} < a_2\}$$

$$= \frac{1}{\sqrt{2\pi T}} \sum_{k=-\infty}^{+\infty} \int_{a_1}^{a_2} \Bigg\{ \exp\left[-\frac{1}{2T} (u + 2k(a_2 - a_1))^2 \right]$$

$$- \exp\left[-\frac{1}{2T} (u - 2a_2 + 2k(a_2 - a_1))^2 \right] \Bigg\} du.$$

Corollary 5.3

For $a > 0$, $[c, d] \subset [-a, a]$,

$$W\{x: \max_{0 \leqslant t \leqslant T} |x(t)| < a, x(T) \in [c, d]\}$$

$$= \frac{1}{\sqrt{2\pi T}} \int_c^d \sum_{k=-\infty}^{+\infty} (-1)^k \exp\left[-\frac{(u - 2ka)^2}{2T} \right] du.$$

Corollary 5.4

Let $\{\xi_{ni}\}$, $i = 1, 2, \ldots, k_n$ be a triangular sequence of real valued random variables satisfying the following conditions:

(1) for each fixed n $\{\xi_{ni}\}$ are independent;
(2) $E\xi_{ni} = 0$, $V(\xi_{ni}) = b_{ni}$, $\sum_{i=1}^{k_n} b_{ni} = 1$, V denoting variance;
(3) for every $\varepsilon > 0$,

$$\lim_{n\to\infty} \sum_{i=1}^{k_n} \int_{|u|>\varepsilon} u^2 \, dF_{ni}(u) = 0,$$

where F_{ni} is the distribution function of ξ_{ni}. Then

$$\lim_{n\to\infty} P\{\max_{1\leqslant k\leqslant k_n} |\xi_{n1} + \ldots + \xi_{nk}| \leqslant a\}$$

$$= \frac{1}{\sqrt{2\pi}} \int_{-a}^{a} \sum_{k=-\infty}^{+\infty} (-1)^k \exp\left[-\frac{(u-2ka)^2}{2}\right] du, \quad a > 0;$$

$$\lim_{n\to\infty} P\{\max_{1\leqslant k\leqslant k_n} (\xi_{n1} + \ldots + \xi_{nk}) < a\}$$

$$= \frac{2}{\sqrt{2\pi}} \int_0^a \exp(-u^2/2)\, du, \qquad a > 0.$$

PROOF. This follows from the fact that

$$\max_{1\leqslant k\leqslant k_n} |\xi_{n1} + \ldots + \xi_{nk}| = \max_{0\leqslant t\leqslant 1} |\xi_n(t)|$$

$$\max_{1\leqslant k\leqslant k_n} (\xi_{n1} + \ldots + \xi_{nk}) = \max_{0\leqslant t\leqslant 1} \xi_n(t),$$

where $\xi_n(t)$ is the stochastic process constructed in Theorem 4.1, Corollary 4.1 to Theorem 4.1, Corollary 5.1 to Theorem 5.1, and Corollary 5.3 to Theorem 5.2.

6. THE SPACE $D[0, 1]$

Let $D[0, 1]$ be the space of all real valued functions $f(t)$ defined on the unit interval and satisfying the following properties:

(1) At every point $t \in [0, 1)$, there exists a limit $f(t+0)$ from the right;
(2) At every point $t \in (0, 1]$, there exists a limit $f(t-0)$ from the left;

(3) At every point $t \in (0, 1)$, $f(t) = f(t + 0)$ or $f(t) = f(t - 0)$ (with possibly a different alternative at different points);

(4) The values at the points 0 and 1 are arbitrary.

The following lemma is obvious.

Lemma 6.1

Every function $f \in D[0, 1]$ is bounded.

Definition 6.1

A function $f \in D[0, 1]$ is said to have at least m ε-oscillations ($\varepsilon > 0$) if there exist points $t_0, t_1, \ldots, t_m$, $0 \leqslant t_0 < t_1 < \ldots < t_m \leqslant 1$ such that $|f(t_{k-1}) - f(t_k)| > \varepsilon$, $k = 1, 2, \ldots, m$.

Lemma 6.2

In order that a function f may belong to $D[0, 1]$ it is necessary and sufficient that for every $\varepsilon > 0$, f has only a finite number of ε-oscillations.

PROOF. Suppose that the condition of the lemma holds. Let $t \in (0, 1]$, and $\varepsilon > 0$ be arbitrary. Let m_0 be the maximum number of $\varepsilon/2$-oscillations of f in the interval $[0, t]$. Then there exist points $0 \leqslant t_0 < t_1 < \ldots < t_{m_0} \leqslant t$ such that $|f(t_{k-1}) - f(t_k)| > \varepsilon/2$, $k = 1, 2, \ldots, m_0$. Suppose $t_{m_0} < t$. For any $t', t'' \in (t_{m_0}, t)$, we have from the maximality of m_0,

$$|f(t_{m_0}) - f(t')| \leqslant \varepsilon/2,$$

$$|f(t_{m_0}) - f(t'')| \leqslant \varepsilon/2,$$

and hence

$$|f(t') - f(t'')| \leqslant \varepsilon$$

If $t_{m_0} = t$, then for any $t', t'' \in (t_{m_0-1}, t)$, the above inequality holds similarly. Since ε is arbitrary it follows that $f(t - 0)$ exists. Similarly it is shown that $f(t + 0)$ exists for all $t \in [0, 1)$. This proves sufficiency.

Suppose at a certain point t_0, $f(t_0 - 0)$ does not exist. Then there exists a sequence $t_n \uparrow t_0$ such that for every n, $\sup_{m>n} |f(t_m) - f(t_n)| > \varepsilon$. This implies the existence of an infinite number of ε-oscillations. The same is the case if $f(t_0 + 0)$ does not exist. This completes the proof.

REMARK. It is also clear that a function $f \in D[0, 1]$ cannot have more than a countable number of discontinuities. Indeed if the contrary is true then there exists an ε such that $|f(t+0) - f(t-0)| > \varepsilon$ for an infinite number of points t. Thus we can construct a sequence $\{t_n\}$ either strictly increasing or decreasing to a t_0 such that

$$|f(t_n + 0) - f(t_n - 0)| > \varepsilon \qquad \text{for all} \quad n.$$

But both $f(t_n + 0)$ and $f(t_n - 0)$ converge to the same limit which is either $f(t_0 + 0)$ or $f(t_0 - 0)$ as $n \to \infty$. This leads to a contradiction.

We shall now consider two functions to be equivalent if they agree at all continuity points of one of them. Then $D[0, 1]$ is divided into equivalence classes and we shall denote the space of equivalence classes by D. We can assume that an equivalence class containing a function f is represented by the function $\tilde{f}$ where

$$\tilde{f}(t) = f(t+0), \qquad \tilde{f}(0) = f(+0), \qquad \tilde{f}(1) = f(1-0).$$

We shall tacitly assume that the space D consists of all functions f with the property

$$f(t+0) = f(t), \qquad f(0) = f(+0), \qquad f(1) = f(1-0).$$

$|f(t+0) - f(t-0)|$ is called the jump at the point t.

Since many stochastic processes have the property that the sample paths have discontinuities of the first kind only with probability one it is useful to introduce a metric topology in the space D and study the weak topology in the space of probability measures on D. The uniform metric

$$d(f, g) = \sup_t |f(t) - g(t)|$$

is not very useful since in such a case the space D becomes nonseparable. In fact the family of functions f_τ, $0 < \tau < 1$, where

$$\begin{aligned} f_\tau(t) &= 0 \qquad \text{if} \quad t < \tau, \\ &= 1 \qquad \text{if} \quad t \geqslant \tau \end{aligned}$$

is uncountable and $d(f_\tau, f_{\tau'}) = 1$ for $\tau \neq \tau'$. We shall introduce a slightly weaker topology, called the Skorohod topology in the space D, in order to make it a separable metric space.

Let H be the space of all homeomorphisms λ of the interval $[0, 1]$ onto itself such that $\lambda(0) = 0$, $\lambda(1) = 1$. H is a group under composition.

For any two $f, g \in D$, let

$$s(f, g) = \inf_{\lambda \in H} [\sup_t |f(t) - g(\lambda(t))| + \sup_t |t - \lambda(t)|].$$

It is clear that $s(f, g) = 0$ if and only if $f = g$. Since H is a group

$$\begin{aligned} s(f, g) &= \inf_{\lambda \in H} [\sup_t |f(t) - g(\lambda(t))| + \sup_t |t - \lambda(t)|] \\ &= \inf_{\lambda \in H} [\sup_t |f(\lambda^{-1}(t)) - g(t)| + \sup_t |t - \lambda^{-1}(t)|] \\ &= s(g, f). \end{aligned}$$

We shall now show that for any $f, g, h \in D$,

$$s(f, h) \leqslant s(f, g) + s(g, h).$$

Indeed, for any $\varepsilon > 0$, there exist $\lambda_1, \lambda_2 \in H$ such that

$$s(f, g) \geqslant \sup_t |f(t) - g(\lambda_1(t))| + \sup_t |t - \lambda_1(t)| - \varepsilon,$$

$$s(g, h) \geqslant \sup_t |g(t) - h(\lambda_2(t))| + \sup_t |t - \lambda_2(t)| - \varepsilon.$$

Hence

$$\begin{aligned} s(f, h) &\leqslant \sup_t |f(t) - h(\lambda_2(\lambda_1(t)))| + \sup_t |t - \lambda_2(\lambda_1(t))| \\ &\leqslant \sup_t |f(t) - g(\lambda_1(t))| + \sup_t |t - \lambda_1(t)| \\ &\quad + \sup_t |g(\lambda_1(t)) - h(\lambda_2(\lambda_1(t)))| + \sup_t |\lambda_1(t) - \lambda_2(\lambda_1(t))| \\ &\leqslant s(f, g) + \varepsilon + \sup_t |g(t) - h(\lambda_2(t))| + \sup_t |t - \lambda_2(t)| \\ &\leqslant s(f, g) + s(g, h) + 2\varepsilon. \end{aligned}$$

Since ε is arbitrary, the required property is proved.

Thus s is a metric in the space D and is called the *Skorohod metric*. The topology induced by s is called the *Skorohod topology*.

For any real valued function f defined on $[0, 1]$ and $\delta > 0$, let

$$\omega_f(\delta) = \sup_{|t'-t''|\leqslant\delta} |f(t') - f(t'')|, \tag{6.1}$$

$$\tilde{\omega}_f(\delta) = \max\{\sup_{t-\delta\leqslant t'\leqslant t\leqslant t''\leqslant t+\delta} (\min[|f(t') - f(t)|; |f(t'') - f(t)|]),$$

$$\sup_{0\leqslant t\leqslant\delta} |f(t) - f(0)|, \sup_{1-\delta\leqslant t\leqslant 1} |f(t) - f(1)|\}. \tag{6.2}$$

Note that $\tilde{\omega}_f(\delta)$ and $\omega_f(\delta)$ monotonically decrease if δ decreases.

Lemma 6.3

For every $f \in D$, $\lim_{\delta\to 0} \tilde{\omega}_f(\delta) = 0$.

Proof. It is clear from the definition of the space D that the last two terms within "max" in (6.2) tend to zero as $\delta \to 0$. Suppose the first term does not tend to zero. Then there exist an $\varepsilon > 0$ and three sequences $t_n' < t_n < t_n''$ such that

$$|f(t_n') - f(t_n)| > \varepsilon, \qquad |f(t_n'') - f(t_n)| > \varepsilon \tag{6.3}$$

for all n and $|t_n' - t_n''| \to 0$ as $n \to \infty$. By passing over to a subsequence if necessary, we may assume that t_n converges to a point $t_0 \in [0, 1]$. Then the sequences $f(t_n'), f(t_n), f(t_n'')$ can have at the most two limit points $f(t_0 - 0)$ and $f(t_0 + 0) = f(t_0)$, so that at least two of them must have the same limit. This contradicts (6.3) and completes the proof.

Lemma 6.4

Let $f \in D$ *and* $[\alpha, \beta] \subseteq [0, 1]$. *If* f *has no jumps of magnitude* $> \varepsilon$ *in the interval* $[\alpha, \beta]$, *then*

$$\sup_{|t'-t''|\leqslant\delta,\, t',t''\in[\alpha,\beta]} |f(t') - f(t'')| \leqslant 2\tilde{\omega}_f(\delta) + \varepsilon.$$

Proof. Let t' and t'' be two fixed points in the interval $[\alpha, \beta]$ such that $|t' - t''| \leqslant \delta$ and $0 < \varepsilon' < \varepsilon$. Let $\tau \in [t', t'']$ be any point with the property

$$|f(t') - f(t)| < \tilde{\omega}_f(\delta) + \varepsilon' \qquad \text{if} \quad t' \leqslant t < \tau,$$

$$|f(t') - f(\tau)| \geqslant \tilde{\omega}_f(\delta) + \varepsilon'.$$

If no such τ exists then $|f(t') - f(t'')| < \tilde{\omega}_f(\delta) + \varepsilon'$. Suppose such a τ exists. From (6.2) we have

$$\min\{|f(\tau) - f(t')|; |f(\tau) - f(t'')|\} \leqslant \tilde{\omega}_f(\delta).$$

Since

$$|f(t') - f(\tau)| \geqslant \tilde{\omega}_f(\delta) + \varepsilon',$$

we have

$$|f(\tau) - f(t'')| \leqslant \tilde{\omega}_f(\delta).$$

Thus

$$\begin{aligned}|f(t'') - f(t')| &\leqslant |f(t'') - f(\tau)| + |f(\tau) - f(\tau - 0)| + |f(\tau - 0) - f(t')| \\ &\leqslant 2\tilde{\omega}_f(\delta) + \varepsilon' + \varepsilon.\end{aligned}$$

Hence in any case

$$|f(t'') - f(t')| \leqslant 2\tilde{\omega}_f(\delta) + \varepsilon' + \varepsilon.$$

Letting $\varepsilon' \to 0$ we complete the proof.

Let $D_{m,n}$ denote the class of all functions in D which are constant in each of the intervals $[k/n, \overline{k+1}/n)$, and taking values which are multiples of $1/m$.

Lemma 6.5

For every function $f \in D$ there exists a function $f^* \in D_{m,n}$ such that

$$s(f, f^*) \leqslant \frac{1}{n} + \frac{1}{m} + 4\tilde{\omega}_f\left(\frac{2}{n}\right).$$

PROOF. We first observe that the function f has the property that in any interval $[k/n, \overline{k+1}/n)$ there cannot exist more than one point at which the magnitude of the jump exceeds $2\tilde{\omega}_f(2/n)$. Indeed if τ is one such point then

$$\begin{aligned}|f(s) - f(\tau - 0)| &= \min\left(|f(s) - f(\tau - 0)|; |f(\tau) - f(\tau - 0)|\right) \\ &\leqslant \tilde{\omega}_f\left(\frac{1}{n}\right) \qquad \text{if} \quad s \in \left[\frac{k}{n}, \tau\right], \\ |f(s) - f(\tau)| &\leqslant \tilde{\omega}_f\left(\frac{1}{n}\right) \qquad \text{if} \quad s \in \left(\tau, \frac{k+1}{n}\right).\end{aligned}$$

(The last inequality follows from the fact that $\min(|f(\tau - 0) - f(\tau)|, |f(\tau) - f(s)|) \leqslant \tilde{\omega}_f(1/n)$ for $s \in (\tau, k+1/n)$ and $|f(\tau - 0) - f(\tau)| \geqslant 2\tilde{\omega}_f(2/n)$). Thus $|f(s) - f(s - 0)| \leqslant 2\tilde{\omega}_f(1/n) \leqslant 2\tilde{\omega}_f(2/n)$, for $s \neq \tau$.

Let τ_k be the point in the interval $[k/n, \overline{k+1}/n)$ at which $|f(\tau_k) - f(\tau_k - 0)| \geqslant 2\tilde{\omega}_f(2/n)$, if such a point τ_k exists. Let $\lambda(t)$ be the continuous function which takes the value 0 at $t = 0$, 1 at $t = 1$, τ_k at $t = \overline{k+1}/n$, $k = 0, 1, 2, \ldots, n-2$ and is linear between k/n and $\overline{k+1}/n$ for every $k = 0, 1, 2, \ldots, n-1$. Then λ is a homeomorphism of the unit interval onto itself. Further $t - 1/n \leqslant \lambda(t) \leqslant t$ for all t. Let

$$\bar{f}(t) = f(\lambda(t)).$$

It is clear that $\bar{f}$ can have jumps of magnitude exceeding $2\tilde{\omega}_f(2/n)$ only at the points k/n, $k = 1, 2, \ldots, n-1$. Further,

$$s(f, \bar{f}) \leqslant \sup_t |\bar{f}(t) - f(\lambda(t))| + \sup_t |t - \lambda(t)| \leqslant \frac{1}{n}. \tag{6.4}$$

Let $\bar{f}^*(t)$ be the function defined by

$$\begin{aligned} \bar{f}^*(t) &= \bar{f}\left(\frac{k}{n}\right) \quad \text{if} \quad t \in \left[\frac{k}{n}, \frac{k+1}{n}\right), \quad k \leqslant n-1 \\ &= \bar{f}\left(\frac{n-1}{n}\right) \quad \text{if} \quad t = 1. \end{aligned}$$

Then $\bar{f}^* \in D$ and

$$\begin{aligned} s(\bar{f}, \bar{f}^*) &\leqslant \sup_t |\bar{f}(t) - \bar{f}^*(t)| \\ &\leqslant \sup_k \sup_{k/n \leqslant t < (k+1)/n} \left| \bar{f}(t) - \bar{f}\left(\frac{k}{n}\right) \right|. \end{aligned}$$

Since the jumps of $\bar{f}$ exceeding $2\tilde{\omega}_f(2/n)$ in magnitude can occur only at the points k/n and there are no such jumps in every closed interval contained in $(k/n, \overline{k+1}/n)$, it follows from Lemma 6.4 that

$$\left| \bar{f}(t) - \bar{f}\left(\frac{k}{n}\right) \right| \leqslant 2\,\tilde{\omega}_{\bar{f}}\left(\frac{1}{n}\right) + 2\tilde{\omega}_f\left(\frac{2}{n}\right) \quad \text{if} \quad t \in \left[\frac{k}{n}, \frac{k+1}{n}\right).$$

We shall now estimate $\tilde{\omega}_{\bar{f}}(1/n)$. We have

$$\begin{aligned} \tilde{\omega}_{\bar{f}}(1/n) = \max\{ &\sup_{t-(1/n) \leqslant t' \leqslant t \leqslant t'' \leqslant t+(1/n)} [\min\{|\bar{f}(t') - \bar{f}(t)|; |\bar{f}(t) - \bar{f}(t'')|\}], \\ &\sup_{0 \leqslant t \leqslant (1/n)} |\bar{f}(t) - \bar{f}(0)|, \quad \sup_{1-(1/n) \leqslant t \leqslant 1} |\bar{f}(t) - \bar{f}(1)|\} \end{aligned}$$

$$= \max\{ \sup_{t-(1/n)\leqslant t'\leqslant t\leqslant t''\leqslant t+(1/n)} [\min\{|f(\lambda(t')) - f(\lambda(t))|; |f(\lambda(t)) - f(\lambda(t''))|\}],$$

$$\sup_{0\leqslant t\leqslant (1/n)} |f(\lambda(t)) - f(0)|, \sup_{1-(1/n)\leqslant t\leqslant 1} |f(\lambda(t)) - f(1)|\}.$$

Since, for $t_1 < t_2 < t_1 + 1/n$, we have $t_1 - 1/n < \lambda(t_1) < \lambda(t_2) \leqslant t_2 < t_1 + 1/n$ and $0 < \lambda(t_2) - \lambda(t_1) \leqslant 2/n$, we have

$$\tilde{\omega}_{\bar{f}}\left(\frac{1}{n}\right) \leqslant \tilde{\omega}_f\left(\frac{2}{n}\right).$$

Hence

$$s(\bar{f}, \bar{f}^*) \leqslant 4\tilde{\omega}_f\left(\frac{2}{n}\right). \tag{6.5}$$

Let $f^*(t)$ be the function defined by

$$f^*(t) = \frac{1}{m}[\text{int}(m\bar{f}^*(t))]$$

where "int" denotes integral part. Since $|f^*(t) - \bar{f}^*(t)| \leqslant 1/m$ for all t, we have from (6.4), (6.5) and the triangle inequality

$$s(f, f^*) \leqslant s(f, \bar{f}) + s(\bar{f}, \bar{f}^*) + s(\bar{f}^*, f^*)$$

$$\leqslant \frac{1}{n} + 4\tilde{\omega}_f\left(\frac{2}{n}\right) + \frac{1}{m}.$$

This completes the proof.

Theorem 6.1

The space D is separable under the Skorohod metric s.

PROOF. This is an immediate consequence of Lemmas 6.3, 6.5, and the fact that the sets $D_{m,n}$ introduced in the proof of Lemma 6.5 are countable.

Now we shall study the compact subsets of the space D under the Skorohod topology. To this end we shall examine the behavior of the sequence $\tilde{\omega}_{f_n}(\delta)$ when f_n converges to f. For any f, $\tilde{\omega}_f(\delta)$ is a monotonic function in δ which decreases to zero as $\delta \to 0$. Let us put

$$\begin{aligned} \bar{\omega}_f(z) &= \tilde{\omega}_f(e^z + 0) && \text{if } z < 0, \\ &= \tilde{\omega}_f(1) && \text{if } z \geqslant 0. \end{aligned}$$

Then $\bar{\omega}_f(z)$ is a monotonic right continuous function on the real line and hence corresponds to a measure $\bar{\omega}_f$.

Lemma 6.6

If $s(f_n, f) \to 0$ as $n \to \infty$, then $\bar{\omega}_{f_n} \Rightarrow \bar{\omega}_f$, where $\Rightarrow$ implies weak convergence.

PROOF. From the conditions of the lemma it is clear that there exists a sequence of homeomorphisms λ_n of $[0, 1]$ onto itself such that $\lambda_n(0) = 0$, $\lambda_n(1) = 1$ and

$$\begin{aligned} \lim_{n \to \infty} |t - \lambda_n(t)| &= 0, \\ \lim_{n \to \infty} \sup_t |f_n(t) - f(\lambda_n(t))| &= 0. \end{aligned} \tag{6.6}$$

It is clear from (6.1) that $\omega_{\lambda_n}(1) = 1$. From (6.2) we have

$$\tilde{\omega}_f(1) = \tilde{\omega}_{f \circ \lambda_n}(1),$$

where $\circ$ denotes composition.

From (6.6) we get

$$\lim_{n \to \infty} \tilde{\omega}_{f_n}(1) = \lim_{n \to \infty} \tilde{\omega}_{f \circ \lambda_n}(1) = \tilde{\omega}_f(1). \tag{6.7}$$

Let now $0 < \delta < 1$ be a continuity point of the monotonic function $\tilde{\omega}_f(\delta)$. For any $\varepsilon > 0$, it is clear from (6.6) that for all sufficiently large n,

$$\begin{aligned} &[\lambda_n(t) - \delta + \varepsilon, \lambda_n(t) + \delta - \varepsilon] \\ &\subseteq [\lambda_n(t - \delta), \lambda_n(t + \delta)] \subseteq [\lambda_n(t) - \delta - \varepsilon, \lambda_n(t) + \delta + \varepsilon] \end{aligned}$$

for all $t \in [0, 1]$. Hence for all sufficiently large n

$$\tilde{\omega}_f(\delta - \varepsilon) \leqslant \tilde{\omega}_{f \circ \lambda_n}(\delta) \leqslant \tilde{\omega}_f(\delta + \varepsilon)$$

Hence

$$\tilde{\omega}_f(\delta - \varepsilon) \leqslant \varliminf_{n\to\infty} \tilde{\omega}_{f\circ\lambda_n}(\delta) \leqslant \varlimsup_{n\to\infty} \tilde{\omega}_{f\circ\lambda_n}(\delta) \leqslant \tilde{\omega}_f(\delta + \varepsilon).$$

Since δ is a continuity point of $\tilde{\omega}_f(\delta)$, we obtain by letting $\varepsilon \to 0$,

$$\lim_{n\to\infty} \tilde{\omega}_{f\circ\lambda_n}(\delta) = \tilde{\omega}_f(\delta).$$

Now from (6.6), we have

$$\lim_{n\to\infty} \tilde{\omega}_{f_n}(\delta) = \lim_{n\to\infty} \tilde{\omega}_{f\circ\lambda_n}(\delta) = \tilde{\omega}_f(\delta). \tag{6.8}$$

Equations (6.7) and (6.8), and the fact that $\tilde{\omega}_f(0) = 0$ for every f, imply that $\bar{\omega}_{f_n} \Rightarrow \bar{\omega}_f$ as $n \to \infty$.

Theorem 6.2

In order that a set $K \subseteq D$ be conditionally compact under the Skorohod topology it is necessary and sufficient that

$$\sup_{f\in K} \sup_t |f(t)| < \infty,$$

$$\lim_{\delta\to 0} \sup_{f\in K} \tilde{\omega}_f(\delta) = 0.$$

PROOF. Suppose K is conditionally compact. Since for any homeomorphism $\lambda \in H$, $\sup_t |f(\lambda(t))| = \sup_t |f(t)|$, it is clear that $\sup_t |f_n(t)| \to \sup_t |f(t)|$ as $n \to \infty$ whenever $s(f_n, f) \to 0$. This shows that the subset

$$\{\sup_t |f(t)|, f \in K\}$$

is conditionally compact in the real line. Hence the first condition of the theorem is fulfilled. Now suppose that the second condition is not fulfilled. Then there exists an $\varepsilon > 0$, a sequence $f_n \in K$ and a sequence $\delta_n \downarrow 0$ such that

$$\tilde{\omega}_{f_n}(\delta_n) \geqslant \varepsilon, \qquad \text{for all } n. \tag{6.9}$$

Because of the conditional compactness of K, we may assume that f_n converges to an $f \in D$ in the metric s. By Lemma 6.6 and Theorem 6.1, Chapter II,

$$\varlimsup_{n\to\infty} \tilde{\omega}_{f_n}(\delta) \leqslant \tilde{\omega}_f(\delta + 0), \qquad 0 < \delta < 1. \tag{6.10}$$

Hence by Lemma 6.3 and (6.10)

$$\lim_{\delta \to 0} \overline{\lim_{n \to \infty}} \, \tilde{\omega}_{f_n}(\delta) = 0.$$

This contradicts (6.9) and completes the proof of necessity.

Suppose now the two conditions of the theorem are fulfilled. Let

$$c = \sup_{f \in K} \sup_t |f(t)|,$$

$$\omega(\delta) = \sup_{f \in K} \tilde{\omega}_f(\delta).$$

It is then clear from the continuity of $\sup_t |f(t)|$ in the Skorohod topology and Lemma 6.6 that

$$\sup_{f \in \bar{K}} \sup_t |f(t)| = c < \infty,$$

$$\lim_{\delta \to 0} \bar{\omega}(\delta) = 0,$$

where

$$\bar{\omega}(\delta) = \sup_{f \in \bar{K}} \tilde{\omega}_f(\delta)$$

and $\bar{K}$ is the closure of K. We shall now prove that $\bar{K}$ is compact. Let $\varepsilon > 0$ be arbitrary. Choose m and n so large that $1/m + 1/n + 4\bar{\omega}(2/n) < \varepsilon$. Then it is clear from Lemma 6.5 that there exist a finite number of elements from $D_{m,n}$ such that the spheres of radius ε around these elements in the s-metric cover $\bar{K}$. Thus in order to prove the compactness of $\bar{K}$ it is enough to prove the completeness of $\bar{K}$ (cf. Lemma 3.1, Chapter II). Let now $\{f_n\}$ be a Cauchy sequence in $\bar{K}$, i.e., $s(f_n, f_m) \to 0$ as n and $m \to \infty$. It is enough to establish that $\{f_n\}$ has a convergent subsequence. Hence we may assume without loss of generality (by going over to a subsequence if necessary) that $s(f_n, f_{n+1}) < 1/2^{n+1}$ for all n. Thus there exists a homeomorphism $\lambda_n \in H$ such that

$$\sup_t |f_n(t) - f_{n+1}(\lambda_{n+1}(t))| \leqslant \frac{1}{2^{n+1}},$$

$$\sup_t |t - \lambda_{n+1}(t)| \leqslant \frac{1}{2^{n+1}}.$$

Let $\mu_1 = \lambda_1$, $\mu_n = \lambda_n \circ \mu_{n-1}$, $n = 2, 3, \ldots$. Then

$$\sup_t |\mu_n(t) - \mu_{n-1}(t)| = \sup_t |t - \lambda_n(t)| \leqslant \frac{1}{2^n}.$$

Hence $\mu_n(t)$ converges to a nondecreasing continuous function $\mu(t)$ satisfying $\mu(0) = 0$, $\mu(1) = 1$. Further,

$$\sup_t |f_n(\mu_n(t)) - f_{n-1}(\mu_{n-1}(t))| =$$

$$\sup_t |f_n(\lambda_n(t)) - f_{n-1}(t)| \leqslant \frac{1}{2^n}.$$

Hence the sequence $\{f_n(\mu_n(t))\}$ converges uniformly to a function $f^*(t)$ belonging to D. We shall now find out the relation between $f^*(t)$ and $\mu(t)$. Suppose $\mu(t)$ is a constant in the interval $[\alpha, \beta]$ and $f^*(\alpha) = f^*(\beta)$. We claim that f^* must be constant in the interval $[\alpha, \beta]$. If not, there is a point $t_0 \in [\alpha, \beta]$ such that $f^*(t_0) \neq f^*(\alpha)$. Hence

$$\begin{aligned} &\lim_{n \to \infty} \min \{|f_n(\mu_n(\alpha)) - f_n(\mu_n(t_0))|, |f_n(\mu_n(\beta)) - f_n(\mu_n(t_0))|\} \\ &= \min \{|f^*(\alpha) - f^*(t_0)|, |f^*(\beta) - f^*(t_0)|\} \\ &= |f^*(\alpha) - f^*(t_0)| > 0. \end{aligned}$$

Since $\mu_n(\alpha)$, $\mu_n(t_0)$ and $\mu_n(\beta)$ converge to $\mu(\alpha)$ as $n \to \infty$, and $\lim_{\delta \to 0} \bar{\omega}(\delta) = 0$, the limit on the left-hand side of the above equation is zero. This is a contradiction. Now suppose that $\mu(t)$ is a constant in $[\alpha, \beta]$ but $f^*(\alpha) \neq f^*(\beta)$. Then we claim that there exists a $\gamma \in [\alpha, \beta]$ such that

$$\begin{aligned} f^*(t) &= f^*(\alpha) \quad \text{if} \quad t \in [\alpha, \gamma), \\ &= f^*(\beta) \quad \text{if} \quad t \in [\gamma, \beta]. \end{aligned}$$

If this were not so, we could find three points $t' < t'' < t'''$ in the interval $[\alpha, \beta]$ such that $f^*(t') \neq f^*(t'')$, $f^*(t'') \neq f^*(t''')$. Then

$$\begin{aligned} &\lim_{n \to \infty} \min \{|f_n(\mu_n(t')) - f_n(\mu_n(t''))|, |f_n(\mu_n(t'')) - f_n(\mu_n(t'''))|\} \\ &= \min \{|f^*(t') - f^*(t'')|, |f^*(t'') - f^*(t''')|\} > 0. \end{aligned}$$

Since $\mu_n(t')$, $\mu_n(t'')$, $\mu_n(t''')$ converge to $\mu(\alpha)$, and $\lim_{\delta \to 0} \bar{\omega}(\delta) = 0$, the limit on the left-hand side of the above equation is zero. This is a contradiction.

Now define the function $\bar{f}$ by the equation

$$\bar{f}(t) = f^*(\max [\tau : \mu(\tau) = t]).$$

Since μ is continuous and $\mu(0) = 0$ and $\mu(1) = 1$, μ takes every value in the interval $[0, 1]$, and therefore $\bar{f}$ is well defined in $[0, 1]$. It is not difficult to verify that $\bar{f} \in D$. Note that if t is a point of strict increase for μ, i.e., $\mu(s) > \mu(t)$ for every $s > t$, then $\bar{f}(\mu(t)) = f^*(t)$. We shall now prove that the sequence f_n converges to $\bar{f}$ in the s-metric.

Let $\tau_1, \tau_2, \ldots, \tau_k \in [0, 1]$ be the points at which $\bar{f}(t)$ has jumps of magnitude $> 1/n$. Let $[\alpha_i, \beta_i]$ be the maximal interval in which $\mu(t)$ takes the value τ_i. It is quite possible that $\alpha_i = \beta_i$. From the discussion in the previous paragraph it is clear that there exists a point $\gamma_i \in [\alpha_i, \beta_i]$ such that

$$\begin{aligned} f^*(t) &= \bar{f}(\tau_i - 0) && \text{if} \quad t \in [\alpha_i, \gamma_i), \\ &= \bar{f}(\tau_i) = \bar{f}(\tau_i + 0) && \text{if} \quad t \in [\gamma_i, \beta_i]. \end{aligned}$$

In particular, if $\alpha_i = \gamma_i$, $f^*(t)$ assumes the unique value $\bar{f}(\tau_i)$. Let $\varepsilon_n < 1/n$ be so chosen that $\tilde{\omega}_{\bar{f}}(\varepsilon_n) < 1/n$. Let $\varphi_n(t)$ be a strictly increasing function such that $\varphi_n(0) = 0$, $\varphi_n(1) = 1$, $\varphi_n(\gamma_i) = \tau_i$ for $i = 1, 2, \ldots, k$ and $\sup_t |\varphi_n(t) - \mu(t)| \leqslant \varepsilon_n$. If $t \notin [\alpha_i, \beta_i]$ for any i, then we have by Lemma 6.4,

$$|f^*(t) - \bar{f}(\varphi_n(t))| \leqslant |f^*(t) - \bar{f}(\mu(t))| + |\bar{f}(\mu(t)) - \bar{f}(\varphi_n(t))|$$

$$\leqslant |f^*(t) - \bar{f}(\mu(t))| + 2\tilde{\omega}_{\bar{f}}(\varepsilon_n) + \frac{1}{n}$$

$$\leqslant |f^*(t) - \bar{f}(\mu(t))| + \frac{3}{n}.$$

Here we have used the fact that $|\mu(t) - \varphi_n(t)| \leqslant \varepsilon_n$ and $\mu(t)$ and $\varphi_n(t)$ do not assume the value τ_i outside $[\alpha_i, \beta_i]$. If t were a point of strict increase the first term on the right-hand side of the above inequality is zero. If t were not a point of strict increase there exists a maximal $t' > t$ at which $\mu(t') = \mu(t)$ and $\bar{f}(\mu(t)) = f^*(t')$. Since f^* can take at most only two values in $[t, t']$, it follows that $|f^*(t) - f^*(t')|$ is less than the maximal jump of f^* in $[t, t']$ which in turn is less than $1/n$. Hence we have

$$|f^*(t) - \bar{f}(\varphi_n(t))| \leqslant \frac{4}{n}, \qquad t \notin \bigcup_{i=1}^{k} ([\alpha_i, \beta_i]). \tag{6.11}$$

Now suppose that $t \in [\alpha_i, \gamma_i)$ for some i. Then

$$|f^*(t) - \bar{f}(\varphi_n(t))| \leqslant \sup_{s \in [\tau_i - \varepsilon_n, \tau_i)} |\bar{f}(\tau_i - 0) - \bar{f}(s)| \leqslant \tilde{\omega}_{\bar{f}}(\varepsilon_n)$$

because $|\bar{f}(\tau_i - 0) - \bar{f}(\tau_i)| > 1/n$ and $\tilde{\omega}_{\bar{f}}(\varepsilon_n) < 1/n$. Similarly,

$$|f^*(t) - \bar{f}(\varphi_n(t))| \leqslant \tilde{\omega}_{\bar{f}}(\varepsilon_n)$$

if $t \in [\gamma_i, \beta_i]$. Thus

$$|f^*(t) - \bar{f}(\varphi_n(t))| \leqslant \frac{1}{n} \qquad \text{for} \quad t \in [\alpha_i, \beta_i]$$

This together with (6.11) gives

$$\sup_t |f^*(t) - \bar{f}(\varphi_n(t))| \leqslant \frac{4}{n}.$$

Hence

$$\begin{aligned} s(f_n, \bar{f}) &\leqslant s(f_n, f^* \circ \mu_n^{-1}) + s(f^* \circ \mu_n^{-1}, \bar{f} \circ \varphi_n \circ \mu_n^{-1}) + s(\bar{f} \circ \varphi_n \circ \mu_n^{-1}, \bar{f}) \\ &\leqslant \sup_t |f_n(\mu_n(t)) - f^*(t)| + \sup_t |f^*(t) - \bar{f}(\varphi_n(t))| \\ &\quad + \sup_t |t - \varphi_n(\mu_n^{-1}(t))| \\ &\leqslant \frac{1}{2^n} + \frac{4}{n} + \sup_t |\varphi_n(t) - \mu(t)| + \sup_t |\mu_n(t) - \mu(t)| \\ &\leqslant \frac{1}{2^n} + \frac{4}{n} + \varepsilon_n + \frac{1}{2^n}. \end{aligned}$$

Thus

$$\lim_{n \to \infty} s(f_n, \bar{f}) = 0.$$

This completes the proof of the theorem.

We shall now introduce another metric in the space D which is equivalent to the Skorohod metric but converts the space D into a complete metric space. To this end we introduce the notion of a graph for functions in D. For any $f \in D$, the graph Γ_f is the set in the two-dimensional plane defined by

$$\Gamma_f = \{(x, t) : t \in (0, 1), x = f(t + 0)\} \cup \{(x, t) : t \in (0, 1), x = f(t - 0)\} \cup \{(f(0), 0)\} \cup \{(f(1), 1)\}. \tag{6.12}$$

It is clear that for every $f \in D$, the graph Γ_f is a closed bounded set in the two-dimensional plane. Further, there exists a one-to-one correspondence between the function $f \in D$ and its graph Γ_f.

For any two closed and bounded sets A and B in the two-dimensional plane, let us introduce the distance $\rho(A, B)$ by

$$\rho(A, B) = \max [\sup_{x \in A} \inf_{y \in B} |x - y|, \sup_{x \in B} \inf_{y \in A} |x - y|] \tag{6.13}$$

where $|x - y|$ is the length of the segment joining x and y.

Lemma 6.7

The space $\mathscr{C}$ of all closed and bounded sets in the two-dimensional plane is a complete metric space under the metric ρ.

Proof. It is easy to verify that ρ is a metric. Indeed $\rho(A, B) = 0$ if and only if $A = B$ and $\rho(A, B) = \rho(B, A)$. Further,

$$\inf_{y \in B} |x - y| \leqslant |x - z| + \inf_{y \in B} |z - y| \qquad \text{for all } z.$$

Hence

$$\inf_{y \in B} |x - y| \leqslant \inf_{z \in C} |x - z| + \sup_{z \in C} \inf_{y \in B} |z - y|.$$

Hence

$$\sup_{x \in A} \inf_{y \in B} |x - y| \leqslant \rho(A, C) + \rho(C, B).$$

Interchanging A and B,

$$\sup_{y \in B} \inf_{x \in A} |x - y| \leqslant \rho(A, C) + \rho(C, B).$$

Hence

$$\rho(A, B) \leqslant \rho(A, C) + \rho(C, B).$$

Let now $A_n \in \mathscr{C}$ and $\rho(A_n, A_m) \to 0$ as n and $m \to \infty$. For any set A and any point x in the two-dimensional plane, let

$$d(x, A) = \inf_{y \in A} |x - y|.$$

Then we have by Theorem 1.1, Chapter I,

$$d(x, A) \leqslant d(y, A) + d(x, y) \qquad \text{for all} \quad y.$$

Hence

$$d(x, A) \leqslant \rho(A, B) + d(x, y) \qquad \text{for all} \quad y \in B.$$

Hence

$$d(x, A) \leqslant \rho(A, B) + d(x, B).$$

Interchanging A and B,

$$d(x, B) \leqslant \rho(A, B) + d(x, A).$$

Thus

$$|d(x, A) - d(x, B)| \leqslant \rho(A, B).$$

It now follows that the sequence of functions $d(x, A_n)$ converges uniformly to a continuous function $g(x)$. If $A_0 = [x : g(x) = 0]$, then $\lim_{n\to\infty} \rho(A_n, A_0) = 0$. This shows that $\mathscr{C}$ is a complete metric space. This completes the proof.

We now introduce the distance $d^*(f, g)$ between f and g in the space D as follows:

$$d^*(f, g) = \rho(\Gamma_f, \Gamma_g) + \rho^*(\bar{\omega}_f, \bar{\omega}_g), \tag{6.14}$$

where ρ is the metric defined by (6.13) in the space $\mathscr{C}$, Γ_f and Γ_g are the graphs of f and g, respectively, $\bar{\omega}_f$, $\bar{\omega}_g$ are the finite measures introduced in Lemma 6.6 and ρ^* is any metric which makes the space of all finite measures on the real line a complete metric space in the topology of weak convergence (see Theorems 6.2 and 6.5, Chapter II).

Theorem 6.3

The metric d^* is equivalent to the Skorohod metric. D is a complete separable metric space under d^*.

PROOF. Suppose f_n is a sequence in D and $s(f_n, f) \to 0$ as $n \to \infty$. Then by Lemma 6.6, $\bar{\omega}_{f_n} \Rightarrow \bar{\omega}_f$ and therefore $\rho^*(\bar{\omega}_{f_n}, \bar{\omega}_f) \to 0$ as $n \to \infty$. Since there exists a sequence of homeomorphisms λ_n of $[0, 1]$ onto itself such that $\lambda_n(0) = 0$ and $\lambda_n(1) = 1$ and

$$\lim_{n\to\infty} \sup_t |\lambda_n(t) - t| = 0,$$

$$\lim_{n\to\infty} \sup_t |f_n(\lambda_n(t)) - f(t)| = 0,$$

we have

$$\begin{aligned}\lim_{n\to\infty} \rho(\Gamma_{f_n}, \Gamma_f) &\leqslant \lim_{n\to\infty} \sup_t \left(|\lambda_n(t) - t|^2 + |f_n(\lambda_n(t)) - f(t)|^2\right)^{1/2} \\ &= 0.\end{aligned}$$

Thus convergence under s implies convergence under d^*. Conversely, let $d^*(f_n, f) \to 0$. Then, in particular, $\rho^*(\bar{\omega}_{f_n}, \bar{\omega}_f) \to 0$ as $n \to \infty$. Hence by Theorem 6.1, Chapter II,

$$\overline{\lim_{n\to\infty}}\, \tilde{\omega}_{f_n}(\delta) \leqslant \tilde{\omega}_f(\delta + 0), \qquad 0 < \delta < 1.$$

By Lemma 6.3 and Theorem 6.2, the sequence f_n is conditionally compact in the topology of Skorohod metric. Let f_0 be any limit of a subsequence f_{n_k}. Then $s(f_{n_k}, f_0) \to 0$ as $k \to \infty$. This implies that $d^*(f_{n_k}, f_0) \to 0$ as $k \to \infty$, and hence $\rho(\Gamma_{f_{n_k}}, \Gamma_{f_0}) \to 0$ as $k \to \infty$. Thus $\Gamma_{f_0} = \Gamma_f$, and therefore $f_0 = f$. In other words, $s(f_n, f) \to 0$. This completes the proof of the first part of the theorem.

Let f_n be a sequence in D such that $\lim_{n,m\to\infty} d^*(f_n, f_m) = 0$. Then $\rho^*(\bar{\omega}_{f_n}, \bar{\omega}_{f_m}) \to 0$. Since ρ^* is a complete metric it follows that there exists a finite measure $\bar{\omega}$ on the real line such that $\rho^*(\bar{\omega}_{f_n}, \bar{\omega}) \to 0$ as $n \to \infty$. Let

$$\omega(\delta) = \bar{\omega}(\log \delta).$$

Then by Theorem 6.1, Chapter II,

$$\overline{\lim_{n\to\infty}}\, \tilde{\omega}_{f_n}(\delta) \leqslant \omega(\delta + 0), \qquad 0 < \delta < 1$$

and

$$\lim_{\delta \to 0} \omega(\delta) = 0.$$

Since $\rho(\Gamma_{f_n}, \Gamma_{f_m}) \to 0$, by Lemma 6.7 there exists a closed bounded set Γ such that $\rho(\Gamma_{f_n}, \Gamma) \to 0$ as $n \to \infty$. Hence all the Γ_{f_n} are contained in a bounded closed set. Thus the sequence f_n is uniformly bounded. By Theorem 6.2, the sequence f_n is conditionally compact in the topology of the metric s and therefore in the metric d^*. Since f_n is a Cauchy sequence, it follows that f_n must converge to a unique limit. Separability of the space D under d^* or equivalently s follows from Theorem 6.1. This completes the proof.

Now we shall examine the space of continuous functions defined on $[0, 1]$ as a subset of the space D. In this connection we have the following lemma.

Lemma 6.8

If a sequence of elements $f_n \in D$ converges in the s-metric to a continuous function f then $\sup_t |f_n(t) - f(t)| \to 0$ as $n \to \infty$.

PROOF. Since f_n converges to f in the s-metric there exists a sequence $\lambda_n \in H$ such that

$$\lim_{n \to \infty} \sup_t |f_n(t) - f(\lambda_n(t))| = 0,$$

$$\lim_{n \to \infty} \sup_t |\lambda_n(t) - t| = 0.$$

It follows from the continuity of f that

$$\lim_{n \to \infty} \sup_t |f(\lambda_n(t)) - f(t)| = 0.$$

Hence

$$\lim_{n \to \infty} \sup_t |f_n(t) - f(t)| = 0.$$

REMARK. It follows from the above lemma that the space C of continuous functions with the uniform topology is nothing but the subset of continuous functions in the space D with the relative topology.

7. PROBABILITY MEASURES IN D

We have seen that the space D with the Skorohod metric is topologically complete and separable. The following theorem asserts that a distribution on the space D is completely determined by its finite dimensional distributions.

By convergence in D we shall always mean convergence in the s-metric.

Theorem 7.1

The class $\mathscr{B}_D$ of the Borel subsets of D coincides with the smallest σ-algebra of subsets of D with respect to which the maps $\pi^t: x \to x(t)$, $x \in D$ are measurable for all $t \in [0, 1]$. If μ and ν are two measures on D, a necessary and sufficient condition that $\mu = \nu$ is that $\mu^{t_1,\ldots,t_k} = \nu^{t_1,\ldots,t_k}$ for all k and $t_1,\ldots, t_k \in [0, 1]$, where $\mu^{t_1,\ldots,t_k}$ and $\nu^{t_1,\ldots,t_k}$ are measures in the k-dimensional vector space R^k induced by μ and ν, respectively, through the map $\pi^{t_1,\ldots,t_k}: x \to (x(t_1),\ldots, x(t_k))$, $x \in D$.

Proof. Let $\mathscr{A}$ be the smallest σ-algebra of subsets of D with respect to which the maps π^t are measurable for all $t \in [0, 1]$. First of all we observe that the maps π^0 and π^1 are continuous on D. Hence π^0 and π^1 are measurable with respect to $\mathscr{B}_D$. Let now $t_0 \in (0, 1)$. We shall prove that π^t is measurable with respect to $\mathscr{B}_D$. For any continuous function f_0 on $[0, 1]$, it is clear that the map $x \to f_0x$, i.e., multiplication by f_0, is a continuous map of D into itself. Since for any $x \in D$, $\lambda \in H$, $\sup_t x(\lambda(t)) = \sup_t x(t)$, it follows that the map $x \to \sup_t x(t)$ is a continuous map of D into the real line. Hence the map $x \to \sup_t [f_0(t)x(t)]$ is continuous. Let f_n be the sequence of continuous functions defined as follows:

$$
\begin{aligned}
f_n(t) &= 0 \quad \text{if} \quad t \in \left[0, t_0 + \frac{1}{2n}\right] \\
&= 1 \quad \text{if} \quad t \in \left[t_0 + \frac{1}{n}, t_0 + \frac{2}{n}\right] \\
&= 0 \quad \text{if} \quad t \in \left[t_0 + \frac{2}{n} + \frac{1}{2n}, 1\right],
\end{aligned}
$$

and f_n is linear in the intervals $[t_0 + 1/2n, t_0 + 1/n]$ and $[t_0 + 2/n, t_0 + 2/n + 1/2n]$. Then f_n is well defined for all sufficiently large n. It follows from the right continuity of x that

$$\pi^{t_0}(x) = \lim_{n\to\infty} \sup_t \,[f_n(t)x(t)].$$

Thus π^{t_0} is a pointwise limit of a sequence of continuous maps on D. In other words π^{t_0} is measurable with respect to $\mathscr{B}_D$. Thus $\mathscr{A} \subseteq \mathscr{B}_D$.

In order to prove that $\mathscr{B}_D \subseteq \mathscr{A}$, we first observe that the measure $\bar{\omega}_x$ associated with any function $x \in D$ (cf. Lemma 6.6) is determined by the monotonic function

$$\bar{\omega}_x'(\delta) = \sup_{\substack{t-\delta\leqslant t'<t\leqslant t''\leqslant t+\delta\\ t,t',t''\text{ rational}}} [\min\{|x(t') - x(t)|; |x(t'') - x(t)|\}]$$

$$+ \sup_{\substack{0\leqslant t\leqslant\delta\\ t\text{ rational}}} |x(t) - x(0)| + \sup_{\substack{1-\delta\leqslant t\leqslant 1\\ t\text{ rational}}} |x(t) - x(1)|.$$

Thus the mapping $x \to \bar{\omega}_x$ is $\mathscr{A}$-measurable when we consider the Borel σ-field of the weak topology in the space of measures on the real line. Hence for any fixed $x_0 \in D$, the real valued function $x \to \rho^*(\bar{\omega}_x, \bar{\omega}_{x_0})$ where ρ^* is as in (6.14) is $\mathscr{A}$-measurable. Further, since

$$\rho(\Gamma_x, \Gamma_{x_0}) = \max\{\sup_t \inf_{t'} |(t, x(t)) - (t', x_0(t'))|,$$

$$\sup_{t'} \inf_{t} |(t, x(t)) - (t', x_0(t'))|\}$$

$$= \max\{\sup_{t\text{ rational}} \inf_{t'\text{ rational}} |(t, x(t)) - (t', x_0(t'))|,$$

$$\sup_{t'\text{ rational}} \inf_{t\text{ rational}} |(t, x(t)) - (t', x_0(t'))|\}$$

where Γ_x, Γ_{x_0} denote the graphs of x and x_0, respectively, ρ is as in (6.14) and $|\cdot|$ denotes the distance in the two-dimensional plane, it follows that the real valued function $x \to \rho(\Gamma_x, \Gamma_{x_0})$ is $\mathscr{A}$-measurable. Thus the function

$$d^*(x, x_0) = \rho(\Gamma_x, \Gamma_{x_0}) + \rho^*(\bar{\omega}_x, \bar{\omega}_{x_0})$$

is $\mathscr{A}$-measurable in x for any fixed x_0. By Theorem **6.3** sets of the form $\{x: d^*(x, x_0) < \varepsilon\}$ when x_0 varies over D and ε over $(0, \infty)$ constitute a basis for the s-topology in D. Hence $\mathscr{B}_D \subseteq \mathscr{A}$. This completes the proof of the first part of the theorem.

The second part is proved exactly in the same manner as Theorem 2.1.

Since D is a separable metric space which is topologically complete, it follows from Theorem 3.2, Chapter II, that every probability measure on D is tight. We shall now get a criterion for compactness of a set of probability measures on D under the weak topology.

Lemma 7.1

Let Γ be a set of probability measures on D. In order that $\bar{\Gamma}$ be compact it is necessary and sufficient that for each $\varepsilon > 0$, there exist a constant $M_\varepsilon > 0$ and a function $\omega(\delta, \varepsilon)$ which is monotonic and right continuous in δ and decreases to zero as $\delta \downarrow 0$ such that

$$\text{(i)} \quad \mu(\{x: \sup_t |x(t)| \leqslant M_\varepsilon\}) > 1 - \frac{\varepsilon}{2}$$

$$\text{(ii)} \quad \mu(\{x: \tilde{\omega}_x(\delta) \leqslant \omega(\delta, \varepsilon) \textit{ for all } \delta\}) > 1 - \frac{\varepsilon}{2}$$

for all $\mu \in \Gamma$.

PROOF. Suppose that Γ is a set of measures satisfying the condition above. For $\varepsilon > 0$, write

$$A_\varepsilon = \{x: \sup_t |x(t)| \leqslant M_\varepsilon\}$$

$$B_\varepsilon = \{x: \tilde{\omega}_x(\delta) \leqslant \omega(\delta, \varepsilon) \text{ for all } \delta\}.$$

Then by Lemma 6.6, $K_\varepsilon = A_\varepsilon \cap B_\varepsilon$ is closed. By Theorem 6.2, K_ε is compact. Further, for any $\mu \in \Gamma$, $\mu(K_\varepsilon) > 1 - \varepsilon$. Hence, by Theorem 6.7, Chapter II, $\bar{\Gamma}$ is compact.

Conversely, suppose $\bar{\Gamma}$ is compact. Then by Theorem 6.7, Chapter II, there exists a compact set K_ε such that $\mu(K_\varepsilon) > 1 - \varepsilon/2$ for all $\mu \in \Gamma$. Let

$$M_\varepsilon = \sup_{x \in K_\varepsilon} \sup_t |x(t)|,$$

$$\omega'(\delta, \varepsilon) = \sup_{x \in K_\varepsilon} \tilde{\omega}_x(\delta), \qquad \omega(\delta, \varepsilon) = \omega'(\delta + 0, \varepsilon), \qquad 0 < \delta < 1.$$

By Theorem 6.2, $M_\varepsilon < \infty$ and $\omega(\delta, \varepsilon)$ is a monotonic function in δ which decreases to zero as $\delta \downarrow 0$. Clearly,

$$\mu(\{x: \sup_t |x(t)| \leqslant M_\varepsilon\}) \geqslant \mu(K_\varepsilon) > 1 - \frac{\varepsilon}{2},$$

$$\mu(\{x: \omega_x(\delta) \leqslant \omega(\delta, \varepsilon) \text{ for all } \delta\}) \geqslant \mu(K_\varepsilon) > 1 - \frac{\varepsilon}{2}$$

for all $\mu \in \Gamma$. This completes the proof.

Theorem 7.2

Let Γ be a set of probability measures on D. In order that $\bar{\Gamma}$ be compact, it is necessary and sufficient that the following conditions be satisfied:

(i) *for each $\varepsilon > 0$, there should exist a constant M_ε such that*

$$\mu(\{x: \sup_t |x(t)| \leqslant M_\varepsilon\}) > 1 - \frac{\varepsilon}{2}$$

for all $\mu \in \Gamma$,

(ii) *for each $\delta > 0$ and $\varepsilon > 0$ there should exist an $\eta = \eta(\delta, \varepsilon) > 0$ such that*

$$\mu(\{x: \tilde{\omega}_x(\eta) \leqslant \delta\}) > 1 - \frac{\varepsilon}{2}$$

for all $\mu \in \Gamma$.

Proof. That (i) is necessary has been proved in the preceding lemma. As for (ii) note that there exists a function $\omega(\delta, \varepsilon)$ which is monotonic in δ and decreases to zero as $\delta \downarrow 0$ such that

$$\mu(\{x: \tilde{\omega}_x(\delta) \leqslant \omega(\delta, \varepsilon) \text{ for all } \delta\}) > 1 - \frac{\varepsilon}{2},$$

for all $\mu \in \Gamma$. We can find an $\eta = \eta(\delta, \varepsilon)$ such that $\omega(\eta, \varepsilon) \leqslant \delta$. Then obviously

$$\mu(\{x: \tilde{\omega}_x(\eta) \leqslant \delta\}) > 1 - \frac{\varepsilon}{2}$$

for all $\mu \in \Gamma$.

To prove the sufficiency we proceed as follows. For each integer $n = 1, 2, \ldots$ and a given $\varepsilon > 0$ there exists an $\eta_{\varepsilon, n}$ such that if

$$F_{\varepsilon, n} = \left\{x : \tilde{\omega}_x(\eta_{\varepsilon, n}) \leqslant \frac{1}{n}\right\},$$

then

$$\mu(F_{\varepsilon, n}) > 1 - \frac{\varepsilon}{2^{n+1}}$$

for all $\mu \in \Gamma$. Let

$$K_\varepsilon = \{x : \sup_t |x(t)| \leqslant M_\varepsilon\} \cap \bigcap_{n=1}^{\infty} F_{\varepsilon, n}.$$

Obviously,

$$\mu(K_\varepsilon) > 1 - \varepsilon$$

for all $\mu \in \Gamma$. If $x \in K_\varepsilon$, then for each n, $x \in F_{\varepsilon, n}$ so that there exists an $\eta_{\varepsilon, n}$ having the property that $\tilde{\omega}_x(\eta_{\varepsilon, n}) \leqslant 1/n$. In other words, $\sup_{x \in K_\varepsilon} \tilde{\omega}_x(\eta) \to 0$ as $\eta \to 0$. Since $\sup_{x \in K_\varepsilon} \sup_t |x(t)| \leqslant M_\varepsilon < \infty$, it follows from Theorem 6.7, Chapter II, that $\bar{\Gamma}$ is compact. This completes the proof.

Corollary 7.1

Let μ_n be a sequence of probability measures in D such that

$$\lim_{\delta \to 0} \overline{\lim_{n \to \infty}} \mu_n(\{x : \tilde{\omega}_x(\delta) > \varepsilon\}) = 0$$

for every $\varepsilon > 0$. Let further the sequence $\{\mu_n^{t_1, \ldots, t_k}\}$ be conditionally compact in the k-dimensional vector space R^k for each fixed k and $t_1, \ldots, t_k \in [0, 1]$, where $\mu_n^{t_1, \ldots, t_k}$ is the measure in R^k induced by μ_n through the map

$$\pi^{t_1, \ldots, t_k} : x \to (x(t_1), \ldots, x(t_k)), \qquad x \in D.$$

Then μ_n is conditionally compact.

PROOF. From the tightness of any fixed measure and the first condition of the corollary it follows that

$$\lim_{\delta \to 0} \sup_n \mu_n(\{x : \tilde{\omega}_x(\delta) > \varepsilon\}) = 0$$

for every $\varepsilon > 0$. Further, for any fixed $x \in D$,

$$\sup_t |x(t)| \leqslant \sup_{0 \leqslant k \leqslant m} \left| x\left(\frac{k}{m}\right) \right| + \tilde{\omega}_x\left(\frac{1}{m}\right)$$

because for $t \in [k/m, \overline{k+1}/m]$, either $|x(t) - x(k/m)| \leqslant \tilde{\omega}_x(1/m)$ or $|x(t) - x(\overline{k+1}/m)| \leqslant \tilde{\omega}_x(1/m)$. Hence,

$$\mu_n(\{x: \sup_t |x(t)| > L\})$$

$$\leqslant \mu_n\left(\left\{x: \sup_{0 \leqslant k \leqslant m} \left| x\left(\frac{k}{m}\right) \right| > L - \varepsilon\right\}\right)$$

$$+ \mu_n\left(\left\{x: \tilde{\omega}_x\left(\frac{1}{m}\right) > \varepsilon\right\}\right).$$

Because of the compactness of finite dimensional distributions we have

$$\lim_{L \to \infty} \sup_n \mu_n\left(\left\{x: \sup_{0 \leqslant k \leqslant m} \left| x\left(\frac{k}{m}\right) \right| > L - \varepsilon\right\}\right) = 0.$$

Hence,

$$\lim_{L \to \infty} \sup_n \mu_n (\{x: \sup_t |x(t)| > L\})$$

$$\leqslant \sup_n \mu_n\left(\left\{x: \tilde{\omega}_x\left(\frac{1}{m}\right) > \varepsilon\right\}\right).$$

Letting $m \to \infty$ we have, from the first condition of the corollary,

$$\lim_{L \to \infty} \sup_n \mu_n(\{x: \sup_t |x(t)| > L\}) = 0.$$

By Theorem 7.2, the sequence $\{\mu_n\}$ is conditionally compact.

8. ERGODIC THEOREMS FOR D-VALUED RANDOM VARIABLES

In this section we shall prove an analog of Theorem 9.4, Chapter VI for D-valued random variables.

Let D^∞ be the product of countable number of copies of the space D. D is given the Skorohod topology and D^∞, the product topology. Then D^∞ is a separable metric space which is topologically complete. As in Section 9 we can consider measures μ on D^∞, which are invariant under the shift transformation T. Let $\mathscr{F} = \{A : A \in \mathscr{B}_{D^\infty}, T^{-1}A = A\}$. $\mathscr{F}$ is called the invariant σ-field. Any point $\mathbf{x} \in D^\infty$ can be expressed as $\mathbf{x} = (x_1, x_2, \ldots)$, where $x_n \in D$ for every n.

Before proceeding to the statement of the ergodic theorem we shall prove a lemma.

Lemma 8.1

Let μ be a probability measure on D such that

$$\int \|x\| \, d\mu(x) < \infty,$$

where

$$\|x\| = \sup_t |x(t)|.$$

Then for any $\varepsilon > 0$, there exists a division $0 = t_0 < t_1 \ldots < t_k = 1$ such that

$$\sup_{t_j \leqslant t, t' < t_{j+1}} \int |x(t) - x(t')| \, d\mu < \varepsilon, \qquad j = 0, 1, \ldots, k-1.$$

PROOF. For any $0 \leqslant \alpha < \beta \leqslant 1$, let

$$\theta(\alpha, \beta) = \sup_{\alpha \leqslant t, t' < \beta} \int |x(t) - x(t')| \, d\mu(x).$$

Let

$$\begin{aligned} \tau_1 &= 1 \qquad \text{if} \quad \theta(0, 1) \leqslant \varepsilon, \\ &= \inf\,[t : \theta(0, t) > \varepsilon], \qquad \text{otherwise.} \end{aligned}$$

We define τ_j inductively as follows:

$$\begin{aligned} \tau_j &= 1 \qquad \text{if} \quad \theta(\tau_{j-1}, 1) \leqslant \varepsilon, \\ &= \inf\,[t : \theta(\tau_{j-1}, t) > \varepsilon], \qquad \text{otherwise.} \end{aligned}$$

The proof of the lemma will be complete if $\tau_j = 1$ at some stage. Suppose $\tau_j < 1$ for all j. Since $|x(t)| \leqslant \|x\|$ for all t, it follows from the dominated convergence theorem that there exist points t_j, t_j' such that $\tau_{j-1} \leqslant t_j < t_j' \leqslant \tau_j$ and $\int |x(t_j) - x(t_j')| \, d\mu(x) \geqslant \varepsilon$ for all j. Since τ_j increases to a limit as $j \to \infty$ and $x \in D$, it follows that $|x(t_j) - x(t_j')| \to 0$ as $j \to \infty$. By the dominated convergence theorem $\lim_{j\to\infty} \int |x(t_j) - x(t_j')| \, d\mu(x) = 0$, which is a contradiction. This completes the proof of the lemma.

Theorem 8.1

Let μ be a probability measure on the space D^∞ which is invariant and ergodic under the shift transformation T. Let $\int \|x_1\| \, d\mu(\mathbf{x}) < \infty$. Then

$$\lim_{n\to\infty} \sup_t \left| \frac{x_1(t) + x_2(t) + \ldots + x_n(t)}{n} - m(t) \right| = 0, \qquad \text{a.e.} \quad \mathbf{x}(\mu),$$

where $\mathbf{x} = (x_1, x_2, \ldots)$, $x_i \in D$ for all i and

$$m(t) = \int x_1(t) \, d\mu(\mathbf{x}).$$

Proof. Since $|x_1(t)| \leqslant \|x_1\|$ for all t, it follows that $m(t)$ is well defined. Since $x_1(t)$ is right continuous and has limits from the left for every $x_1 \in D$, it follows from the dominated convergence theorem that $m(t)$ has the same properties and hence belongs to D.

For any $\mathbf{x}$, let $\mu_{n,\mathbf{x}}$ be the measure in D which has mass $1/n$ at the points $x_1, x_2, \ldots, x_n$. For any $\mathbf{x} \in D^\infty$, let

$$S_n(t, \mathbf{x}) = \frac{x_1(t) + x_2(t) + \ldots + x_n(t)}{n}$$

Then

$$S_n(t, \mathbf{x}) = \int_D w(t) \, d\mu_{n,\mathbf{x}}(w)$$

$$m(t) = \int_D w(t) \, d\mu_1(w),$$

where μ_1 is the distribution of x_1. We have for any compact subset $K \subseteq D$,

$$|S_n(t, \mathbf{x}) - m(t)| \leqslant |\varepsilon_n{}^K(t)| + \int_{K'} ||w||\, d\mu_{n,\mathbf{x}}(w) + \int_{K'} ||w||\, d\mu_1(w), \tag{8.1}$$

where K' denotes the complement of K and

$$\varepsilon_n{}^K(t) = \int_K w(t)\, d\mu_{n,\mathbf{x}}(w) - \int_K w(t)\, d\mu_1(w).$$

Let $\varepsilon > 0$ be arbitrary. By Theorem 6.2, there exists a $\delta > 0$ such that for any $\alpha \leqslant t < \beta < \alpha + \delta$ and all $x \in K$,

$$\min\,(|x(t) - x(\alpha)|,\, |x(t) - x(\beta - 0)|) < \varepsilon.$$

Hence

$$|x(t) - x(\alpha)| \leqslant |x(\alpha) - x(\beta - 0)| + \varepsilon$$

for all $x \in K$, $\alpha \leqslant t < \beta < \alpha + \delta$. Consequently,

$$\sup_{\alpha \leqslant t < \beta} |\varepsilon_n{}^K(t)| \leqslant \left| \int_K w(\alpha)\, d\mu_{n,\mathbf{x}}(w) - \int_K w(\alpha)\, d\mu_1(w) \right| + \int |w(\alpha) - w(\beta - 0)|\, d(\mu_{n,\mathbf{x}} + \mu_1) + 2\varepsilon.$$

Letting $n \to \infty$, we have from the ergodic theorem of Birkhoff for real valued random variables,

$$\lim_{n \to \infty} \sup_{\alpha \leqslant t < \beta} |\varepsilon_n{}^K(t)| \leqslant 2 \int |w(\alpha) - w(\beta - 0)|\, d\mu_1 + 2\varepsilon \tag{8.2}$$

for each $\alpha \leqslant \beta < \alpha + \delta$ with probability one. But by Lemma 8.1 there exists a division $0 = t_0 < t_1 < \ldots < t_N = 1$ such that (a) $|t_j - t_{j+1}| < \delta$ and (b) for $j = 0, \ldots, N - 1$,

$$\int |w(t_j) - w(t_{j+1} - 0)|\, d\mu_1(w) \leqslant \frac{\varepsilon}{2}.$$

Hence (8.2) implies that

$$\limsup_{n\to\infty} \sup_t |\varepsilon_n^K(t)| \leqslant 3\varepsilon, \qquad \text{a.e.} \quad \mathbf{x}(\mu).$$

The above inequality, (8.1) and Birkhoff's ergodic theorem imply

$$\limsup_{n\to\infty} \sup_t |S_n(t, \mathbf{x}) - m(t)| \leqslant 3\varepsilon + 2\int_{K'} ||w||\, d\mu_1(w), \qquad \text{a.e.} \quad \mathbf{x}(\mu).$$

Since D is topologically complete and hence every finite measure is tight (Theorem 3.2, Chapter II), the compact set K can be so chosen that

$$\int_{K'} ||w||\, d\mu_1(w) < \frac{\varepsilon}{2} \qquad \limsup_{n\to\infty} \sup_t |S_n(t, \mathbf{x}) - m(t)| \leqslant 4\varepsilon, \qquad \text{a.e.} \quad \mathbf{x}(\mu).$$

Letting $\varepsilon \to 0$ we complete the proof.

Corollary 8.1

If in Theorem 8.1, μ is not necessarily ergodic but invariant under T, then

$$\limsup_{n\to\infty} \sup_t |S_n(t, \mathbf{x}) - m(t, \mathbf{x})| = 0 \qquad \text{a.e.} \quad \mathbf{x}(\mu),$$

where

$$m(t, \mathbf{x}) = \int_{D^\infty} w_1(t) \lambda(\mathbf{x}, d\mathbf{w})$$

and $\lambda(\mathbf{x}, A)$ is the conditional probability of A given the invariant σ-field $\mathscr{F}$ in the probability space $(D^\infty, \mathscr{B}_{D^\infty}, \mu)$.

PROOF. This is an immediate consequence of Theorem 8.1 and the fact that in a complete separable metric space every measure invariant under a homeomorphism can be expressed as a direct integral of ergodic measures (cf. Oxtoby [27]).

Corollary 8.2

In Corollary 8.1, if in addition $\int ||x_1||^{1+\alpha}\, d\mu(\mathbf{x}) < \infty$ for some $\alpha \geqslant 0$, then

$$\lim_{n\to\infty} E\|S_n(t, \mathbf{x}) - m(t, \mathbf{x})\|^{1+\alpha} = 0,$$

where E denotes expectation.

PROOF. This is deduced from Theorem 8.1 exactly in the same way as Theorem 9.5, Chapter VI.

9. APPLICATIONS TO STATISTICAL TESTS OF HYPOTHESIS

One of the most important problems in statistics is to test the hypothesis on the basis of observations that a population is distributed according to a given distribution function.

Suppose we make n independent observations $\xi_1, \xi_2, \ldots, \xi_n$ on a statistical population which is distributed according to a continuous distribution function $F(x)$. The most natural way to estimate $F(x)$ on the basis of these observations is to construct the sample distribution $F_n^*(x)$ where

$$F_n^*(x) = \nu_n(x)/n$$

and $\nu_n(x)$ is the number of ξ_k in the interval $(-\infty, x]$. From the classical theorem of Glivenko-Cantelli we have

$$\lim_{n\to\infty} \sup_x |F_n^*(x) - F(x)| = 0$$

with probability one. For testing the hypothesis mentioned above it would be useful to find the asymptotic distribution of $\sup_x |F_n^*(x) - F(x)|$. We shall solve this problem by making use of the results of Section 7.

We consider

$$\eta_n(x) = \sqrt{n}(F_n^*(x) - F(x)), \qquad -\infty < x < \infty,$$

as a random process by taking x as time.

Lemma 9.1

The finite dimensional distributions of the process $\eta_n(x)$ converge weakly to the corresponding finite dimensional distributions of the Gaussian *process* $\eta(x)$ *for which* $E\eta(x) = 0$, $E\eta(x)\eta(y) = F(x)(1 - F(y))$ *for* $-\infty < x \leqslant y < \infty$.

PROOF. We have

$$\eta_n(x) = \frac{1}{\sqrt{n}} \sum_{k=1}^{n} [\varepsilon(x - \xi_k) - F(x)],$$

where

$$\varepsilon(z) = 0 \quad \text{if} \quad z < 0,$$
$$= 1 \quad \text{if} \quad z \geqslant 0.$$

It is clear that

$$E\varepsilon(x - \xi_k) = F(x),$$

$$E[\varepsilon(x - \xi_k)\varepsilon(y - \xi_k)] = F(x) \qquad \text{if} \quad x < y.$$

Since $\varepsilon(x - \xi_k) - F(x)$ are independent for different k, the lemma follows from the classical central limit theorem in finite-dimensional vector spaces.

Let now the function $F^{-1}(t)$ be defined as

$$F^{-1}(t) = \inf\,[x : F(x) = t].$$

Since $F(x)$ is continuous it takes every value between 0 and 1 as x varies in $[-\infty, +\infty]$. Thus $F^{-1}(t)$ is well defined and monotonic in the interval $[0, 1]$. We shall write

$$\xi_n'(t) = \eta_n(F^{-1}(t)),$$

$$\xi'(t) = \eta(F^{-1}(t)),$$

where η_n and η are as in the preceding lemma. It is then clear that

$$\xi_n'(t) = \frac{1}{\sqrt{n}} \sum_{1}^{n} [\varepsilon(t - \zeta_k) - t], \qquad 0 \leqslant t \leqslant 1,$$

where $\zeta_k = F(\xi_k)$ are independently distributed according to the uniform distribution in the interval $[0, 1]$.

Lemma 9.2

$\xi_n'(t) \in D$ with probability one. Further, the finite dimensional distributions of the process $\xi_n'(t)$ converge weakly to the corresponding finite dimensional distributions of $\xi'(t)$ as $n \to \infty$. The process $\xi'(t)$ is Gaussian with $E\xi'(t) = 0$ and $E\xi'(t)\xi'(s) = t(1 - s)$, whenever $t \leqslant s$.

PROOF. This is an immediate consequence of Lemma 9.1.

Lemma 9.3

The finite-dimensional distributions of the process $\xi'(t)$ of Lemma 9.2 are the conditional finite-dimensional distributions of the Brownian motion process $w(t)$ under the condition that $w(1) = 0$.

PROOF. It is clear that the conditional finite-dimensional distributions of the process $w(t)$ under the condition $w(1) = 0$ are Gaussian. Hence, it is enough to prove that

$$E(w(t)|w(1) = 0) = E\xi'(t) = 0,$$

$$E(w(t)w(s)|w(1) = 0) = E\xi'(t)\xi'(s).$$

Let

$$\xi(t) = w(t) - tw(1).$$

Then

$$\begin{aligned} E\xi(t)w(1) &= Ew(t)w(1) - t \\ &= E[w(t)(w(1) - w(t)) + w(t)^2] - t \\ &= 0, \end{aligned}$$

since $w(1) - w(t)$ and $w(t)$ are independent. Thus $\xi(t)$ and $w(1)$ are independent. Hence

$$E(\xi(t)|w(1)) = 0$$

$$E(\xi(t)\xi(s)|w(1)) = E\xi(t)\xi(s).$$

Since $w(t) = \xi(t) + tw(1)$, we obtain

$$E(w(t)|w(1)) = tw(1),$$

$$\begin{aligned} E(w(t)w(s)|w(1)) &= E\xi(t)\xi(s) + tsw(1)^2 \\ &= \min[t, s] - ts + tsw(1)^2. \end{aligned}$$

If $w(1)$ is assumed to be zero then

$$E[w(t)w(s)|w(1) = 0] = t(1 - s) \qquad \text{if} \quad t \leqslant s,$$

$$E[w(t)|w(1) = 0] = 0.$$

This completes the proof.

Theorem 9.1

The distribution of the process $\xi_n'(t)$ converges weakly to the distribution of the process $\xi'(t)$ in the space D.

PROOF. It follows from Lemma 9.3 that $\xi'(t)$ is continuous with probability one, and hence its distribution can be considered as a measure in D. By Lemma 9.2, the distribution of the process $\xi_n'(t)$ can be considered as a measure in D.

It is clear that for any $\delta > 0$ and $x \in D$,

$$\tilde{\omega}_x(\delta) \leqslant \sup_{|t' - t''| \leqslant \delta} |x(t') - x(t'')|,$$

where $\tilde{\omega}_x(\delta)$ is defined by (6.2). Thus in order to establish the conditional compactness of the sequence of distributions of ξ_n' it is enough to prove that for any $\varepsilon > 0$,

$$\lim_{\delta \to 0} \overline{\lim_{n \to \infty}} P\{ \sup_{|t' - t''| \leqslant \delta} |\xi_n'(t') - \xi_n'(t'')| > \varepsilon\} = 0. \tag{9.1}$$

Indeed, this follows immediately from Lemma 9.2 and Corollary 7.1 to Theorem 7.2. Since $\xi_n'(t) + \sqrt{n}\,t$ is monotonic increasing in t, we have for any $t_1 < t_2 < t_3 < t_4$, $-\sqrt{n}(t_3 - t_2) \leqslant \xi_n'(t_3) - \xi_n'(t_2) \leqslant \xi_n'(t_4) - \xi_n'(t_1) + \sqrt{n}(t_2 - t_1 + t_4 - t_3)$. By an easy calculation we obtain

$$\sup_{|t' - t''| \leqslant \delta} |\xi_n'(t') - \xi_n'(t'')|$$
$$\leqslant 3 \sup_{|k_1/2^m - k_2/2^m| \leqslant \delta + 1/2^{m-1}} \left| \xi_n'\left(\frac{k_1}{2^m}\right) - \xi_n'\left(\frac{k_2}{2^m}\right) \right| + 4\frac{\sqrt{n}}{2^m}$$

for any fixed positive integer m. Let m_n be so chosen that $\sqrt{n}/2^{m_n} \to 0$ as $n \to \infty$ and $n/2^{m_n} \geqslant 1$. Then in order to prove (9.1) it is sufficient to establish that for any $\varepsilon > 0$,

$$\lim_{\delta \to 0} \overline{\lim_{n \to \infty}} P\left\{ \sup_{|k_1/2^{m_n} - k_2/2^{m_n}| \leqslant \delta} \left| \xi_n'\left(\frac{k_1}{2^{m_n}}\right) - \xi_n'\left(\frac{k_2}{2^{m_n}}\right) \right| > \varepsilon \right\} = 0. \tag{9.2}$$

Let $m(\delta)$ be the largest positive integer such that $\delta 2^{m(\delta)} \leqslant 1$. Then

$$\sup_{|k_1/2^{m_n} - k_2/2^{m_n}| \leqslant \delta} \left| \xi_n'\left(\frac{k_1}{2^{m_n}}\right) - \xi_n'\left(\frac{k_2}{2^{m_n}}\right) \right|$$

$$\leqslant \sup_{|k_1/2^{m_n} - k_2/2^{m_n}| \leqslant 1/2^{m(\delta)}} \left| \xi_n'\left(\frac{k_1}{2^{m_n}}\right) - \xi_n'\left(\frac{k_2}{2^{m_n}}\right) \right|. \tag{9.3}$$

If $|k_1/2^{m_n} - k_2/2^{m_n}| \leqslant 1/2^{m(\delta)}$ we can find an integer j_n such that

$$\frac{j_n}{2^{m(\delta)}} \leqslant \frac{k_1}{2^{m_n}} \leqslant \frac{k_2}{2^{m_n}} \leqslant \frac{(j_n+1)}{2^{m(\delta)}}.$$

Hence

$$\frac{k_1}{2^{m_n}} = \frac{j_n}{2^{m(\delta)}} + \frac{1}{2^{\tau_1}} + \dots + \frac{1}{2^{\tau_s}},$$

where $m(\delta) \leqslant \tau_1 < \tau_2 < \dots < \tau_s \leqslant m_n$ are positive integers. Similarly,

$$\frac{k_2}{2^{m_n}} = \frac{j_n}{2^{m(\delta)}} + \frac{1}{2^{\tau_1'}} + \dots + \frac{1}{2^{\tau'_{s'}}},$$

where $m(\delta) \leqslant \tau_1' < \tau_2' < \dots < \tau'_{s'} \leqslant m_n$ are positive integers. Hence,

$$\left| \xi_n'\left(\frac{k_1}{2^{m_n}}\right) - \xi_n'\left(\frac{k_2}{2^{m_n}}\right) \right|$$

$$\leqslant \left| \xi_n'\left(\frac{k_1}{2^{m_n}}\right) - \xi_n'\left(\frac{j_n}{2^{m(\delta)}}\right) \right| + \left| \xi_n'\left(\frac{j_n}{2^{m(\delta)}}\right) - \xi_n'\left(\frac{k_2}{2^{m_n}}\right) \right|$$

$$\leqslant \sum_{i=1}^{s} \left| \xi_n'\left(\frac{j_n}{2^{m(\delta)}} + \sum_{k=1}^{i} \frac{1}{2^{\tau_k}}\right) - \xi_n'\left(\frac{j_n}{2^{m(\delta)}} + \sum_{k=1}^{i-1} \frac{1}{2^{\tau_k}}\right) \right|$$

$$+ \sum_{i'=1}^{s'} \left| \xi_n'\left(\frac{j_n}{2^{m(\delta)}} + \sum_{k=1}^{i'} \frac{1}{2^{\tau_k'}}\right) - \xi_n'\left(\frac{j_n}{2^{m(\delta)}} + \sum_{k=1}^{i'-1} \frac{1}{2^{\tau_k'}}\right) \right|$$

$$\leqslant 2 \sum_{r=m(\delta)}^{m_n} \sup_i \left| \xi_n'\left(\frac{i+1}{2^r}\right) - \xi_n'\left(\frac{i}{2^r}\right) \right|.$$

Thus from (9.3) and the above inequality we obtain

$$\sup_{|k_1/2^{m_n} - k_2/2^{m_n}| \leqslant \delta} \left| \xi_n'\left(\frac{k_1}{2^{m_n}}\right) - \xi_n'\left(\frac{k_2}{2^{m_n}}\right) \right|$$

$$\leqslant 2 \sum_{s=m(\delta)}^{m_n} \left[\sup_i \left| \xi_n'\left(\frac{i+1}{2^s}\right) - \xi_n'\left(\frac{i}{2^s}\right) \right| \right].$$

Let now $0 < a < 1$ be such that $2a^4 > 1$. If the left-hand side of the above inequality exceeds ε, then the sth term within the summation sign must exceed $(1 - a)a^{s - m(\delta)}\, \varepsilon/2$ for at least one s. Otherwise, the left-hand side will be $\leqslant \varepsilon$. Thus, by Chebyshev's inequality,

$$P\left\{ \sup_{|k_1/2^{m_n} - k_2/2^{m_n}| \leqslant \delta} \left| \xi_n'\left(\frac{k_1}{2^{m_n}}\right) - \xi_n'\left(\frac{k_2}{2^{m_n}}\right) \right| > \varepsilon \right\}$$

$$\leqslant \sum_{s=m(\delta)}^{m_n} \sum_{i=0}^{2^s - 1} P\left\{ \left| \xi_n'\left(\frac{i+1}{2^s}\right) - \xi_n'\left(\frac{i}{2^s}\right) \right| > (1 - a)a^{s - m(\delta)} \frac{\varepsilon}{2} \right\}$$

$$\leqslant \sum_{s=m(\delta)}^{m_n} \sum_{i=0}^{2^s - 1} \frac{2^4}{(1 - a)^4 \varepsilon^4 a^{4(s - m(\delta))}} E \left| \xi_n'\left(\frac{i+1}{2^s}\right) - \xi_n'\left(\frac{i}{2^s}\right) \right|^4. \quad (9.4)$$

But for any $h > 0$

$$\xi_n'(t + h) - \xi_n'(t) = \sqrt{n}\left(\frac{z_n}{n} - h\right),$$

where z_n is a random variable taking integral values $0 \leqslant k \leqslant n$, with probability

$$P\{z_n = k\} = \binom{n}{k} h^k (1 - h)^{n - k}.$$

The standard calculation of moments of a binomial distribution yields

$$E|\xi_n'(t + h) - \xi_n'(t)|^4 = \frac{1}{n} h(1 - h)(h^3 + (1 - h)^3) + 3\frac{(n - 1)}{n} h^2 (1 - h)^2$$

$$\leqslant \frac{2h}{n} + 3h^2$$

$$\leqslant \frac{2h}{2^{m_n}} + 3h^2,$$

since $n/2^{m_n} \geqslant 1$. Thus when $h \geqslant 1/2^{m_n}$, we have

$$E|\xi_n'(t+h) - \xi_n'(t)|^4 \leqslant 5h^2.$$

Substituting this estimate in (9.4), we get

$$P\left\{\sup_{|k_1/2^{m_n} - k_2/2^{m_n}| \leqslant \delta} \left| \xi_n'\left(\frac{k_1}{2^{m_n}}\right) - \xi_n'\left(\frac{k_2}{2^{m_n}}\right) \right| > \varepsilon \right\}$$

$$\leqslant \sum_{s=m(\delta)}^{mn} \frac{2^4}{(1-a)^4\varepsilon^4} \cdot \frac{5}{2^s a^{4(s-m(\delta))}}$$

$$\leqslant \frac{80}{(1-a)^4\varepsilon^4}\left[\sum_{r=0}^{\infty} \frac{1}{(2a^4)^r}\right] \cdot \frac{1}{2^{m(\delta)}}$$

$$= c_\varepsilon \cdot \frac{1}{2^{m(\delta)}},$$

where

$$c_\varepsilon = \frac{80}{(1-a)^4\varepsilon^4}\left(\sum_{r=0}^{\infty} \frac{1}{(2a^4)^r}\right).$$

Since $m(\delta) \to \infty$ as $\delta \to 0$, (9.2) is proved. This shows that the sequence of distributions of ξ_n' is conditionally compact in D.

Let now the distribution of ξ_n' in D be μ_n. We shall now show that any limit of μ_n must be concentrated in the subset C of continuous functions in D. For any $x \in D$, let $j_\lambda(x)$ be the number of jumps whose absolute value is greater than λ. It is clear that the function $x \to j_\lambda(x)$ is continuous in the Skorohod topology for every $\lambda > 0$. Hence, if any subsequence μ_{n_k} of μ_n converges weakly to a μ_0, then the distribution of j_λ according to μ_{n_k} converges weakly to the distribution of j_λ according to μ_0. But from (9.1) we see that for all sufficiently large n, the distribution of j_λ according to μ_n is degenerate at the origin. This shows that $\mu_0(C) = 1$. Hence, for every fixed $t_1, t_2, \ldots, t_k \in [0, 1]$, the map

$$x \to (x(t_1), \ldots, x(t_k))$$

is μ_0—almost everywhere continuous in D. Therefore, the finite-dimensional distributions of μ_{n_k} converge weakly to the finite-dimensional distributions of μ_0. Now Lemma 9.3 and Theorem 2.1 imply that μ_0 is the distribution of the process ξ'. This completes the proof.

Theorem 9.2

Let $\xi_1, \xi_2, \ldots, \xi_n$ be n-independent and identically distributed random variables with a continuous distribution function $F(x)$. Let $F_n^*(x)$ be the sample distribution function based on $\xi_1, \xi_2, \ldots, \xi_n$. Then for all $\alpha > 0$,

$$\lim_{n\to\infty} P\{\sqrt{n} \sup_{-\infty<x<\infty} |F(x) - F_n^*(x)| < \alpha\} = \sum_{k=-\infty}^{+\infty} (-1)^k \exp - 2k^2\alpha^2,$$

$$\lim_{n\to\infty} P\{\sqrt{n} \sup_{-\infty<x<\infty} [F_n^*(x) - F(x)] < \alpha\} = 1 - \exp(-2\alpha^2).$$

PROOF. It is clear that the functionals

$$f_1(x) = \sup_t |x(t)|, \qquad x \in D,$$

$$f_2(x) = \sup_t x(t), \qquad x \in D$$

are continuous in Skorohod topology. Further,

$$\sqrt{n} \sup_{-\infty<x<\infty} |F_n^*(x) - F(x)| = f_1(\xi_n'), \tag{9.5}$$

$$\sqrt{n} \sup_{-\infty<x<\infty} [F_n^*(x) - F(x)] = f_2(\xi_n') \tag{9.6}$$

where ξ_n' is the process in Theorem 9.1. Since by Theorem 9.1 the distribution of the process ξ_n' converges weakly to the distribution of $\xi'(t)$ in the space D, it follows that the distributions of (9.5) and (9.6) converge weakly to the distributions of $f_1(\xi')$ and $f_2(\xi')$, respectively. By Lemma 9.3, the distribution of $\xi'(t)$ is the same as the conditional distribution of the Brownian motion process $w(t)$ under the condition that $w(1) = 0$. But by Theorem 5.2 we have for all $\alpha > 0$, $x < \alpha$,

$$P\{\sup_{0\leqslant t\leqslant 1} |w(t)| < \alpha, w(1) < x\}$$

$$= \frac{1}{\sqrt{2\pi}} \sum_{-\infty}^{+\infty} \int_{-\alpha}^{x} \{\exp[-\tfrac{1}{2}(u + 4k\alpha)^2] - \exp[-\tfrac{1}{2}(u + 4k\alpha - 2\alpha)^2]\} \, du,$$

$$P\{\sup_{0\leqslant t\leqslant 1} w(t) < \alpha, w(1) < x\}$$

$$= \frac{1}{\sqrt{2\pi}} \int_{-\infty}^{x} \left\{\exp(-u^2/2) - \exp\left[-\frac{(u-2\alpha)^2}{2}\right]\right\} du.$$

Differentiating the two expressions in the above equations with respect to x, putting $x = 0$, and dividing by $1/\sqrt{2\pi}$, we have

$$P\{\sup_t |w(t)| < \alpha | w(1) = 0\} = \sum_{k=-\infty}^{+\infty} (-1)^k \exp(-2k^2\alpha^2)$$

$$P\{\sup_t w(t) < \alpha | w(1) = 0\} = 1 - \exp(-2\alpha^2).$$

This completes the proof.

BIBLIOGRAPHICAL NOTES

The comments made below indicate the literature that has been used in the preparation of this monograph. No attempt is made to give a complete bibliography or illuminate the history of the subject. Further references can be obtained from the literature indicated.

CHAPTER I

§ 1–3. A systematic study of the Borel subsets of a metric space is contained in Kuratowski [21].

§ 4–5. Theorem 4.2 on Borel cross sections in compact metric spaces is due to Federer and Morse [6]. Lemma 5.1 is due to Mackey [25]. We have taken most of the material from Kuratowski [21] and Varadarajan [44].

CHAPTER II

§ 1–5. Most of the material is contained in Halmos [12].

§ 6. The proof of Theorem 6.1 is taken from Billingsley [2]. Theorems 6.2 and 6.5 are due to Prohorov [33] but their proofs have been adopted from Varadarajan [42]. Theorem 6.9 has been taken from Ranga Rao [34]. For a deeper analysis of the weak topology in the space of measures the reader may refer to [43].

§ 7. Theorem 7.1 is due to Varadarajan [42].

§ 8. Theorem 8.1 has been taken from Parthasarathy et al. [28].

CHAPTER III

§ 1–5. Most of the results here are contained in Parthasarathy et al. [28].

CHAPTER IV

§ 1–12. Almost all the results have been taken from Parthasarathy et al. [28], [29] and Parthasarathy and Sazonov [30]. That Theorem 12.1 is not true in the case of a compact group is an unpublished result of H. Heyer. For limit theorems in the case of homogeneous spaces and Lie groups the reader may refer to [7], [8], [15], [31], [40], and [41]. Except in the case of symmetric spaces [8], the results obtained so far are not final. For a survey of these results see [38].

CHAPTER V

§ 1–8. All the results here are quite well known. The consistency theorem in the case of products of real lines is due to Kolmogorov [19]. The proofs of the consistency theorem and the existence of conditional and regular conditional probability have been taken from Varadarajan [44]. The case of analytic Borel spaces is purposely omitted for the sake of simplicity.

CHAPTER VI

§ 1–2. The theorems on characteristic functions and compactness criteria are due to Prohorov [33]. Theorems 2.4 and 2.5 are due to Sazonov [37].
§ 3–8. All the theorems here are due to Varadhan [45].
§ 9. The ergodic theorems are due to Mourier [26] but their proofs have been taken from Ranga Rao [34].

CHAPTER VII

§ 1–9. Most of the proofs have been adopted from Gikhman and Skorohod [9] and Prohorov [33]. For different proofs of the results on Skorohod topology see Kolmogorov [20]. The proof of the ergodic theorem is taken from Ranga Rao [35].

BIBLIOGRAPHY

1. A. D. Alexandroff, Additive set functions in abstract spaces, *Mat. Sb.* **8**, 307–348 (1940); **9**, 536–628 (1941); **13**, 169–238 (1943).
2. P. Billingsley, Invariance principle for dependent random variables, *Trans. Amer. Math. Soc.* **83**, 250–282 (1956).
3. E. T. Copson, "Theory of Functions of a Complex Variable." Oxford Univ. Press, London and New York 1935.
4. H. Cramér, "Mathematical Methods of Statistics." Princeton Univ. Press, Princeton, New Jersey, 1946.
5. J. L. Doob, "Stochastic Processes." Wiley, New York, 1953.
6. H. Federer and A. P. Morse, Some properties of measurable functions, *Bull. Amer. Math. Soc.* **49**, 270–277 (1943).
7. H. Furstenberg, Noncommuting random products, *Trans. Amer. Math. Soc.* **108**, 377–428 (1963).
8. R. Gangolli, Isotropic infinitely divisible measures on symmetric spaces, *Acta Math.* **111**, 213–246 (1964).
9. I. I. Gikhman and A. V. Skorohod, "Introduction to the Theory of Random Processes." Moscow, 1965 (In Russian).
10. B. V. Gnedenko and A. N. Kolmogorov, "Limit Distributions for Sums of Independent Random Variables." Addison-Wesley, Cambridge, Massachusetts, 1954 (Translated from Russian).
11. U. Grenander, "Probabilities on Algebraic structures." Wiley, New York, 1963.
12. P. R. Halmos, "Measure Theory." Van Nostrand, Princeton, New Jersey, 1962.
13. E. J. Hannan, Group representations and applied probability, *J. Appl. Prob.* **2**, 1–68 (1965).
14. E. Hille and R. S. Phillips, "Functional Analysis and Semigroups." (*Amer. Math. Soc. Colloquium Publ.*, Vol. 31). *Amer. Math. Soc.*, Providence, Rhode Island, 1957.
15. G. A. Hunt, Semigroups of measures on Lie groups, *Trans. Amer. Math. Soc.* **81**, 264–293 (1956).
16. J. L. Kelley, "General Topology." Van Nostrand, New York, 1961.
17. A. I. Khinchine, Contributions à l'arithmétique des lois de distribution, *Bull. Math. Univ. Moscow* **1**, 6–17 (1937).
18. B. M. Kloss, Stable distributions on locally bicompact groups, *Theor. Prob. Appl.* **7**, 237–257 (1962) (Translated from Russian).
19. A. N. Kolmogorov, "Foundations of Probability Theory." Chelsea, New York, 1950 (Translated from German).

20. A. N. Kolmogorov, On Skorohod convergence, *Theor. Prob. Appl.* **1**, 215–222 (1956) (Translated from Russian).
21. C. Kuratowski, "Topologie I." Warszawa-Lwow, **1933**.
22. P. Lévy, L'addition des variables aléatoires définies sur une circonférence, *Bull. Soc. Math.* **67**, 1–41 (1939).
23. P. Lévy, Sur une classe de lois de probabilité indecomposables, *C. R. Acad. Sci. Paris* **235**, 489–492 (1952).
24. P. Lévy, "Theorie de l'Additions des Variables Aléatoires." Gauthier-Villars, Paris, 1954.
25. G. W. Mackey, Representations of locally compact groups I, *Ann. Math.* **55**, 101–139 (1952).
26. E. Mourier, Eléments aléatoires à valeurs dans un espace de Banach, These de doctorat, Paris, 1952.
27. J. C. Oxtoby, Ergodic sets, *Bull. Amer. Math. Soc.* **58**, 116–136 (1952).
28. K. R. Parthasarathy, R. Ranga Rao and S. R. S. Varadhan, On the category of indecomposable distributions on topological groups, *Trans. Amer. Math. Soc.* **102**, 200–217 (1962).
29. K. R. Parthasarathy, R. Ranga Rao, and S. R. S. Varadhan, Probability distributions on locally compact abelian groups, *Illinois. J. Math.* **7**, 337–369 (1963).
30. K. R. Parthasarathy and V. V. Sazonov, On the representation of infinitely divisible distributions on locally compact abelian groups, *Theor. Prob. Appl.* **9**, 118–122 (1964) (Translated from Russian).
31. K. R. Parthasarathy, The central limit theorem for rotation groups, *Theor. Prob. Appl.* **9**, 248–257 (1964).
32. L. S. Pontrjagin, "Topological Groups." Princeton University Press, Princeton, New Jersey, 1946 (Translated from Russian).
33. Yu. V. Prohorov, Convergence of random processes and limit theorems in probability theory, *Theor. Prob. Appl.* **1**, 157–214 (1956).
34. R. Ranga Rao, Relations between weak and uniform convergence of measures with applications, *Ann. Math. Stat.* **33**, 659–680 (1962).
35. R. Ranga Rao, The law of large numbers for $D[0, 1]$-valued random variables, *Theor. Prob. Appl.* **8**, 70–74 (1963).
36. W. Rudin, "Fourier Analysis on Groups." Wiley (Interscience), New York, 1962.
37. V. V. Sazonov, On characteristic functionals, *Theor. Prob. Appl.* **3**, 201–205 (1958) (Translated from Russian).
38. V. V. Sazonov and V. N. Tutubalin, Probability distributions in topological groups, *Teor. Veroyat. i. Primenen.* **11**, 3–55 (1966) (In Russian).
39. W. Sierpinski, "General Topology." Univ. of Toronto Press, Toronto, 1952.
40. V. N. Tutubalin, Asymptotic behaviour of compositions of measures in certain homogeneous spaces, *Trud. Mat. Inst. Stekl. USSR Acad. Sci.* **36**, 1301–1342 (1963) (In Russian).
41. V. N. Tutubalin, Limit theorems for the product of random matrices, *Theor. Prob. Appl.* **10**, 15–27 (1965).

42. V. S. Varadarajan, Weak convergence of measures on separable metric spaces, *Sankhya* **19**, 15–22 (1958).
43. V. S. Varadarajan, Measures on topological spaces, *Mat. Sbornik* **55**, 35–100 (1961) (In Russian).
44. V. S. Varadarajan, Special topics in probability theory, Lecture notes, *Courant Inst. Math. Sci.*, 1962.
45. S. R. S. Varadhan, Limit theorems for sums of independent random variables with values in a Hilbert space, *Sankhya* **24**, 213–238 (1962).
46. A. Weil, "L'integrations dans les groupes topologiques et ses applications." Hermann & Co., Paris, 1940.

LIST OF SYMBOLS

Symbols are defined on the pages listed.

AUTHOR INDEX

Numbers in parentheses are reference numbers and indicate that an author's work is referred to, although his name is not cited in the text. Numbers in italics show the page on which the complete reference is listed.

SUBJECT INDEX